WORKBOOK for
Clinical Pharmacy
and Therapeutics

WORKBOOK for Clinical Pharmacy and Therapeutics

edited by

Linda Lloyd Hart, Pharm.D.

Clinical Professor, Division of Clinical Pharmacy
Director, Drug Information Analysis Service
School of Pharmacy
University of California, San Francisco
San Francisco, California

Dick R. Gourley, Pharm.D.

Dean and Professor of Pharmacy Practice
Mercer University
Southern School of Pharmacy
Atlanta, Georgia

Eric T. Herfindal, Pharm.D.

Chairman and Clinical Professor, Division of Clinical Pharmacy
Director, Department of Pharmaceutical Services
School of Pharmacy
University of California, San Francisco
San Francisco, California

WILLIAMS & WILKINS

Baltimore • Hong Kong • London • Sydney

Editor: John P. Butler
Associate Editor: Linda Napora
Copy Editor: Elia A. Flanegin
Design: Norman W. Och
Production: Raymond E. Reter

Copyright © 1988
Williams & Wilkins
428 East Preston Street
Baltimore, Maryland 21202, USA

Accurate indications, adverse reactions, and dosage schedules for drugs are provided in this book, but it is possible that they may change. The reader is urged to review the package information data of the manufacturers of the medications mentioned.

Printed in the United States of America

Library of Congress Cataloging-in-Publication Data

Workbook for Clinical pharmacy and therapeutics / [edited by] Linda
   Lloyd Hart, Dick R. Gourley, Eric T. Herfindal.
      p.   cm.
   ISBN 0-683-03935-0
   1. Chemotherapy—Case studies.   2. Chemotherapy—Examinations,
questions, etc.   3. Pharmacy—Case studies.   4. Pharmacy—
Examinations, questions, etc.   I. Hart, Linda L.   II. Gourley, D.
R. H., 1922–   .   III. Herfindal, Eric T.   IV. Clinical pharmacy and
therapeutics.
   [DNLM: 1. Drug Therapy—examination questions.   2. Therapeutics—
examination questions. WB 330 C641 Suppl.]
RM263.W67 1988
615.5'8—dc19
DNLM/DLC
for Library of Congress   88-10682
                                                               CIP

                                                          90 91 92
                                      3   4   5   6   7   8   9   10

Preface

The purpose of this *Workbook* is to help the student develop skills in therapeutics. Clinical pharmacy has long had as its function the selection of the right drug for the right patient in the right dose and at the right time. However, the ability to select and assess therapy is a complex process that takes time and experience to develop and refine. Integration, anticipation, and judgment are higher cognitive functions than memorization of facts and require active participation in the learning process. Therefore, this is a *Workbook* with space for written answers.

Students are encouraged to write in the book and by so doing to commit themselves to an answer that they can defend. The format of the workbook is case presentations. The cases are to be used to learn to select or to assess therapy and to solve therapeutic problems. By following the suggested problem-oriented approach to therapy, the student will develop an organized and comprehensive way of looking at drug therapy that will avoid omitting any important patient or drug, variable or consideration. The first few cases are simple, but they become progressively more complicated and realistic.

In some cases, questions and answers are provided. In other cases, specific answers are replaced by hints as to where the answers may be found in *Clinical Pharmacy and Therapeutics, Fourth Edition.* Finally, cases are presented with neither answers nor questions to simulate the presentation of a patient in the clinical setting. Knowledge of previous coursework and information from references other than *Clinical Pharmacy and Therapeutics* may be required to develop a drug therapy plan. Each case should represent a process and not an end in itself because the most important aspect of this *Workbook* is to learn to apply knowledge and to make decisions, not to learn facts. Current answers may be incorrect in the future as new knowledge or drugs become available. There are few absolutes in therapeutics and while one answer may in fact be correct, another answer may be a better choice for a particular patient. In some cases, several answers may be equally acceptable and a practitioner may have an individual preference. In other cases, the available information may be conflicting or controversial and the risks versus benefits must be weighed for each patient. The *Workbook* allows the student to make mistakes and to learn from those mistakes without harming a patient. This is a *Workbook* and the student must work to organize thoughts, develop drug therapy plans, and solve therapeutic problems. Skill develops as one repeats an action or function many times. This *Workbook* gives the student the opportunity to repeat the process of selecting, assessing, and/or monitoring therapy in 115 cases.

The contributors and reviewers have provided cases that allow the student to practice so as to develop skill in therapeutics. The cases do not cover all of the material from the fourth edition of *Clinical Pharmacy and Therapeutics*, but they are representative of patients with these diseases and should be useful as a supplement to the textbook.

L.L.H.

Acknowledgments

We gratefully acknowledge the work of all of the contributors and reviewers:

SECTION 1
GAIL W. McSWEENEY, *Contributor*
KATHRYN M. KUDZIA, *Reviewer*

SECTION 2
THERESA A. SALAZAR, *Contributor*
JOAN E. KAPUSNIK, *Contributor*
PETER J. S. KOO, *Contributor*
ROBERT M. MOWERS, *Reviewer*

SECTION 3
ILENE K. AUER, *Contributor*
LINDA LLOYD HART, *Contributor*
Y. W. FRANCES LAM, *Contributor*
PAULINE J. LEW, *Contributor*
BETTY J. DONG, *Reviewer*

SECTION 4
JOHN R. WHITE, JR, *Contributor*
MAUREEN S. BORO, *Reviewer*

SECTION 5
LINDA LLOYD HART, *Contributor*
JOAN E. KAPUSNIK, *Contributor*
PETER J. S. KOO, *Contributor*
DAYNA L. McCAULEY, *Contributor*
NANCY C. SAMBOL, *Contributor*
GAIL W. McSWEENEY, *Reviewer*

SECTION 6
STEPHEN A. ECHAVES, *Contributor*
LINDA LLOYD HART, *Contributor*
MASSIE SO, *Contributor*
DORIS SUE, *Reviewer*

SECTION 7
LINDA LLOYD HART, *Contributor*
MARY F. HEBERT, *Contributor*
BRIAN K. ALLDREDGE, *Reviewer*

SECTION 8
MAUREEN S. BORO, *Contributor*
JOAN E. KAPUSNIK, *Contributor*
PETER J. S. KOO, *Contributor*
ROBERT M. MOWERS, *Contributor*
STEVEN R. KAYSER, *Reviewer*

SECTIONS 9 AND 10
LINDA LLOYD HART, *Contributor*
MARK L. HOLTSMAN, *Contributor*
DORIS SUE, *Contributor*
ANN M. BOLINGER, *Reviewer*

SECTION 11
BRIAN K. ALLDREDGE, *Contributor*
LINDA LLOYD HART, *Contributor*
ROBERT M. MOWERS, *Reviewer*

SECTION 12
C. Y. JENNIFER CHAN, *Contributor*
RON R. FINLEY, *Contributor*
LINDA LLOYD HART, *Contributor*
JAMES T. YOUNG, *Contributor*
LUCY A. RICHMAN, *Reviewer*
JAMES T. YOUNG, *Reviewer*

SECTION 13
KIM A. BERGSTROM, *Contributor*
ANN M. BOLINGER, *Contributor*
BETTY J. DONG, *Contributor*
JOAN E. KAPUSNIK, *Contributor*
LISA C. RODONDI, *Contributor*
DIANE M. ROMAC, *Contributor*
ROBERT J. STAGG, *Contributor*
JOHN F. FLAHERTY, *Reviewer*
B. JOSEPH GUGLIELMO, *Reviewer*

SECTION 14
JUDY J. CHASE, *Contributor*
BETTY J. DONG, *Contributor*
RANDELL K. MIYAHARA, *Contributor*
ROBERT J. STAGG, *Contributor*
JUDY J. CHASE, *Reviewer*
ROBERT J. STAGG, *Reviewer*

SECTION 15
ANN M. BOLINGER, *Contributor*
DONALD CHANG, *Contributor*
BETTY J. DONG, *Contributor*
LINDA LLOYD HART, *Contributor*
SUSAN Y. KIM, *Contributor*
RONALD J. RUGGIERO, *Contributor*
ROBERT J. STAGG, *Contributor*
KIM A. BERGSTROM, *Reviewer*
MARK L. HOLTSMAN, *Reviewer*
PAULINE J. LEW, *Reviewer*
MARY F. HEBERT, *Reviewer*
LORI A. REISNER, *Reviewer*
ALVIN F. WONG, *Reviewer*

Contributors

BRIAN K. ALLDREDGE, Pharm.D.
Assistant Clinical Professor, University of California, Division of Clinical Pharmacy, School of Pharmacy, San Francisco, California

ILENE K. AUER, Pharm.D.
Pharmacy Researcher, University of California, Division of Clinical Pharmacy, School of Pharmacy, San Francisco, California

KIM A. BERGSTROM, Pharm.D.
Resident in Pharmacy Administration, University of California, Pharmaceutical Services, School of Pharmacy, San Francisco, California

ANN M. BOLINGER, Pharm.D.
Assistant Clinical Professor, University of California, Division of Clinical Pharmacy, School of Pharmacy, San Francisco, California

MAUREEN S. BORO, Pharm.D.
Resident in Pharmacokinetics, University of California, Division of Clinical Pharmacy, School of Pharmacy, San Francisco, California

C. Y. JENNIFER CHAN, Pharm.D.
Assistant Clinical Professor, University of California, Division of Clinical Pharmacy, School of Pharmacy, San Francisco, California; Staff Pharmacist II, University of California Davis Medical Center, Sacramento, California

DONALD CHANG, Pharm.D.
Resident in Clinical Pharmacy, University of California, Division of Clinical Pharmacy, School of Pharmacy, San Francisco, California

JUDY J. CHASE, Pharm.D.
Oncology Fellow, University of California, Division of Clinical Pharmacy, School of Pharmacy, San Francisco, California

BETTY J. DONG, Pharm.D.
Associate Clinical Professor, University of California, Division of Clinical Pharmacy, School of Pharmacy, San Francisco, California

STEPHEN A. ECHAVES, Pharm.D.
Assistant Clinical Professor, University of California, Division of Clinical Pharmacy, School of Pharmacy, San Francisco, California

RON R. FINLEY, Pharm.D.
Adjunct Lecturer, University of California, Division of Clinical Pharmacy, School of Pharmacy, San Francisco, California

LINDA LLOYD HART, Pharm.D.
Clinical Professor and Director, Drug Information Analysis Service, University of California, Division of Clinical Pharmacy, School of Pharmacy, San Francisco, California

MARK L. HOLTSMAN, Pharm.D.
Resident in Clinical Pharmacy, University of California, Division of Clinical Pharmacy, School of Pharmacy, San Francisco, California

JOAN E. KAPUSNIK, Pharm.D.
Assistant Clinical Professor, University of California, Division of Clinical Pharmacy, School of Pharmacy, San Francisco, California

SUSAN Y. KIM, Pharm.D.
Assistant Clinical Professor, University of California, Division of Clinical Pharmacy, School of Pharmacy, San Francisco, California; Pharmacist, Bay Area Poison Control Center, San Francisco General Hospital, San Francisco, California

PETER J. S. KOO, Pharm.D.
Assistant Clinical Professor, University of California, Division of Clinical Pharmacy, School of Pharmacy, San Francisco, California

Y. W. FRANCES LAM, Pharm.D.
Assistant Professor, University of Texas Health Center at San Antonio, Department of Pharmacology, San Antonio, Texas

PAULINE J. LEW, Pharm.D.
Resident in Clinical Pharmacy, University of California, Division of Clinical Pharmacy, School of Pharmacy, San Francisco, California

DAYNA L. MCCAULEY, Pharm.D.
Assistant Clinical Professor, University of California, Division of Clinical Pharmacy San Francisco, California

GAIL W. MCSWEENEY, Pharm.D.
Assistant Clinical Professor, University of California, Division of Clinical Pharmacy, School of Pharmacy, San Francisco, California

RANDELL K. MIYAHARA, Pharm.D.
Assistant Professor of Pharmacy Practice, Mercer University Southern School of Pharmacy, Atlanta, Georgia

ROBERT M. MOWERS, Pharm.D.
Assistant Clinical Professor, University of California, Division of Clinical Pharmacy, School of Pharmacy, San Francisco, California

MARY F. HEBERT, Pharm.D.
Resident in Clinical Pharmacy, University of California, Division of Clinical Pharmacy, School of Pharmacy, San Francisco, California

LISA C. RODONDI, Pharm.D.
Assistant Clinical Professor, University of California, Division of Clinical Pharmacy, School of Pharmacy, San Francisco, California; Staff Pharmacist, Veterans Administration Medical Center, Department of Pharmacy Service, Palo Alto, California; Adjunct Professor of Pharmacy, University of the Pacific, School of Pharmacy, Stockton California

DIANE M. ROMAC, Pharm.D.
Assistant Clinical Professor, University of California, Division of Clinical Pharmacy, School of Pharmacy, San Francisco, California; Satellite Pharmacist, University of California David Medical Center, Sacramento, California

RONALD J. RUGGIERO, Pharm.D.
Associate Clinical Professor, University of California, Division of Clinical Pharmacy, School of Pharmacy, San Francisco, California

THERESA A. SALAZAR, Pharm.D.
Assistant Clinical Professor, University of California, Division of Clinical Pharmacy, School of Pharmacy, San Francisco, California

NANCY C. SAMBOL, Pharm.D.
Assistant Clinical Professor, University of California, Division of Clinical Pharmacy, School of Pharmacy, San Francisco, California

ROBERT J. STAGG, Pharm.D.
Assistant Clinical Professor, University of California, Division of Clinical Pharmacy, School of Pharmacy, San Francisco, California

DORIS SUE, Pharm.D.
Resident in Drug Information, University of California, Division of Clinical Pharmacy, School of Pharmacy, San Francisco, California

JOHN R. WHITE JR., Pharm.D.
Pharmacokinetics Fellow, University of California, Division of Clinical Pharmacy, School of Pharmacy, San Francisco, California

JAMES T. YOUNG, Pharm.D.
Assistant Professor of Pharmacy Practice, Mercer University Southern School of Pharmacy, Atlanta, Georgia

Contents

INTRODUCTION

Guidelines for Using This Book

This *Workbook* was developed to accompany the fourth edition of *Clinical Pharmacy and Therapeutics* and is organized in sections that correspond to those in the textbook. The cases within each section of this *Workbook* represent the diseases of that section of the textbook as well as diseases that have been discussed in the previous sections of the textbook. There are four types of cases in each of the sections of this *Workbook*: In the first type, cases are fully analyzed (the method of analysis will be discussed later in this introduction). In these cases, we have assessed and recommended drug therapy for the patient. In the second type of case, questions about specific aspects of the therapy are presented and answers to these questions are provided in the back of this *Workbook* (Appendix A). The student should fully analyze these cases prior to answering the questions to avoid giving incorrect or incomplete responses. The answers that are provided are not meant to be extensive discussions of the topic; the student should refer to the corresponding discussion in the fourth edition of *Clinical Pharmacy and Therapeutics* for a more thorough explanation. The third type of case presents questions about specific aspects of therapy. We have developed questions that are likely to be asked by health practitioners as well as questions that test the student's understanding of the material. Answers are not provided for these questions; the reader is referred to the corresponding section of the fourth edition of *Clinical Pharmacy and Therapeutics* (Appendix B). In a few cases, the answers to the questions will not be discussed in the textbook, and the student should rely on previous coursework such as pharmacokinetics or should consult other reference sources for the answer. As in the second type of case, the student should fully analyze the case prior to answering the questions. The final type of case has neither questions nor answers. This type of case more accurately represents the presentation of a patient in the clinical setting. It is important for students to practice with this type of case because they need to begin to anticipate the types of questions that will be asked in the clinical setting. In addition, the clinical pharmacist is frequently the one who is asking questions as well as providing the answers to therapeutic questions. Therefore, the student needs to develop the skill of identifying the questions that need to be asked about a patient's therapy.

The first two types of cases, those that are analyzed and those that have questions and answers, are considered *study cases;* those cases with only questions and those with neither questions nor answers are considered *practice cases.* All the diseases and potential therapeutic problems within a section of the textbook cannot be discussed in cases in this *Workbook.* Therefore, this *Workbook* cannot be used to ensure understanding of all the material in a section. However, it is likely that a student who is able to analyze the cases in this *Workbook* and to answer or to pose and answer questions about these cases has a good grasp of the material. The cases will become more difficult within a section and as the student progresses through the *Workbook.*

Problem-Oriented Approach

An understanding of the "problem-oriented approach" to medical care is necessary to use this *Workbook.* In 1964, Lawerence E. Weed published the problem-oriented approach to medical records, patient care, and medical education. The method differed from the previous method in which health care practitioners approached the patient from the point of view of their medical specialties. The "source method," as the previous method was called, was cited as a cause of fragmented patient care. The problem-oriented method, in addition to being comprehensive due to better communication among all persons contributing to health care, allows auditing of care to assure quality. Today, nearly all health care providers follow some form of the problem-oriented method of patient care and the medical record.

The pharmacist should learn the problem-oriented method of health care so that a systematic, disciplined approach to each patient is used and no important therapeutic considerations are missed. The approach should always be the same regardless of the simplicity or complexity of the problem. Although the pharmacist must focus on drug therapy, he or she should not ignore other problems including social, psychological, and financial problems.

The two main components to the problem-oriented method, the problem list and the SOAP note are discussed next.

Problem List

A problem is defined as a patient concern, a health professional concern, or a concern of both the patient and the health professional. Problems are not confined to diagnoses. A problem may be a patient complaint (i.e., a symptom), abnormal results from a laboratory test or abnormal finding from a physical examination (i.e., a sign), a social or financial situation, a psychological concern, or a physical limitation. A problem is identified as generally or as specifically as possible based on available information. A symptom may become a sign after the physical examination is completed; this may lead to a diagnosis after the completion of the appropriate diagnostic tests. The diagnosed disease may then be cured by treatment. For example, a patient may complain of cough, fever, and sputum production. A physician hears rales and rhonchi on chest auscultation and orders a sputum culture and chest radiograph, which leads to the diagnosis of pneumococcal pneumonia. Penicillin is administered and the pneumonia is cured. Thus, problems are dynamic: problems are resolved and new problems develop. Patients frequently have some stable and some inactive problems, but they usually have one problem that is the most severe or that demands attention before the others.

The problem list is developed from the data in a medical record, which would typically include the chief complaint, history of the present illness, past medical history, social history, family history, drug history, review of systems, results of laboratory tests and diagnostic procedures such as electrocardiogram and radiographs, and the physical examination. Health care providers gather information to contribute to the data and organize the data to develop the problem list. However, each health care provider may not interpret the data in exactly the same manner nor will he or she consider each problem in the same rank of importance; ranking will depend upon the perspective of the health care provider. The problem list is the table of contents of the medical record and the framework for patient care. With each hospital admission or clinic visit, the problem list should be rearranged into hierarchical order with the most serious problem listed first.

Each of the cases in the first 14 sections of this *Workbook* has a problem list that is considered complete for the medical problems. However, therapeutic problems such as adverse drug reactions and drug toxicity are not always identified. The cases in Section 15 do not have a problem list. While it is recognized that pharmacists will not be diagnosing medical problems, it is important for the pharmacist to be able to develop a working problem list from the information in the medical record. When a problem list is provided, it is not necessarily in the correct order for the present hospital admission or clinic visit. Therefore, the student must rearrange the problem list so that the most important problem is discussed first. *Although the ranking will differ, the numbers for each of the problems do not change and all new problems are added to the problem list with sequential numbers.* Therefore, it is not uncommon for Problem 4 to be discussed first because it is important and Problem 1 to be discussed last because it is inactive. All problems must be considered in the treatment of any other problem, and the treatment of a given problem is affected by the presence of all of the other problems.

Soap Note

The second component of the problem-oriented medical record is the organization of the data into the SOAP (subjective, objective, assessment, and plan) note. Each chart entry is recorded in this format. For each problem, the subjective and objective data are recorded and the data are assessed or interpreted in order to develop a plan. The plan may be to gather more data or to treat. All the analyzed cases in this *Workbook* are analyzed in the SOAP format. In addition, the student should analyze the other cases using this format; space is provided on a case worksheet for the SOAP notes following each case.

Each component of the SOAP note is discussed next and an example follows the discussion:

Subjective

Subjective data include patient complaints or symptoms. In addition, observations of health care providers may be subjective in nature. The primary means of gathering subjective data is by talking to the patient. This is frequently done in a systematic fashion called the review of systems (ROS).

Objective

Objective data include vital signs, results of laboratory tests, the findings from a physical examination, and the results of various procedures such as radiographs, CT scans, electrocardiograms, etc.

The pharmacist uses subjective and objective data to monitor or assess therapy and to document adverse drug reactions. The subjective data required by the pharmacist may be different from that required by other health professionals who use the information for different purposes. The pharmacist must select the data that are necessary to follow drug therapy, and the efficacy of therapy is usually defined as the return of the subjective and objective data to normal. However, sometimes patient-specific considerations dictate other endpoints for therapy. The pharmacist must be familiar with all the subjective and objective information in the medical record to determine the therapeutic implications of the data and to recognize adverse drug reactions.

Assessment

The pharmacist should interpret the subjective and objective data for each problem so as to develop a therapeutic plan, to follow the response to therapy, or to document an adverse drug reaction. The pharmacist should develop a systematic method for assessing each problem so that the assessment is complete and accurate. The following is a suggested method of assessment:

1. A pharmacist should always consider whether a problem is drug induced. Many problems are not diseases but are actually adverse drug reactions, and the plan for treatment is obviously very different in each instance. The pharmacist may be the only health care practitioner who recognizes the problem as an adverse drug reaction.
2. The pharmacist should consider whether drug therapy is required; nondrug therapy such as diet may be a better solution to the problem. The problem may not yet be severe enough to require drug therapy or an isolated abnormal laboratory test may not be the rational basis for drug therapy.
3. If the patient is already receiving drug therapy, the pharmacist should assess the current therapy for appropriateness. He or she should consider the following:
   a. Are all the drugs necessary? All the drugs taken by the patient should be for problems identified in the problem list. Duplication of drugs from the same therapeutic category frequently occurs, and the maximum dose of a single agent may be preferred to two drugs for the same problem.
   b. Is this the drug of choice for this patient? The drug should be the best drug for this patient considering all the patient's other problems and drugs, age, renal and hepatic function, and any other relevant factors such as allergies, risk factors for adverse drug reactions, convenience, and cost.
   c. Is this the correct dose? The patient should be given the appropriate dose for age, sex, weight, renal and hepatic function, the other drugs included in his or her regimen, and other problems/factors such as nutritional status. Pharmacokinetic calculations should be performed if possible.
   d. Is this the correct dosage form? The dosage form and the route of administration should be appropriate for the patient. Sustained release formulations may or may not be indicated. A liquid preparation may be more easily administered and compliance may determine the dosage form that is chosen.
   e. Is this the best schedule for administration of this drug to this patient? Some drugs require around-the-clock administration while others should be given with meals. Patients with a history of noncompliance should be given simplified regimens.
   f. Is the duration of therapy appropriate? Some treatments should be given for the lifetime of the patient while others should only be given for a specific length of time. Patients are frequently started on therapy that is never discontinued although the problem has resolved. Some patients need to be treated for a longer period because the disease is severe while other patients need only to be treated when they have an exacerbation of their disease.
4. If the patient is receiving drug therapy, the pharmacist should assess the response to therapy and decide whether the response is adequate and/or the response is that which was expected. An appropriate response may be the resolution of the patient's complaints and the return of all objective data to normal, or an appropriate response may be a decrease in the patient's complaints and the return of the objective data toward normal. In some patients, it is neither possible nor appropriate to return all subjective and objective data to normal. Noncompliance or failure to follow prescribed therapy may be the reason for an inadequate response. Therefore, the pharmacist should always assess compliance, and it is inappropriate and dangerous to increase a dose of medication because of inadequate response due to noncompliance.
5. The pharmacist should assess any drug interactions or adverse drug reactions that have occurred or may occur in this patient.

Any drug interactions should be managed so that the dose of each drug is appropriate. In addition, potential drug interactions should be documented so that they are avoided. Any adverse drug reaction and the appropriate action taken to treat it should be documented.

The SOAP note should contain all the reasons for any action taken regarding therapy. The pharmacist should document the reasons for changing therapy in the assessment portion of the SOAP note. This is important for other health care practitioners who need to understand the reasons for the change, for auditing the quality of care, and for helping the pharmacist remember the reasons for the changes. The pharmacist should state the reasons for selecting this drug for this patient, the reasons for discontinuing a drug, the reasons for avoiding certain drugs, the reasons for changing the dose, the reasons for adding a second-line agent, etc.

Plan

The plan includes treatment, monitoring parameters and endpoints of therapy, patient education, and, perhaps, additional studies necessary to evaluate the problem. The pharmacist who has selected the drug of choice in the correct dose for this patient in the assessment portion of the note initiates therapy in the plan. The pharmacist must decide how therapy will be initiated and if full doses will be started immediately or if the dose will be titrated to the desired dose. If the dose is to be titrated, then the frequency of dosage changes must be identified in the plan.

The pharmacist must select the appropriate subjective and objective data that will be followed to assess response to therapy and the intervals for these measurements. Usually the same subjective and objective data that were used to diagnose the disease are used to monitor therapy. However, expensive or invasive tests are not usually repeated as monitoring parameters. The pharmacist must also select the appropriate subjective and objective data that will be observed for assessment of adverse drug effects. Any specific tests required to assess toxicity should be identified in the plan. Any abnormalities revealed by routine screening tests that would indicate adverse effects should also be identified in the plan along with the frequency of these observations. The plan may include the action that should be taken if an adverse drug reaction occurs. The plan may be to discontinue therapy if certain adverse reactions occur yet to continue therapy if other side effects occur or to treat certain toxicities.

The plan should include the patient education that the pharmacist will give to the patient. The patient should know the name(s), dose, indication, quantity, schedule, precautions, drug interactions, storage, and side effects of each drug. The patient should be able to administer the drug properly; any information necessary for the safe use of this drug should be discussed. Any patient concerns about the medication should be addressed.

An example case will be analyzed using the SOAP format to illustrate the method that is used in this *Workbook*. The information is obtained from the medical record. For the sake of saving space in this *Workbook*, all information from the chart has been abbreviated and condensed. The laboratory data have been reported in standard units. Abbreviations have been used less frequently than they are used in medical charts, but common abbreviations are used to save space and to familiarize the student with these abbreviations.

EXAMPLE CASE

CC: R.J. is a 74-year-old male who comes to clinic today with a complaint of weakness and lethargy for 2 months.

Past Medical History (PMH)

R.J. has seizures because of a motor vehicle accident 2 years ago. The seizures have been well con-

trolled and R.J. only suffers one seizure about every 6 months.

R.J. has suffered from hemorrhoids for 12 years.

R.J. has degenerative joint disease in his knees and hips. His complaints are slight pain and stiffness that do not interfere with his activities.

Medication History

Phenytoin, 300 mg p.o. qhs
Aspirin, 650 mg p.o. q.i.d.
Over-the-counter (OTC) hemorrhoid ointment applied prn

R.J. is a compliant patient.

Social History

Tobacco—negative
Alcohol—heavy in the last 6 months since his wife's death

Physical Examination (PE)

GEN (General): Well-developed, well-nourished male in no distress
VS (Vital signs): BP 120/80 HR 80 RR 20 T 37 Wt 62 kg (70 kg 6 months ago) Ht 6'0"
HEENT (Head, eyes, ear, nose, and throat): Pale mucous membranes and skin, no nystagmus
COR (Coronary): Normal S1 and S2, no murmurs, rubs, or gallop
CHEST: Clear to auscultation and percussion
ABD (abdomen): Soft, nontender, with no masses or organomegaly
GU (Genitourinary): WNL (within normal limits)
RECTAL: Guaiac-positive, large inflamed hemorrhoids
EXT (Extremities): Pale nail beds, tenderness of both knees but no signs of inflammation, limited range of motion of both hips
NEURO (Neurological): Oriented to time, place, and person; cranial nerves intact; normal deep tendon reflexes (DTRs).

Results of Laboratory Tests

Hct 32	MCV 80
Hgb 10	MCHC 28
RBC 4	Serum FE 38
Plts 320k	TIBC 510

Peripheral blood smear: microcytic and macrocytic RBCs

Problem List

1. Degenerative joint disease
2. Hemorrhoids
3. Seizures
4. Mixed anemia

The student analyzing this case should first rearrange the problem list into the appropriate order for this clinic visit. R.J.'s complaint today is consistent with the problem of anemia and this problem should be discussed first. The hemorrhoids are contributing to the anemia and should be discussed second. The other two problems appear to be well controlled and are stable. Remember that the number of the problem does not change although the order may. The student then needs to analyze each of the problems using the SOAP format and following the systematic approach outlined previously.

Problem 4. Mixed Anemia

S: R.J. complains of weakness and lethargy. The physician noted pale mucous membranes and pale nail beds.

O: The Hct, Hgb, MCHC, RBC, and serum Fe are decreased. The TIBC is increased while iron saturation is decreased. The MCV is normal but the smear shows microcytic and macrocytic cells. The stool is guaiac-positive.

A: R.J. is suffering from iron deficiency anemia and is likely to have folate deficiency as well. The iron deficiency is due to his blood loss secondary to his bleeding hemorrhoids and perhaps due to gastrointestinal (GI) blood loss secondary to bleeding caused by aspirin and alcohol. His diet may be low in iron and folate due to his drinking and his recent weight loss may indicate inadequate intake. He may not be eating appropriately since his wife died. In addition, both the phenytoin and the alcohol decrease the absorption of folate. However, because treating a B_{12} deficiency anemia with folate can correct the anemia but will allow the nervous system damage to progress, a B_{12} deficiency must be ruled out prior to treating the folate deficiency. The suspicion of folate deficiency must be confirmed. Because R.J. is not in acute distress, the oral route may be used for iron replacement. Ferrous sulfate is the cheapest form of oral iron. The dose of iron required to reverse the signs and symptoms and to replete his iron stores is about 40 mg/day of elemental iron for 6 months. This may be achieved with 325 mg $FeSO_4$ t.i.d. R.J. should avoid aspirin and alcohol. Acetaminophen may be effective for treating his degenerative joint disease (DJD) inasmuch as no inflammation is present (see below).

P: Begin $FeSO_4$ 325 mg p.o. t.i.d. for 6 months. Obtain a folate and a B_{12} level and a reticulocyte count. Monitor weakness, lethargy, pallor, and reticulocyte count (expect an increase in 7 days and a return to normal in 2–3 weeks), Hct (expect a 6% increase in 3 weeks and a return to normal in 6 weeks), Hgb (expect a 2 mg% increase in 3 weeks and a return to normal in 6 weeks), and peripheral blood smear. R.J. should take the iron on an empty stomach if possible. If this causes too much GI distress, he may take the iron with food but the duration of treatment may need to be longer. He should not take the iron with milk or antacids. The iron may cause his stools to turn black but this may be distinguished from tarry-looking stools that would indicate GI bleeding. The iron may cause constipation so he should increase the fiber in his diet and he should take a bulk laxative such as psyllium 1 teaspoonful t.i.d. but not at the same time as the iron. The iron must be kept away from children; iron poisoning in children may be fatal. R.J. should also increase the iron in his diet by eating more red meat, liver, and other sources of iron. If the suspicion of folate deficiency is confirmed, R.J. should begin folic acid 1 mg p.o. q.d. for 2–3 weeks to reverse the signs and symptoms of anemia and to replete his body stores. Because R.J. is taking phenytoin, he may require folate supplementation for as long as he requires phenytoin. R.J. should decrease his alcohol consumption and should be referred for appropriate counseling. The social worker should evaluate R.J.'s need for help with cooking and housekeeping. In 2 weeks, R.J. should have another stool guaiac test to rule out other sources of GI bleeding.

Problem 2. Hemorrhoids

S: None.

O: Large inflamed hemorrhoids noted on physical examination. Guaiac-positive stool.

A: His hemorrhoids should be treated to stop the bleeding. The drugs for treating hemorrhoids are only useful for treating the symptoms and the inflammation. Over-the-counter preparations do not contain steroids needed for effective treatment of the inflammation.

P: Refer R.J. to a proctologist. Discontinue the topical hemorrhoidal ointment. Begin Anusol hydrocortisone (HC) suppositories, 1 rectally b.i.d. R.J. should remove the foil from the suppository and insert the suppository into the rectum in the morning and at bedtime for 3–6 days until the inflammation subsides. If the suppositories cause staining, the stains may be removed from the fabric by washing. Begin the bulk laxative as in Problem 4 to decrease straining at stool.

Problem 1. Degenerative Joint Disease

S: R.J. complains of slight pain and stiffness in his knees.

O: Pain in both knees without evidence of inflammation and limited range of motion in both hips were noted on physical examination.

A: R.J. has pain and stiffness that does not interfere with his activities and has no signs of inflammation. The aspirin may be contributing to his iron deficiency anemia and should be discontinued. Because the degenerative joint disease (DJD) does not appear to involve an inflammatory process at this time, acetaminophen may be adequate to treat the DJD. However, large doses of acetaminophen would be hepatotoxic in this patient with a history of heavy alcohol intake. If acetaminophen is ineffective or causes an adverse reaction, then ibuprofen in analgesic doses is likely to cause less GI blood loss than aspirin.

P: Obtain liver function tests. Discontinue the aspirin. Begin acetaminophen 650 mg p.o. q.i.d. Do not exceed 4 g/day of acetaminophen. Avoid any other products that might contain either acetaminophen or aspirin. Discontinue or limit the ingestion of alcohol to no more than two drinks per day. Monitor liver function tests every month for 3 months. If R.J. is unable to tolerate acetaminophen or it is ineffective, begin ibuprofen 400 mg q.i.d. and monitor stool guaiac and renal function tests.

Problem 3. Seizures

S: None.

O: R.J. has only one seizure every 6 months. Nystagmus was not present on physical examination.

A: R.J.'s seizure disorder appears to be well controlled and he is not suffering any adverse effects from his phenytoin therapy other than the contribution of the phenytoin to his anemia. If R.J. is given folic acid therapy, his phenytoin dose may have to be adjusted due to decreased serum concentrations from this drug interaction.

P: Obtain a serum phenytoin level. Monitor for an increase in seizure frequency or a decrease in serum concentration if folate therapy is begun. Monitor for adverse drug reactions to phenytoin including nystagmus, ataxia, GI distress, skin reactions, liver function tests, CBC, and signs and symptoms of hypothyroidism, lymphadenopathy, and intoxication. Explain the need for good oral hygiene to avoid gingival hyperplasia and for regular dental appointments. Explain that all health care providers should know about his phenytoin therapy because of the numerous drug interactions with phenytoin.

The student who has analyzed this case in this manner is now in a position to answer specific questions concerning the case. For example, the student could answer questions about how this patient's anemia should be treated or what monitoring parameters should be followed to assess the efficacy of the treatment of the anemia. Likewise, the student could also answer questions about the treatment of R.J.'s DJD or the efficacy of the treatment of his seizures. The student should anticipate the questions that are likely to be asked in a clinical setting concerning this patient's therapy. These questions may also include predicting a phenytoin level for R.J. The student who has analyzed the case in the suggested fashion is unlikely to give inaccurate or incomplete answers to these questions because no important therapeutic considerations have been omitted.

The SOAP format allows a systematic approach to therapy and is widely used in pharmacy education and practice. However, each practitioner would analyze a case slightly differently. In many cases, the correct therapy for an individual patient will be agreed upon by all who analyze the case because in these situations there is only one possible therapy based upon the contraindications or other patient variables. In other cases, the correct therapy is not so straightforward and two or three alternatives may be equally acceptable. In these cases, the choice of therapy frequently rests with the individual practitioner's preference. In other cases, there may be one therapy that would be the best for the patient but other alternatives may be acceptable because of extenuating circumstances such as a history of noncompliance. Therefore, the student should use the cases in the *Workbook* to learn the method of analyzing cases rather than to learn specific facts. The answers given in these cases are usually not the only acceptable answers and other available alternatives would be equally efficacious and safe. The therapy and information given in these cases may become incorrect as new knowledge is accumulated. In some cases, the available literature is conflicting or controversial and two practitioners may have different opinions based on the available information. In all cases, the case analysis and answers to the questions pertain only to the patient involved. The information may or may not be applicable to other patients with the same problem. Therefore, the student is warned against memorizing these cases and thinking that he or she knows the material and will then be able to pass examinations. This *Workbook* allows the student to practice analyzing cases and making decisions concerning therapeutics in a situation that cannot harm a patient. By this process, the student should develop skill in therapeutics. If this *Workbook* is used as intended, the student will make a commitment to a method of treating the patient. This will be useful in developing the skills that are necessary for performance in a clinical setting. Thus, the student is encouraged to write the SOAP notes in the space provided. A single book cannot be responsible for the development of a clinical pharmacist, but this *Workbook*, in conjunction with the fourth edition of *Clinical Pharmacy and Therapeutics* and with the guidance of faculty in appropriate courses, will serve in preparing students for pharmacy practice.

Nutrition

CASE 1

CC: R.M. is a 32-year-old male who presents to the emergency room complaining of extreme tiredness, weakness, and dizziness when he stands up. He reports a 3-day history of diarrhea (3–4 times a day), nausea, and occasional vomiting.

Past Medical History

Noncontributory.

Problem List

1. Hypovolemia
2. Dehydration
3. Electrolyte abnormalities
4. Fever of unknown origin

Medication History

Multivitamin, 1 tablet q.d.
Aspirin (ASA), 650 mg q4h prn fever for the past week
Dristan, 1–2 tablets q6h prn nasal congestion for the past week

Physical Examination

GEN: Pale, thin man complaining of dry mouth, mild abdominal cramping, and feeling "sick to his stomach"
VS: BP 130/85 (lying) 120/60 (standing) HR 100 (lying) 120 (standing) T 38.2 RR 20 Wt 65 kg (usual Wt 69 kg) Ht 6'2"
HEENT: Dry mucous membranes
COR: Sinus tachycardia
CHEST: WNL
ABD: Hyperactive bowel sounds, no guarding or pain on palpation
GU: Normal
EXT: Pale, cool fingers and toes; decreased skin turgor

Results of Laboratory Tests

Na 131   BUN 30
K 2.7   Cr 1.3
Cl 92
HCO_3 29

Problem 1. Hypovolemia

S: R.M. complains of dizziness.
O: He has orthostatic hypotension, BUN/Cr >20, sinus tachycardia, and cool extremities.
A: R.M. has hypovolemia (intravascular salt and water loss) from vomiting, diarrhea, and reduced intake.
P: Begin normal saline at 500 cc/hour, reassess in 1 hour. Monitor BP, HR, urine output, and serum Na.

Problem 2. Dehydration

S: None.
O: R.M. has dry mucous membranes and decreased skin turgor.
A: R.M. is suffering from dehydration (total body salt and water loss), vomiting, diarrhea, and reduced intake; his fluid deficit is 4 liters and the sodium deficit is 350 mEq.
P: Give a total of 2 liters of normal saline (to replace the sodium deficit) and then change the intravenous solution to D5¼–½NS at 250 cc/hour for the next 24 hours. This will replace the fluid deficit and meet maintenance needs for salt and water. Reassess every 4 hours. Monitor serum Na, BP, HR, urine output, skin turgor, and mucous membranes.

Problem 3. Electrolyte Abnormalities

S: R.M. complains of weakness and tiredness.
O: K = 2.7, Cl = 92, HCO_3 = 29
A: This is hypokalemic alkalosis from vomiting, diarrhea, and reduced intake.
P: The normal saline infusion will correct the serum Cl and HCO_3. Check urinary output and if adequate, give KCl 10 mEq in 100 ml D5½ NS per hour i.v. × 4; check serum K 2 hours later, repeat potassium boluses until serum level is >4.
Monitor serum electrolytes.

Problem 4. Fever of Unknown Origin

S: A history of a "cold" is reported by patient.
O: T = 38.2
A: This is probably a self-limiting viral illness.
P: Give ASA or acetaminophen for fever q4h prn, reassess in 12 hours (at least 4 hours after last antipyretic dose). Monitor fever and GI symptoms.

CASE 2

CC: B.A. is a 5-year-old girl brought to the pediatric walk-in clinic by her parents. Three hours ago she drank 3 oz of methyl salicylate liniment that her father keeps in the bathroom medicine cabinet for treatment of minor muscular aches and pains. Since the ingestion, she progressed from irritable to agitated but is now somnolent; vomiting was not induced.

Past Medical History

Noncontributory.

Problem List

1. Metabolic acidosis
2. Respiratory alkalosis
3. Hyperkalemia
4. Hypercalcemia

Medication History

Noncontributory

Physical Examination

GEN: B.A. is a well-developed, well-nourished tachypneic girl, arousable when shaken but otherwise unresponsive. She exhibits slight muscular twitching.

VS: BP 135/80 HR 95 T 37.1 RR 34 Wt 17 kg

EXT: Small amount of muscular twitching

Remainder of physical examination is normal.

Results of Laboratory Tests

Na 142 BUN 6 Arterial blood gases (ABGs):
K 7.3 Cr 0.9 Po_2 92
Cl 96 Ca 9.3 Pco_2 29
HCO_3 13 Alb 4.3 pH 7.20

ECG: peaked T waves

Problem 1. Metabolic Acidosis

S: None.

O: pH = 7.20, HCO_3 = 13, anion gap = 38, bicarbonate deficit = 100 mEq.

A: This is primary metabolic acidosis with a positive anion gap secondary to salicylate ingestion. There has been increased renal excretion of bicarbonate to maintain electrical neutrality (not a true "bicarbonate deficit" but a compensatory mechanism).

P: Begin gastric lavage and/or charcoal to remove any remaining liniment from stomach and hemodialysis to remove the salicylate from the blood. Give 100 cc of sodium bicarbonate 8.4%, over 5–10 minutes. Reassess in 15 minutes and repeat if necessary to maintain pH >7.30.
Monitor ABGs, serum electrolytes, salicylate level, and mental status.

Problem 2. Respiratory Alkalosis

S: None.

O: Pco_2 = 32

A: B.A. has primary respiratory alkalosis secondary to central nervous system stimulation by salicylates and as a compensatory mechanism for primary metabolic acidosis.

P: As for Problem 1: Hemodialysis will remove the salicylate and correction of the metabolic acidosis will obviate the need for respiratory compensation.
Monitor RR and ABGs.

Problem 3. Hyperkalemia

S: None.

O: K = 7.3, pH = 7.20, muscular twitching, peaked T waves on ECG.

A: This is hyperkalemia secondary to a shift of potassium ions from the intracellular to the intravascular space in metabolic acidosis.

P: Rapidly correct the acidosis and maintain the pH >7.30 with sodium bicarbonate infusion. Repeat ECG, if peaked T waves persist, begin D5W with 25 U regular insulin/liter.
Monitor ECG, serum K, blood glucose, and muscle activity.

Problem 4. Hypercalcemia

S: None.

O: Ca = 9.3, Alb = 4.3, pH = 7.20

A: The free serum calcium concentration is increased secondary to displacement by hydrogen ions from albumin binding sites.

P: Correct the acidosis.
Monitor serum Ca, ABGs, and muscular twitching.

CASE 3

CC: J.L. is a 52-year-old woman admitted to the general surgery service.

Past Medical History

J.L. was in her usual state of health until 3 months ago. She began to have gnawing abdominal pain, early satiety, and occasional nausea and vomiting; these symptoms have been a chronic problem for her since a partial gastrectomy and truncal vagotomy were performed for duodenal ulcers 3 years ago. J.L. has lost 20 lb in the last 3 months. An extensive gastrointestinal workup by her private physician demonstrated a delayed gastric emptying time and a high-grade obstruction at the site of the gastrectomy. J.L. was referred for management of this problem.

Problem List

1. Gastric dysmotility syndrome
2. Malnutrition

Medication History

No current prescription or OTC medications.

Physical Examination

GEN: Thin female appears in no acute distress and is pleasant and cooperative

VS: BP 135/75 HR 78 T 36.7 RR 12 Wt 40 kg Ht 5'5"

The remainder of physical examination is normal and noncontributory.

Results of Laboratory Tests

Na 138	Glu 102	Mg 2.6
K 4.1	LFTs WNL	PO$_4$ 4.3
Cl 101	H/H 27/7.5	Ca 8.6
HCO$_3$ 24	MCV 78	TG 105
BUN 25	Alb 3.1	
Cr 0.4	TP 5.1	

Problem

S:_____

O:_____

A:_____

P:_____

Problem

S:_____

O:_____

A:_____

P:_____

Questions

1. What are the signs and symptoms of malnutrition in J.L.?
2. How should J.L.'s malnutrition be treated and what should be monitored?

CASE 4

CC: T.C. is a 45-year-old male with acute pancreatitis, peripheral edema, and a distended abdomen. His breathing is rapid and shallow secondary to his abdominal girth and severe pain. Due to intractable nausea and vomiting, he has a nasogastric tube in place that puts out 2000 cc/day.

Past Medical History

T.C. presented to the emergency room 1 week ago complaining of severe abdominal pain, nausea, and vomiting of 24 hours duration. On abdominal examination, he had extreme left upper quadrant tenderness and no other remarkable findings on physical examination. Serum amylase was 822; other lab results were within normal limits. A CT scan revealed a large inflammatory mass in the area of the pancreas. A diagnosis of acute pancreatitis was made. Since admission, T.C.'s abdominal findings have remained unchanged.

Problem List

1. Cadaver renal transplant, 12/85
2. Acute pancreatitis
3. Hypovolemia with increased total body water
4. Respiratory alkalosis
5. Electrolyte abnormalities
6. Renal dysfunction
7. Lack of oral intake for 7 days

Medication History

Medications prior to admission:

Prednisone 40 mg qd since 12/85
Azathioprine 50 mg qd since 12/85
Cyclosporine 300 mg qd since 12/85

Current medications:

Hydrocortisone 100 mg i.v. q8h
Ranitidine 50 mg i.v. q8h
Morphine SO_4 15–20 mg. i.m./s.c. q3–4h prn pain
D5½ NS with 20 mEq KCl/liter at 200 cc/hour

Physical Examination

VS: BP 100/60 HR 135 T 37.2 RR 26 Wt 73 kg (Adm. Wt 58) Ht 6'0"
HEENT: Normal
COR: Sinus tachycardia
CHEST: Diminished breath sounds, both bases
ABD: Rigid, distended abdomen; no bowel sounds; pain and guarding on palpation
GU: Normal
EXT: 3+ Peripheral and sacral edema

Results of Laboratory Tests

Na 130	BUN 18	LFTs WNL	ABGs:
K 3.2	Cr 1.2	Alb 2.2	P_{O_2} 92
Cl 96	Amy 520	Mg 1.2	P_{CO_2} 32
HCO_3 21	Glu 102	PO_4 2.1	pH 7.50

Urinalysis: SG 1.035, U_{Na} 10, U_K 48
Urine output for last 12 hours = 150 cc

Problem _____

S: _____

O: _____

A: _____

P: _____

Problem _____

S: _____

O: _____

A: _____

P: _____

Problem

S:————————————

O:————————————

A:————————————

P:————————————

Problem

S:————————————

O:————————————

A:————————————

P:————————————

problem

S:————————————

O:————————————

A:————————————

P:————————————

Problem

S:————————————

O:————————————

A:————————————

P:————————————

Problem

S:

O:

A:

P:

Diseases of the Blood

CASE 5

CC: R.J. is a 62-year-old female admitted to the hospital with a chief complaint of worsening abdominal pain and diarrhea.

History of Present Illness

R.J. has a 6-week history of abdominal pain and diarrhea. Symptoms were most severe following meals. This caused her to decrease her food intake and has resulted in a 15-lb weight loss. She claims to have taken Mylanta-II 30–45 cc every 3–6 hours to alleviate the pain, but it did not give much relief. R.J. states that the pain has become especially severe over the last 2 days. Angiography is consistent with ischemic bowel and the patient is being evaluated for surgery.

Past Medical History

R.J. has suffered mild hypertension for 7 years; it has been treated with diuretics and diet. She also has had hypercholesterolemia for 2 years; a trial of niacin therapy was discontinued 9 months ago by the patient secondary to headache and flushing. R.J. had a gastrectomy 5 years ago secondary to peptic ulcer disease. She also had a mitral valve replacement 3 years ago; since that time she has been on the anticoagulant, warfarin.

Problem List

1. Ischemic bowel
2. Iron deficiency anemia
3. Over anticoagulation
4. Hypertension
5. Hypercholesterolemia

Medication History

Warfarin 2.5 mg alternating with 5 mg qhs
Hydrochlorothiazide 25 mg q AM
Cimetidine 300 mg q hs
Mylanta II 30–45 cc q3–6h (self-prescribed)
Diazepam 5 mg qhs prn sleep

Allergies

None known.

Social History

R.J. has been smoking 2 packs of cigarettes per day for 20 years; she has unsuccessfully attempted to quit several times. R.J. drinks 3–5 glasses of wine per week.

Physical Examination

GEN: Well-developed, pale woman appears alert and in moderate distress. Patient notes that she has been feeling weak and tired.
VS: BP 130/85 HR 90 T 37.2 RR 27 Wt 54 kg
HEENT: WNL
COR: Slight tachycardia, regular rhythm, no murmurs
CHEST: Clear to auscultation and percussion
ABD: Decreased bowel sounds, no guarding or pain on deep palpation, no spleen, kidney or other masses noted
GU: Deferred
RECT: Guaiac-positive, but no bright red blood per rectum
EXT: Pale, dry skin noted; femoral pulses R 2+, L 3+; old and new bruises noted on shins, left thigh, and arms

Results of Laboratory Tests

Na 134	RBC 3.6	MCHC 30	PT 26 sec
K 4.1	Hct 27.4	Rectic 1%	PTT 89 sec
Cl 100	Hgb 8.6	Alb 2.2	Ferritin 4.6
HCO₃ 25	Plts 187k	Glu 156	Fe 33
BUN 8	MCV 72	Chol 310	TIBC 460
Cr 0.5	MCH 24	TG 175	

Problem 1. Ischemic Bowel

S: R.J. has abdominal pain, diarrhea, decreased food tolerance and decreased appetite, and nutritional deficits.

O: R.J.'s angiography is consistent with ischemic bowel. She has experienced a 15-lb weight loss. Her albumin measures 2.2; indices are consistent with iron deficiency anemia.

A: R.J. will most likely require surgery in the near future. Decreased food intake has led to nutritional deficits. SCr may be a poor indicator of renal function, since it could be low due to muscle wasting. Electrolytes are currently WNL.

P: Nothing by mouth (NPO) for now. Monitor frequency, duration, and intensity of abdominal pain. Monitor frequency of diarrhea, watch for symptoms of dehydration. Initiate total parenteral nutrition (TPN) to meet caloric and protein requirements, monitor appropriate laboratory parameters. Reassess nutrition status postoperatively.

Problem 2. Iron Deficiency Anemia

S: Pale, dry skin, feeling weak and tired, guaiac-positive, slight tachycardia

O: Hgb 8.6   Hct 27.4   RBC 3.6
   MCV 72   MCH 24   MCHC 30
   Fe 33   TIBC 460   Ferritin 4.6

A: The indices are consistent with iron deficiency anemia. In addition, the iron saturation index (Fe × 100/TIBC) = 7.1% and the corrected reticulocyte count = 0.6%.

R.J. has multiple contributing factors including a decreased intake, decreased absorption (due to gastrectomy, antacid use), and chronic GI blood loss (possibly due to anticoagulation.) The patient is going to surgery soon, so iron stores will need to be replenished. Intravenous replacement will be necessary, since the patient is n.p.o. and i.m. administration is not possible in an anticoagulated patient. There are no contraindications for intravenous iron therapy in this patient.

Total iron deficit:

$$TID = 0.66 \times (54 \text{ kg}) \times \left(100 - \frac{8.6 \times 100}{14.8}\right) = 1493 \text{ mg}$$

Volume of iron dextron injection:

$$1493 \text{ mg} \times \frac{1 \text{ ml}}{50 \text{ mg}} = 30 \text{ ml iron dextran}$$

P: Check the peripheral blood smear to assess RBC morphology. Check vitamin B_{12} and folate levels to rule out deficiencies of these since gastrectomy and decreased dietary intake could also deplete these stores. Begin parenteral iron therapy: Dilute 30-ml preservative-free iron dextran in 250–500 ml NS. Give a 10-mg test dose (1.5–3 ml) and observe for 1 hour for acute reactions. Infuse the remaining dose over 2–3 hours. During the infusion, monitor for thrombophlebitis, flushing, fever, and dyspnea. Monitor over the next week for arthralgias and myalgias, an increase in reticulocytes, Hgb, and a normalization of indices.

Problem 3. Over Anticoagulation

S: Guaiac-positive; bruises on shins, arms, and left thigh.

O: PT 26 sec   PTT 89 sec   Plts 187 k

A: The over anticoagulation is likely due to inadequate intake of dietary vitamin K and depletion of stores. Keep the patient therapeutically anticoagulated until surgery. Since the patient is n.p.o., give heparin; the goal is to maintain PTT 60–90 sec. Discontinue heparin 2–3 hours prior to surgery. Give fresh frozen plasma (FFP) if PT has not returned to a normal value.

P: Discontinue warfarin now. Initiate heparin therapy; a bolus is not required since the PTT is elevated. Monitor PTT, PT, and Hct. Check for symptoms of bleeding; continue to guaiac stools and check urine for hematuria. If bleeding occurs, discontinue the heparin infusion and give fresh-frozen plasma. Avoid intramuscular injections. Initiate education of the patient regarding anticoagulant therapy. Suggest obtaining identification (Medi-Alert) bracelet, if not done already.

Problem 4. Hypertension

S: No symptoms.

O: BP 130/85

A: The hypertension is fairly well controlled but R.J. will require monitoring.

P: Since the patient will be n.p.o., change to furosemide 10 mg i.v. q.d. Monitor BP, Na, K, and fluid status. Encourage the patient to stop smoking, or at least to decrease the amount. (Determine what methods the patient tried in the past and make suggestions for increased success.)

Problem 5. Hypercholesterolemia

S: R.J. has decreased femoral pulses and hypertension.

O: Cholesterol 310 mg/dl.

A: This is not an immediate problem, but will need to be addressed when patient is taking oral feeding.

P: Provide dietary counseling. If necessary, consider a second trial of niacin starting at low doses and titrating up. Alternatives include bile acid binding resins or lovastatin.

CASE 6

CC: P.S. is an obese (82 kg) 61-year-old male with a chief complaint of a progressive ulceration of the left medial heel.

History of Present Illness

P.S. was in his usual state of health until 2 weeks ago when he noticed what looked like an infected blister on his left heel. Since the blister was not painful, he assumed it was "getting better." Two days prior to admission P.S. went on a long walk. That evening he noted that the area had become deeper and larger with a purulent discharge. The surrounding area was red and tender to touch. P.S. has a long history of diabetes that has been poorly controlled. He occasionally monitors his urine glucose, and states he would be willing to perform blood glucose monitoring but he does not know how. He says that he lacks his usual energy, even though he has given up drinking. Morning stiffness lasts 2–4 hours with decreased range of motion (ROM) in hands and wrists.

Past Medical History

P.S. has had non-insulin-dependent diabetes for 31 years. He had a seizure disorder diagnosed 10 years ago. He has renal insufficiency, which has progressively worsened over the last 2–3 years. P.S. also has had rheumatoid arthritis for 8 years; severe flare-ups have been managed with steroids. The flares have involved his hips, feet, shoulder, and particularly his wrists and hands.

Problem List

1. Infected heel ulcer
2. Mixed anemia
3. Diabetes
4. Rheumatoid arthritis

Current Medications

Phenytoin 100 mg p.o. t.i.d. × 10 years
Glyburide 7.5 mg po q AM × 3 years
Enteric-coated aspirin 325 mg 3 tablets q.i.d. × 6 years
Maalox 15–30 ml prn (usually 2–3 × week)

Allergies

P.S. is allergic to penicillin; he experienced hives and swelling 15 or 20 years ago. He is also allergic to sulfa; he had severe nausea from cotrimoxazole during a prior hospitalization 2 years ago.

Social History

P.S. has had a history of alcoholism for 15 years; he is now a member of Alcoholics Anonymous. His last drink was 8 months ago. P.S. has smoked 1–2 packs of cigarettes a day for 30 years; he claims to be smoking less now than in previous years.

Physical Examination

GEN: Obese, well-developed male appears alert, cooperative, and in no apparent distress.
VS: BP 130/85 HR 85, regular RR 18 T 37.9 Wt 82 kg
HEENT: WNL
COR: WNL
CHEST: Clear to auscultation and percussion, no rales or rubs
ABD: Obese and protruding, no palpable masses
GU: WNL
RECT: WNL
EXT: 3-cm red ulcer on left medial heel with purulent discharge. Scratches on shins. Diffuse synovial thickening in small joints, especially MCP and MTP joints bilaterally.

Results of Laboratory Tests

Na 138	Hct 28	MCHC 31	TIBC 220
K 4.8	Hgb 7	Retic 1.2%	Glu 310
Cl 101	WBC 8.2k	Alb 2.8	PT 12.6 sec
HCO$_3$ 25	Plt 105k	Folate 2	PTT 34 sec
BUN 36	MCV 90	Fe 39	Hgb A$_1$^{c} 13.4%
Scr 2.1	MCH 23	Vit B$_{12}$ 186	Sed rate 63
RBC 3.7			

Urinalysis: Pending.
Culture from ulcer: Pending.
Peripheral blood smear: Macrocytic hypersegmented cells, many bizarre poikilocytes and target cells.

Problem 1: Infected Heel Ulcer

S: Patient has red ulcer on heel with purulent discharge.
O: Cultures are pending; WBC 8.2k, T 37.9
A: The infected heel ulcer is probably due to poor circulation and foot care in this diabetic patient.
P: Administer empiric i.v. antibiotics until cultures and sensitivities return, then adjust appropriately. Avoid penicillins and possibly cephalosporins in light of the patient's penicillin allergy history. Check blood cultures if his temperature spikes or an increase in WBCs occurs. Start patient education on proper foot care for a diabetic patient.

Problem 2: Mixed Anemia

S: Patient complains of "lack of usual energy".
O:

Hgb 28	Findings	Folate 2
Hct 7	on smear	Vit B$_{12}$ 186
Retic 1.2%	MCV 90	Fe 39
Plts 105k	MCH 23	TIBC 220
	MCHC 31	

A: The laboratory data are consistent with a mixed anemia due to folate deficiency and anemia of chronic disease (ACD). Factors contributing to folate deficiency include prior history of alcoholism with poor dietary intake and prolonged phenytoin use. Factors contributing to ACD include chronic renal insufficiency and rheumatoid arthritis. P.S. does not currently have iron deficiency (iron saturation index WNL) or vitamin B$_{12}$ deficiency (vitamin B$_{12}$ level WNL).
P: Give folate to meet metabolic demands and replace body stores. Prescribe folate 1–5 mg p.o. qd × 2–3 weeks. Check Hct, Hgb. indices, and folate level to assess efficacy of treatment. Hgb, and RBC indices may not normalize in the face of ACD. Iron therapy will not normalize Fe or TIBC. Monitor for seizures.

Problem 3. Diabetes

S: Patient has history of diabetes.
O: Glu 310 HgbA$_{1c}$ 13.4%
A: His diabetes is poorly controlled by his current regimen. Assess patient compliance. The stress of the foot infection may be aggravating glucose control.
P: While patient is in the hospital, continue the current regimen of glyburide 7.5 mg p.o. qd, 1 hour before breakfast and also cover with sliding scale insulin. If necessary, devise a regimen

that gives better control. Monitor blood glucose (goal is 140–180 mg/100 ml), urine glucose, and signs of hypoglycemia or hyperglycemia. Begin patient education regarding diet, home blood glucose monitoring, recognizing signs of hypoglycemia and hyperglycemia, and how to manage these.

Problem 4. Rheumatoid Arthritis

S: P.S. has morning stiffness, decreased hand/wrist ROM, and a history of RA flares.

O: P.S. has bilateral MTP and MCP swelling and stiffness.

A: This is not a major problem at this time.

P: Continue current enteric-coated aspirin.

CASE 7

CC: E.T. is a 65-year-old male admitted to the hospital for evaluation of fever and changing mental status.

History of Present Illness

Three days ago E.T. was found by his roommate drunk on the floor of their apartment; 1 day later E.T. started to experience chills and fever.

Past Medical History

E.T. has a history of alcoholism, alcoholic liver disease, and peptic ulcer disease. He had aspiration pneumonia three times in the past 2 years. He also has had analgesic nephropathy and is G-6-P-D deficient. E.T. also has hypertension, which is being controlled with medications.

Problem List

1. Alcoholism
2. Alcoholic liver disease
3. Peptic ulcer disease
4. History of aspiration pneumonia (3 times in the past 2 years)
5. History of analgesic nephropathy
6. G-6-P-D deficient
7. History of hypertension (controlled on medications)
8. Rule out sepsis, possible aspiration pneumonia
9. Fluid and electrolyte imbalance
10. Anemia
11. Renal impairment

Medication History

Furosemide 80 mg p.o. q.d.
Aspirin 650 mg p.o. for fever and headaches
Methyldopa 500 mg p.o. b.i.d.
Naproxen 250 mg p.o. b.i.d.
Cimetidine 800 mg p.o. qhs
Acetaminophen 500 mg with hydrocodone 5 mg p.o. q.i.d.
Quinine sulfate 650 mg p.o. qhs prn for leg cramps

Physical Examination

VS: BP 100/50 HR 108 (sitting) BP 120/80 HR 85 (supine) RR 34 T 39 Wt 70 kg (normal 75 kg)

HEENT: Scleral icterus, two facial bruises

ABD: Girth 50″, with (+) fluid wave (ascites)

RECT: Guaiac-positive

EXT: Multiple bruises and petechiae were noted on thighs and legs

SKIN: Dry and warm, poor turgor

Results of Laboratory Tests

Na 155	Hct 25	MCH 32	Glu 80	Fe 29
K 5.6	Hgb 9	Ast 120	Ca 8.5	TIBC 350
Cl 109	WBC 19.5	Alt 260	PO$_4$ 1.6	Coombs (+)
HCO$_3$ 18	Plts 250	Alb 3.0	Mg 1.3	Folate 1.8
BUN 90	MCV 95	T Bili 5.2	PT 16.2	B$_{12}$ 200
Cr 4.0				

Peripheral blood smear: Microcytes and macrocytes with hemolyzed RBCs

ABGs (on room air): pH 7.32, Po$_2$ 60, Pco$_2$ 60

Problem

S:

O:

A:

P:

Problem

S:

O:

A:

P:

Problem

S:

O:

A:

P:

Problem

S:

O:

A:

P:

Problem

S:

O:

A:

P:

Problem

S:

O:

A:

P:

Problem

S:

O:

A:

P:

Problem

S:

O:

A:

P:

Problem

S:

O:

A:

P:

Problem
S:
O:
A:
P:

Problem
S:
O:
A:
P:

Questions

1. List the most likely drug-related causes for E.T.'s anemia.
2. How would you treat E.T.'s anemia?
3. What monitoring parameters and patient education would you give to E.T.?
4. Define this patient's fluid and acid-base status.
5. How would you acutely treat E.T.'s fluid and acid-base abnormalities? Specifically include the type of fluid, rate, electrolytes, and monitoring parameters.

CASE 8

CC: M.S. is an 18-year-old male with hemophilia A, admitted to the ER with acute abdominal pain. The patient has never had abdominal pain in the past.

History of Present Illness

M.S. was in his usual state of health until last evening when he noted the onset of mild to moderate abdominal pain. The pain remained mild until noon today, when it became localized and much worse in intensity. The pain has been steadily worsening, and the patient reports dizziness and headaches when standing. Ibuprofen makes the abdominal pain worse and lying still relieves it. The patient had nausea today, but no vomitting or diarrhea. He noted mild discomfort with urination. He denies any history of trauma, but went white-water rafting 48 hours prior to admission.

The patient received 1600 U of Factor VIII concentrate intravenously at home before coming to the ER. A "trough" Factor VIII level was obtained in the ER before an additional 1600 U of Factor VIII concentrate was given.

Past Medical History

Multiple previous admissions for bleeding episodes.

Problem List

1. Hemophilia A
2. Acute abdominal pain
3. Pain control
4. Nausea

Medication History

Patient currently on Factor VIII concentrate prn.

Allergies

Hives with ampicillin.
Multiple environmental allergens.

Social History

M.S. denies tobacco, alcohol, or recreational drug use.

Physical Examination

GEN: Well-developed, well-nourished male. Alert and cooperative in distress, but stoic and without diaphoresis.

VS: BP 120/78 HR 100 (sitting); BP 108/72 HR 120 (standing) T 36.7 RR 16

HEENT: Nose and mouth clear, PERRLA, tympanic membranes normal

COR: Regular rhythm, normal heart sounds

CHEST: Clear, without rubs

ABD: High-pitched bowel sounds throughout, nondistended, (+) percussion tenderness, especially in midleft abdominal region. No masses.

GU: WNL, patient notes mild discomfort with urination, incomplete bladder emptying and some dribbling.

RECT: Deferred secondary to hemophiliac status.

EXT: WNL

NEURO: WNL

SKIN: Clear, no visible bruising or marks

Results of Laboratory Tests

Na 136	BUN 19	WBC 6.8	PTT 38.2
K 3.8	Cr 0.8	Plts 206k	Factor VIII
Cl 106	Hct 44.7	Glu 100	Activity level 46%
HCO$_3$ 20	Hgb 15.8	PT 11.8 sec	

Problem _____

S: _____

O: _____

A: _____

P: _____

Problem _____

S: _____

O: _____

A: _____

P: _____

Problem _____

S: _____

O: _____

A: _____

P: _____

Problem

S:

O:

A:

P:

SECTION/3

Endocrine and Metabolic Disease

CASE 9

CC: R.S. is a 65-year-old male who was brought to the emergency room in a semicomatose state. His wife reports that he has not felt well since his last clinic visit 4 weeks ago. He complained of muscle aches, nausea, and loss of appetite; he vomited often. She says that this week his flu got much worse; he became much weaker, was dizzy even in bed, had severe vomiting and diarrhea, ran a fever, and complained that every muscle in his body ached. She made sure that he took all of his medications in addition to taking two aspirin every 4 hours for the fever and terrible headaches that made him confused.

Past Medical History

R.S. first presented to the medical clinic 6 months ago with signs and symptoms of Cushing's syndrome. The diagnosis of adenocarcinoma of the left adrenal gland was made. Three months ago he underwent a left adrenalectomy and was placed on steroid replacement therapy. Over the past 2 months his prednisone was tapered, and on his last clinic visit it was reduced to 5 mg q.d. for 3 weeks, after which it was discontinued. Other past medical history includes essential hypertension previously controlled with diuretics.

Problem List

1. Addisonian crisis
2. Hypovolemia
3. Hyponatremic dehydration
4. Hyperkalemia
5. Hypoglycemia
6. Anemia
7. Hypertension

Medication History

Prednisone 5 mg q.d., discontinued 1 week prior to admission
Hydrochlorothiazide (HCTZ) 50 mg q.d.
Aspirin 325 mg q.d. and 650 mg prn headache
KCl 20 mEq b.i.d.

Physical Examination

GEN: Febrile, unresponsive male in acute distress
VS: BP 80/45 HR 130 RR 30 T 39.6 Wt 65 kg (80 kg 4 weeks ago)
HEENT: Moon facies; pale gums
CHEST: Lungs clear
COR: NLS1, S2, no S3; heart rate rapid and irregular
ABD: Nontender, bowel sounds present
EXT: No palpable pulses; proximal muscle weakness and wasting; cool, cyanotic hands and feet; pale nail beds
SKIN: Dry, papery, tenting; numerous ecchymoses especially at pressure points; striae over chest and abdomen

Results of Laboratory Tests

Na 125	Hct 36	MCHC 33
K 7	Hgb 12	FBS 50
Cl 90	WBC 3.5	Ca 9.8
HCO_3 25	Plts 50	PO_4 4.5
BUN 45	MCV 90	Alb 4
Cr 1.6	MCH 32	

Lung function tests: WNL
WBC Differential: PMN 50, lym 40, eos 10, mono 5
ECG: Tachycardia, irregular rate, 8 premature ventricular beats per minute, peaked T waves

Problem 1: Addisonian Crisis

S: R.S. complains of flu-like symptoms, muscle aches, nausea, anorexia, vomiting, confusion, dizziness, and headaches.

O: R.S. had a left adrenalectomy and recently discontinued his prednisone. His vital signs are BP 80/45, HR 130, and RR 30; there has been a 15-kg weight loss in the last 4 weeks. His Hct, Hgb, WBC, and PMN are decreased and eosinophils are increased. He is hypoglycemic (FBS 50); his Na and Cl are decreased, while his K is increased and there is evidence of hypovolemic dehydration including an increased BUN and Cr and a BUN/Cr >20.

A: R.S. had an adrenal carcinoma with a left adrenalectomy 3 months prior to admission and was treated with prednisone, which was recently tapered and discontinued. Because of the adrenal carcinoma, R.S. has HPA axis suppression and right adrenal atrophy. Stress due to the flu without corticosteroid management for stress precipitated the current problem. Although the patient has signs of Cushing's syndrome, he is in adrenal crisis. R.S. is in acute distress (near shock); the potentially life-threatening situation requires immediate treatment.

P: Immediately give an i.v. dose of hydrocortisone sodium succinate or phosphate 100 mg, repeat q8h for 48 hours, then taper rapidly by decreasing the dose by 20–30% q.d. (see schedule below) to a maintenance dose of oral hydrocortisone 30 mg q.d. Change to an oral dosage form as soon as tolerated and split the maintenance dose 20 mg q AM and 10 mg in late afternoon. Hydrocortisone is preferred because it has mineralocorticoid activity.

Taper schedule:	75 mg q8h	Each dose should
	50 mg q8h	be given for
	40 mg q8h	1–2 days
	30 mg q8h	
	20 mg q8h	
	20, 20, 10 mg given t.i.d.	
	20 mg b.i.d.	
	Maintenance	

If required, give fludrocortisone 0.1 mg p.o. qd for 2 days; titrate the dose between 0.05 and 0.2 mg. Generally this treatment is not required because hydrocortisone possesses enough mineralocorticoid activity. Obtain cortisol and ACTH levels prior to giving the hydrocortisone; follow levels at 4-week intervals for return of endogenous cortisol production. Follow signs and symptoms of adrenal insufficiency: muscle aches, nausea, vomiting, anorexia, diarrhea, confusion, headache, dizziness, dehydration, changes in serum electrolytes, and signs and symptoms of excess steroids; Na and water retention, personality changes, elevated blood sugar, and insomnia. Provide R.S. with patient education including compliance with steroid dosing and the details of stress management (doubling daily dose for illnesses); signs and symptoms of steroid deficiency (may expect mild fatigue) and steroid excess. R.S. should get an identification (Medi-Alert) bracelet.

Problem 2. Hypovolemia

S: R.S. complains of being dizzy in bed, vomiting, and diarrhea.

O: BP 80/45. HR 130. There are no palpable peripheral pulses and his hands and feet are cyanotic.

A: R.S. is semicomatose with an elevated heart rate, low blood pressure, and no peripheral pulses; he requires immediate fluid support to increase his intravascular volume and maintain tissue perfusion.

P: Infuse 1 liter of D10NS over an hour. D10 will correct the hypoglycemia and NS will replete the intravascular volume. Monitor BP, HR, peripheral pulses, temperature of hands and feet, and urine output.

Problem 3. Hyponatremic Dehydration

S: R.S. complains of dizziness, anorexia, vomiting, diarrhea, and a fever.

O: BP 80/45, HR 130, RR 30, T 39.6, weight loss, cyanotic hands and feet, skin dry and tenting. BUN/Cr ratio >20:1, Na 125

A: R.S. has severe hyponatremia and dehydration due to lack of mineralocorticoid (aldosterone), diuretic use, and probable low intake in combination with vomiting and diarrhea. He needs immediate fluid and sodium replacement as well as maintenance fluids.

P: Discontinue the diuretic. Infuse 1 liter D10NS as above.

Calculate the fluid deficit:

$$[(140 - 125)/140] \times 0.6(65) = 4 \text{ liters}$$

Add to daily fluid maintenance requirement:

$$2.4 \text{ liters} + 4 \text{ liters} = 6.4 \text{ liters}$$

Calculate Na deficit:

$$(140 - 125) \times 0.6(65) = 585 \text{ mEq}$$

Add to daily Na maintenance requirement:

$$72 + 585 = 657 \text{ mEq}$$

The patient's 24-hour fluid requirement is 6.4 liters, each containing 66 mEq Na. This is not a practical i.v. fluid, therefore, give 3 liters of D10NS over the next 12 hours (250 ml/hour) and follow with 2.4 liters of D10½NS at a rate of 200 ml/hour. Monitor BP, HR, RR, serum and urine Na, BUN, Cr, mental status, urine output, skin turgor and color, peripheral pulses, and temperature.

Problem 4. Hypoglycemia

S: R.S. complains of nausea and is confused.

O: Semicomatose, FBS 50.

A: The patient is unresponsive and currently hemoconcentrated, therefore his blood glucose is lower than that measured by the laboratory. He has no history of diabetes or insulin use, therefore, his hypoglycemia probably stems from his lack of cortisol. He needs treatment to avoid coma and possible brain damage.

P: Give 50 ml of 50% dextrose immediately and follow with D10 as above. Monitor blood glucose, mental status, and urine for glucose and ketones.

Problem 5. Hyperkalemia

S: R.S. complains of weakness and muscle aches.

O: K 7.0, ECG: irregular heart rate and peaked T waves

A: A lack of aldosterone and potassium supplementation have precipitated this problem. The patient has cardiac symptoms of hyperkalemia and requires immediate treatment. Long-term treatment may not be necessary with resolution of the acute situation and adequate fluid replacement.

P: Discontinue KCl. Give 5–10 mEq calcium chloride or gluconate stat, by slow i.v. push while monitoring the ECG for resolution of the arrhythmia and alternation of the T wave morphology. Add 20 units of regular insulin to each liter of i.v. fluid until the serum K is within normal limits. Adding 1 U of regular insulin for every 2–3 g of dextrose given will drive the potassium into the cells and temporarily reduce the serum potassium. For permanent removal of potassium, use an ion exchange resin such as sodium polystyrene sulfonate 30–50 g (available as a suspension in 50 ml of 70% sorbitol) added to 100 ml of tap water as a retention enema (0.5–1 hour). This will reduce the serum potassium by 0.5–2 mEq/liter by exchanging it for an equivalent amount of Na. Monitor the serum K q4h during fluid replacement and the ECG constantly until the patient is stabilized.

Problem 6. Anemia/Thrombocytopenia/Leukopenia

S: Patient complains of weakness.

O: HR 130 and irregular, RR 30, pale gums and nail beds, Hct 36, Hgb 12, RBC 3.5, MCV 90, MCH 32, MCHC 33, WBC 3.5, and Plts 50

A: RBC indices are within normal limits, but the RBC, WBC and platelet count are decreased. The patient is dehydrated, therefore although below normal, the Hct and Hgb are falsely elevated. The patient's HPA axis is suppressed, which may have resulted in decreased androgenic steroid production and consequent bone marrow hypoplasia. He also has been taking aspirin frequently and may have blood loss anemia. R.S. needs further evaluation and long-term treatment may be required.

P: Check the blood smear, a reticulocyte count, serum iron, Fe/TIBC ratio, and stool guaiac for occult bleeding. If androgenic steroids are required, give testosterone 200–400 mg/kg i.m. 2 times a week or fluoxymesterone 2–30 mg qd. Transfusion for blood loss is not required unless the hematocrit falls below 20–30%. Monitor CBC with platelets, reticulocyte count, and signs and symptoms of anemia, bleeding or infection and of androgen excess: virilization, Na and water retention, and muscle aches.

Problem 7. Hypertension

S: None.

O: History.

A: R.S. is not currently hypertensive, and no treatment is required at the present time.

P: Discontinue HCTZ and have the patient return to the clinic after discharge for follow-up. Monitor BP and HR.

CASE 10

CC: I.V. is a 70 year-old woman who was admitted to the hospital after being found wandering in the hallways of the general medicine clinic disoriented, vomiting, and complaining of bone pain, fatigue, and thirst.

History of Present Illness

I.V. has a 3-year history of diffuse bone pain that has become progressively worse over the last 60 months. She also complains of several months of increasing lethargy, muscle weakness, and feeling cold all the time. A bone scan 6 months ago revealed multiple areas of uptake with osteoblastic lesions in the midshaft of the femur, and skull films showed diffuse demineralization. A bone biopsy showed osteitis fibrosis cystica and a subsequent parathyroid hormone level (PTH) was 9600 and serum calcium was 10.1. The patient had been lost to follow-up until her presentation in clinic today.

Past Medical History

I.V. has had hypothyroidism for 15 years; she had a thyroid irradiation in 1972. I.V. also has had hypertension for 1.5 years. She has had hyperparathyroidism with osteitis fibrosis cystica for 6 months.

Problem List

1. Acute hypercalcemia
2. Hyperparathyroidism
3. Hypovolemia/dehydration
4. Hypothyroidism
5. Hypertension

Medication History

Levothyroxine 50 μg p.o. q.d.
Hydrochlorothiazide 50 mg p.o. b.i.d
Calcium carbonate 1250 mg 1 tablet p.o. t.i.d.
Multivitamin 1 tablet p.o. q.d.
Docusate 100 mg p.o. b.i.d.
Acetaminophen and codeine 60 mg p.o. prn pain
Diphenhydramine 25 mg p.o. qhs prn sleep

Physical Examination

GEN: Chronically ill-appearing female in moderate distress.

VS: BP 130/85 HR 80 (sitting) BP 110/70 HR 90 (standing) RR 16 T 37 Wt 43.4 kg

HEENT: Normal cephalic atraumatic (NC/AT); pupils: equal, round, reactive to light and accommodation (PERRLA); extraocular muscles intact (EOMI)

COR: Negative jugular venous distention (JVD), normal carotids, regular rhythm and rate (RRR), first and second heart sounds (S1,S2) normal

CHEST: Clear

ABD: (+) Bowel sounds (BS), soft without masses, no organomegaly

GU: Deferred

RECTAL: Guaiac-negative

EXT: Diffuse bone tenderness; (+) swelling (L) fourth finger; (+) tenderness (R) forearm; cold dry skin, poor turgor

NEURO: Decreased deep tendon reflexes (DTRs)

Results of Laboratory Tests

Na 137	Hct 38.1	Alb 2.8
K 3.6	Hgb 12.3	FBS 120
Cl 101	WBC 9.9	Ca 14.1
HCO_3 35	Plts 209k	PO_4 3.2
Bun 36	AST 18	Mg 2.0
Cr 1.2	Alk Phos 77	PTH >9000

Thyroid function tests: T_4 4, RT_3U 25, TSH 20
Urine electrolytes: Pending
CT scan: > 1 cm adenoma in parathyroid gland

Problem 1. Acute Hypercalcemia

S: I.V. complains of diffuse bone pain, vomiting, fatigue, and thirst, and is disoriented.

O: The PTH level, alkaline phosphatase, and serum calcium are increased. The serum calcium must be corrected for a low albumin; Ca = 14.1. Choose normal albumin = 4 so 4 − 2.8 = 1.2. 1.2 × 0.8 (correction factor) = 0.96 or 1. 14.1 + 1 = 15.1, which is the corrected serum Ca. I.V. also has bone disease and orthostatic blood pressure changes.

A: This is an acute hypercalcemic crisis. Contributory factors include supplementary calcium intake and a thiazide diuretic. The serum calcium must be lowered, as the patient is symptomatic and more serious manifestations such as cardiac arrhythmias must be avoided, before the underlying disease is treated.

P: Discontinue the calcium and hydrochlorothiazide. Replace her fluids with normal saline 1 liter i.v. over 2–4 hours or until urine output is 100 ml/hour. Then add furosemide 20–100 mg i.v. q1–2h and monitor urine volume hourly, check urinary Mg and K periodically to assess the extent of losses and determine the need for intravenous replacement. Get a 24-hour urine creatinine, urine Ca and hydroxyproline, and another serum Ca and PO_4. If the Ca is still high, add mithramycin 12.5–25 μg/kg i.v. over 30 minutes, which should lower the serum calcium within 48 hours. Monitor liver function tests, CBC with a differential, prothrombin time, partial thromboplastin time, fever, vomiting and an urinalysis. Ambulate the patient as much as possible because immobilization may increase serum Ca in some patients. The goal is to lower the serum Ca to a reasonably safe level of <12 mg/dl.

Problem 2. Hyperparathyroidism

S: I.V. complains of bone pain, vomiting, fatigue, and thirst and is disoriented.

O: The PTH level, alkaline phosphatase, and serum calcium are increased. There is evidence of bone disease, hypertension, and dehydration; the CT scan shows an adenoma.

A: I.V. has hypercalcemia, elevated PTH levels, bone disease; CT findings are consistent with hyperparathyroidism.

P: I.V. will require surgery when the hypercalcemic crisis is resolved and she is stable. Her fluid intake should be maintained, and oral furosemide and oral phosphate (not to exceed 1 g elemental per day) should be continued to control serum calcium until that time.

Problem 4. Hypothyroidism

S: I.V. complains of fatigue, lethargy, muscle weakness, cold intolerance, and dry skin.

O: Laboratory data shows a decreased T_4, low-normal RT_3U, decreased FTI, and increased TSH; her DTRs are decreased.

A: Her treatment is inadequate since the patient is hypothyroid clinically as well as objectively; she should be euthyroid. The dose is low for her weight, i.e., approximately 1 μg/lb would be appropriate. Elderly patients often require less.

P: Increase dose of levothyroxine to 75 μg p.o. q.d. for 1 month and reassess. Monitor thyroid function tests (TFTs) in 4–6 weeks. Provide patient education about cardiotoxicity of thyroid including palpitations, chest pain, and shortness of breath. Instruct I.V. to call the clinic if any of these occur.

Problem 3. Hypovolemia/Dehydration

S: I.V. complains of thirst and has dry skin with poor turgor.

O: Her blood pressure and pulse change on standing and sitting, and she has an increased BUN.

A: The signs and symptoms are consistent with hypovolemia/dehydration secondary to hypercalcemia, the use of the thiazide diuretic, and possible inadequate fluid intake.

P: Rehydrate as in Problem 1. Monitor BP and HR, standing and sitting. Monitor skin turgor, fluid input and output, serum electrolytes, and BUN and Cr. Maintain fluid intake.

Problem 5. Hypertension

S: None.

O: BP 130/85; history of hypertension for 1.5 years

A: I.V. is not hypertensive by the evidence presented; her hypertension could be masked by the hypovolemia. Also, hypertension could be a complication of hyperparathyroidism.

P: Once the patient is rehydrated, reassess BP. Need to measure blood pressure two to three times in the clinic after discharge.

On day 5 of hospitalization and day 2 postparathyroidectomy, I.V.'s chief complaint is recurrent muscle spasms in her limbs as well as acute abdominal pain. She is visibly agitated. On physical examination, her vital signs are stable and her laboratory values are within the normal limits with the exception of Ca 5.9, albumin 3.0, and PTH, which is pending.

Problem List

1. Acute hypercalcemia, resolved
2. Hyperparathyroidism, resolved
3. Hypovolemia, resolved
4. Hypothyroidism
5. Hypertension
6. Severe hypocalcemia
7. Hypoparathyroidism

Problem 6. Severe Hypocalcemia

S: I.V. complains of muscle spasms in her limbs and abdominal pain and is agitated.

O: Her corrected Ca level is 6.7 mg/100 ml.

A: I.V. has severe hypocalcemia complicated by tetany, most likely due to hypoparathyroidism after parathyroidectomy. Her serum Ca levels must be increased to prevent further tetany and other life-threatening sequalae such as laryngeal stridor and convulsions.

P: Administer calcium gluconate 10% i.v. at a rate of 10–20 ml/hour and maintain that rate until her serum Ca is >7 mg/100 ml. The goal is a Ca between 8–9 mg/100 ml. Also, start calcium 1–2 g q.d. and calcitriol 1–3 μg/day as soon as the patient is able to take oral medications in order to taper her off of the intravenous calcium once the serum Ca is under control. Vitamin D2 10,000–25,000 units/day p.o. could be used instead of calcitriol since it is cheaper. Monitor serum Ca, PO_4, and Mg levels. Monitor renal function if giving calcitriol. Monitor muscle spasms and abdominal pain as well.

Problem 7. Hypoparathyroidism

S: I.V. has muscle spasms, abdominal pain, and agitation.

O: I.V. has a low serum Ca.

A: The hypocalcemia and the history of parathyroidectomy are consistent with hypoparathyroidism.

P: Check a PTH level, monitor serum Ca, PO_4 levels when hypocalcemia is resolved. The goal is to maintain eucalcemia with vitamin D. Once past the "hungry bone" syndrome, try to taper off the calcium preparations.

I.V. is discharged from the hospital after 18 days with the following medication: calcium carbonate 1250 mg p.o. q.i.d., levothyroxine 75 μg p.o. q.d., and docusate 100 mg p.o. b.i.d. She returns to the general medicine clinic 2 weeks later for follow-up of her hypertension, hypothyroidism, and hypoparathyroidism. She is feeling more "peppy" and her bone pain does not bother her as much.

Physical examination

VS: BP 130/85 HR 78 RR 16 T 37

Results of Laboratory Tests

Na 138	Cr 1.2	Alb 3.1
K 3.8	Hct 38.4	FBG 135
HCO_3 24	Hgb 12.8	Ca 8.4
Cl 103	WBC 9k	PO_4 3.1
BUN 16	Plts 21k	Mg 2.0

Thyroid function tests: T_4 9, RT_3U 30, TSH 3.5

Medication History

Levothyroxine 75 μg p.o. qd
Calcium carbonate 1250 mg p.o. q.i.d.
Docusate 100 mg p.o. b.i.d.
Multivitamin p.o. q.d.
Diphenhydramine 25 mg p.o. qhs prn insomnia
Acetaminophen 1 caplet p.o. prn pain (never takes more than 4/day)
Vitamin D2 25,000 U q.d.

Problem List

4. Hypothyroidism
5. Hypertension
7. Hypoparathyroidism

Problem 7. Hypoparathyroidism

S: None.

O: Her Ca level is within normal limits.

A: There is good control of her serum calcium.

P: Continue calcium and vitamin D supplements. Monitor serum Ca every 3 months or sooner if patient becomes symptomatic again.

Problem 4. Hypothyroidism

S: Patient states she is "feeling more peppy."

O: T_4, TSH, RT_3U within normal limits. FTI = $T_4 \times RT_3U$ = 2.7 normal

A: I.V. is subjectively and objectively euthyroid.

P: Continue levothyroxine 75 μg p.o. q.d. Monitor TFTs every 6 months. If I.V. become symptomatic of either hypothyroidism or hyperthyroidism, she should come to the clinic.

Problem 5. Hypertension

S: None.

O: BP 130/85 HR 78

A: I.V. is not currently hypertensive, however two more BP readings are required to make final assessment.

P: Get two more BP readings.

CASE 11

CC: A.H. is a 57-year-old male referred to the diabetic clinic by his local physician for evaluation of his diabetic control. He was diagnosed as an obese, type II diabetic about 15 months ago. Despite numerous attempts with diet control, A.H. failed to have satisfactory weight reduction. His fasting blood glucose concentration has risen lately and ranged from 230–260 mg/100 ml over the last 2 weeks and his HgbA$_{1c}$ has ranged from 11–13%. He denies nausea, vomiting, palpitations, chest pain, or shortness of breath, however, he complains of weakness, fatigue, increased urination and increased thirst. He states that his allergies have started again, and he needs more pseudoephedrine for his nasal congestion.

Past Medical History

A.H. has had hypertension (HTN) for 10 years.

He has Type II diabetes mellitus (DM), atrial flutter, and seasonal allergies.

Problem List

1. Type II diabetes mellitus
2. Hypertension
3. Atrial fluttter
4. Seasonal allergies

Family History

A.H.'s father died of myocardial infarction at age 60. His mother is alive; she has DM and HTN.

Social History

A.J. smokes one to two packs per day and drinks three to four beers per day

Allergies

Pollen
Dust
Sulfa→rash

Medication History

Hydrochlorothiazide (HCTZ) 50 mg qd
KCL 20 mEq q AM
Propranolol 10 mg q.i.d.
Digoxin 0.25 mg qd
Pseudoephedrine 60 mg p.o. q6h prn congestion

Physical Examination

GEN: Obese man in no acute distress
VS: BP 154/96 (previous BP readings have ranged from 150/90 to 160/96) HR 88-regular RR 18 T 37.4 Wt 90 kg (up 3 kg) Ht 5'8"

Results of Laboratory Test

Na 140   BUN 21
K 4.5   Cr 1.9
Cl 100
HCO_3 30

Random BG = 340 mg/100 ml, (last week 360 mg/100 ml)
$HgbA_{1c}$ = 10% (last week 11%)
Urinalysis: 2+ glucose, negative ketone, negative protein, (last week 2+ glucose, negative ketone)

Problem 1. Diabetes Mellitus

S: A.H. complains of polyuria, polydipsia, weakness, and fatigue.
O: Random blood glucose = 340–360 mg/100 ml, FBS 230–260 mg/100 ml, $HgbA_{1c}$ = 11–13%, UA: 2+ glucose, Wt = 90kg, Ht 5'8"
A: The diabetes is poorly controlled; A.H. is symptomatic and needs better control to pre-

vent long-term complications. Since the patient has failed nonpharmacological intervention, and his blood glucose has been increasing, drug treatment is indicated.

Cross-sensitivity may occur between sulfonamides and sulfonylureas but this is not a contraindication to their use. A trial of an oral sulfonylurea should be started. Tolazamide is a good choice because it requires less frequent dosing, and hence may improve compliance; also it is metabolized and excreted by the liver, not the kidneys. Other possible choices are second-generation sulfonylureas, although they have no particular advantage. Glyburide may accumulate in renal failure, resulting in prolonged hypoglycemia secondary to the long duration of action. Tolbutamide requires more frequent dosing and therefore may decrease compliance. Chlorpropamide is not a good choice in renal failure and has a disulfiram effect which would be a problem in this patient, who drinks alcohol. Chlorpropamide may also cause SIADH. Acetohexamide is not a good choice. The metabolite is 2.5 times more active and is eliminated by the kidneys. Therefore, it should not be used in patients with renal insufficiency.

Hydrochlorothiazide (HCTZ) may induce hyperglycemia but is not absolutely contraindicated in diabetes. Propranolol may increase (by decreasing insulin release) or decrease (by decreasing gluconeogenesis) blood glucose; propranolol will mask all hypoglycemic symptoms except sweating and decrease hypoglycemic recovery. Although propranolol is only relatively contraindicated in DM, a cardioselective β antagonist or an alternative agent should be considered.

P: Begin tolazamide 250 mg q.d. and titrate the dose by 250 mg/day at weekly intervals until a maximum dose of 1 g is reached. Institute urine testing or home glucose monitoring to attempt better control. Monitor blood and urine glucose and for symptoms of hypoglycemia and hyperglycemia.

Problem 2. Hypertension

S: No complaints.
O: BP = 154/96. History of HTN. A.H. uses pseudoephedrine.
A: A.H. needs better control of his BP to prevent long-term complications particularly in view of other risk factors for coronary artery disease such as DM, smoking, obesity and a family history. Propranolol is at a subtherapeutic dose as evidenced by his pulse. Another agent should be considered because of the effect of propranolol on diabetes. Also the patient should comply with nonpharmacological intervention (diet control, weight loss). Avoid clonidine, because

A.H. may be noncompliant, and stopping this medication abruptly may precipitate withdrawal hypertension.

P: Discontinue propranolol. Instruct A.H. to stop smoking and to decrease his weight. Begin a low-salt, low-cholesterol diet. Start metoprolol 50–100 mg/day. Reevaluate in 1 week. Metoprolol loses its cardioselectivity at dose >100 mg/day. Other alternatives include a calcium channel blocker such as verapamil for controlling both HTN and atrial flutter. Monitor BP, HR, dizziness, weight, constipation (if using verapamil). Monitor signs and symptoms of digitalis toxicity and digoxin levels because they can increase 50–70% with the addition of verapamil.

Problem 3. Atrial Flutter

S: None.
O: P 88, regular
A: Current regimen appears to be adequate without apparent side effects.
P: Discontinue propranolol. Use verapamil or metoprolol as above. Monitor HR, renal failure, and for symptoms of digoxin toxicity.

Problem 4. Seasonal Allergies

S: Patient's complaint.
O: History.
A: Sympathomimetics block insulin release and may increase BP, blood glucose, and potentially could induce cardiac arrhythmias.
P: Discontinue pseudoephedrine and begin oxymetazoline nasal spray.

CASE 12

CC: C.K. is a 52-year-old male who comes to clinic for a follow-up visit for multiple medical problems. He complains of increased fatigue, thirst, and urination. The pain in his knees and hips has progressed until he is no longer able to work as a janitor.

Problem List

1. Type I diabetes since age 13 with complications of retinopathy, nephropathy and neuropathy.
2. Congestive heart failure (CHF): onset about 6 months ago.
3. Renal impairment secondary to DM
4. Hyperuricemia with no acute attacks of gout
5. Type IV hyperlipidemia
6. Degenerative joint disease diagnosed in June 1981 affecting his knees and hips.
7. Anemia

Medication History

C.C. is compliant with medications and takes them according to the following schedule:

Insulin: NPH 20 U s.c. q 8 AM and 15 U s.c. q 6 PM; Reg 5 U s.c. q 8 AM and 15 U s.c. q 6 PM

Digoxin 0.375 mg qd at 9 AM
Furosemide 20 mg q am 8 AM and 80 mg q 6 PM
Klotrix 10 mEq bid (8 AM and 6 PM)
Colbenemid (probenecid 0.5 g, colchicine 0.5 mg) one bid (8 AM and 6 PM) for 2 years
Prednisone 15 mg q.d. 8 AM since June 1981
Questran (cholestyramine resin) 4-g packet q.i.d. at 8 AM, 1 PM, 4 PM, 10 PM

Allergies

None known.

Physical Examination

GEN: Obese, cushingnoid appearing male in no apparent distress
VS: BP 150/80 HR 88-regular T 37 RR 20 Wt 100 kg Ht 178 cm
HEENT: Jugular venous distension (JVD)
COR: + S3, no murmurs
CHEST: Bilateral rales
ABD: Obese, soft, no masses
GU: BPH
RECT: WNL guaiac-negative
EXT: Thin, wasted lower extremities, 3+ ankle edema, multiple ecchymoses
NEURO: DTRs WNL

Results of Laboratory Tests

Na 138	BUN 53	WBC 12	Ca 7.8	Tri 660
K 4.0	Cr 3.6	Plts 198	PO$_4$ 6.1	Uric acid 10
Cl 109	Hct 33	Alb 3.4	Mg P	Dig level <0.5
HCO$_3$ 19	Hgb 11	FBG 320	Chol 150	

Urinalysis: 2% glucose; (+) protein; (−) ketones; (−) crystals; (−) WBCs

Over the last week blood glucose recorded at home:

	7 AM	12 noon	4 PM	10 PM
Mon	310	250	80	120
Wed	300	240	90	110
Fri	310	250	100	100
Mon	310	260	90	120

Problem 1. Type I Diabetes Mellitus

S: C.K. complains of polyuria, polydipsia, and fatigue.
O: Urine glucose 2%, FBS 320 mg/100ml, home glucose monitoring data: 7 AM = 300–310, 12 noon = 240–260, 4 PM = 80–100, 10 PM = 100–120
A: C.K.'s diabetes is not well controlled and adjustments in his insulin dosing are needed to achieve control. C.K.'s current AM insulin mixture is greater than a 2:1 ratio of NPH to regular; the regular is probably taking on the properties of NPH insulin because of the excess protamine in NPH. This and/or the low dose of regular is leading to the high blood glucose at 12 noon. The dose of NPH in the evening may be too high and C.K. may be experiencing the Somogyi phenomena. The peak action of

the NPH insulin probably occurs around 2 AM and C.K.'s 10 PM blood sugars are 100–120. C.K. could be hypoglycemic around 2 AM and the counterregulatory hormones could be responsible for the hyperglycemia seen at 7 AM. Furosemide and prednisone may be contributing to C.K.'s hyperglycemia, but this effect is probably slight.

P: Ask C.K. if he eats a snack at 10 PM and if he is experiencing night sweats or vivid dreams. Continue the previous insulin regimen today and obtain a 2 AM blood glucose tonight to document hypoglycemia. Tomorrow begin an AM regimen of 10 U regular and 15 U NPH. Adjust the PM regimen according to the results of the 2 AM blood glucose. If 2 AM blood glucose is below 80, decrease the PM dose to 10 U regular and 10 U NPH. Add a sliding scale for coverage during the period of dose adjustment. Monitor blood glucose 6 times per day until the new dose is established. Maintain constant food intake and activities. Monitor signs and symptoms of both hypoglycemia and hyperglycemia. Assess C.K.'s insulin injection technique and need for additional education about his disease. Obtain a glycosylated hemoglobin.

Problem 5. Type IV Hyperlipidemia

S: None.

O: Triglycerides = 660, cholesterol = 150

A: C.K. has an elevated triglyceride level, however, it is not clear that this is an independent risk factor for atherosclerosis and atherosclerotic vascular disease. Since C.K.'s diabetes is out of control, this may be contributing to the elevated TG level. The cholesterol is not elevated but cholesterol is a definite risk factor for coronary artery disease. Colestipol can decrease the cholesterol level, is not indicated for an elevated triglyceride level, and may be binding digoxin (see below). However, since the triglyceride level is > 500 mg/100 ml, C.K. should be treated.

P: Discontinue colestipol. Improve control of the diabetes as above. Get a dietary consultant to discuss weight loss and a decrease in calories and fat in the diet. Begin gemfibrozil 600 mg b.i.d. Reassssess in 6 weeks. Monitor for GI side effects. If GI upset occurs, advise patient to take with food or milk. If severe diarrhea or abdominal pain occurs, C.K. should contact the clinic. Monitor triglycerides and cholesterol.

Problem 2. Congestive Heart Failure

S: C.K. complains of fatigue.

O: JVD, ankle edema, rales, (+) S3, digoxin level <0.5

A: C.K.'s CHF is not well controlled although he is on appropriate drug therapy. The dose of digoxin is high for his renal function, and a predicted level using population parameters is 4.5 µg/ml. However, the measured level is <0.5 and C.K. is compliant. The colestipol, furosemide, and digoxin are being administered together, resulting in decreased digoxin absorption. C.K. is not in acute distress so there is no need for rapid digitalization. Furosemide should not be administered in the evening, if possible, to avoid nocturia. Furosemide is required because of his decreased Cr Cl. The need for such a small dose of KCl is unclear. Patients who become hypokalemic with diuretics usually require KCl 40–80 mEq/day. However, C.K. does have renal impairment. C.K.'s prednisone could also contribute to hypokalemia.

P: Discontinue colestipol as in Problem 5. Begin digoxin 0.125 mg q AM along with furosemide 80 mg. Discontinue KCl. Monitor for resolution of signs and symptoms of CHF including JVD, ankle edema, rales, S3 and signs and symptoms of digoxin toxicity such as anorexia, arrhythmias, confusion, and visual disturbances. Monitor serum K.

Problem 3. Renal Impairment

S: None.

O: Elevated BUN, Cr, and PO₄. Ca = 8.3 when corrected for decreased albumin. Cr Cl = 25 ml/minute.

A: C.K.'s renal function is decreased secondary to diabetes. Drug therapy for this problem is unavailable. Improved control of diabetes may decrease the rate of decline. Hyperphosphatemia should be treated to prevent the bone disease that results from renal failure. Improvement in CHF may lead to improvement in his renal function.

P: Begin aluminum hydroxide concentrated gel 15 ml q.i.d. with meals. Separate the dose of digoxin and antacid by 2 hours. Monitor serum Ca and PO₄, BUN, Cr, and constipation.

Problem 4. Hyperuricemia

S: None.

O: Uric acid by autoanalyzer = 10. No acute attacks of gout.

A: The current therapy is inappropriate since C.K.'s uric acid would be <10 when measured by the uricase method. He has had no acute attacks of gout and is asymptomatic. Probenecid may cause urate nephropathy, worsening C.K.'s renal function and it is ineffective with a creatinine clearance <30 ml/min. Colchicine prophylaxis is only needed for the first 6 months of uricosuric therapy, not for 2 years. Furosemide may be increasing his serum uric acid level, but only weak diuretics such as spironolactone and triamterene do not have this side effect. Allopurinol has the risk of serious side effects and is not currently indicated in this patient.

P: Discontinue colbenemid. Monitor signs and symptoms of gout, urate nephropathy, and serum uric acid level. No treatment unless an attack of gout occurs.

Problem 8. Steroid Toxicity

S: C.K. complains of fatigue.

O: C.K. is an obese, cushingnoid-appearing male with ecchymoses and an elevated WBC.

A: C.K. has signs and symptoms of steroid excess. Corticosteroids are not indicated in the management of degenerative joint disease (see below). Steroids may be aggravating C.K.'s CHF and DM and could cause serious side effects such as aseptic necrosis of the hip or femur. C.K. probably has HPA axis suppression because of his prolonged steroid therapy since 1981.

P: Slowly taper the steroids by decreasing the prednisone by 2.5 mg/day/week until C.K. is receiving 7.5 mg prednisone per day. Check an AM cortisol and if >10, discontinue prednisone. If <10, taper by 1 mg/day every 2 weeks until AM cortisol is >10 or C.K. is off prednisone. In 9 months, perform a cortrosyn stimulation test to assess adrenal reserve. Provide stress coverage until adrenal reserve is documented. Monitor for signs and symptoms of adrenal insufficiency including fatigue, myalgias, arthralgias, BP, glucose and electrolytes. Educate C.K. about the taper, the need to inform health care providers about his steroid history, and how to obtain a Medi-Alert bracelet.

Problem 6. Degenerative Joint Disease

S: C.K. complains of pain in his knees and hips.

O: C.K. is unable to work.

A: Degenerative joint disease can only be symptomatically treated by drug therapy and analgesia is the primary goal. Low-dose ASA may inhibit uric acid secretion. NSAID may worsen C.K.'s renal impairment.

P: Begin acetaminophen 4 g/day. Have physical therapy; discuss rest, exercises, heat, etc. with C.K. Decrease weight as above. Monitor pain and ability to walk, etc. Monitor liver function tests every 6 months.

Problem 7. Anemia

S: C.K. complains of fatigue.

O: Hct 33%, Hgb 11 g/dl, guaiac-negative

A: C.K. is probably anemic secondary to his renal failure and other chronic diseases, but other causes need to be ruled out by obtaining appropriate laboratory data such as serum Fe, vitamin B_{12}, folate, ferritin, and a peripheral blood smear. The anemia of chronic renal failure is due to a decreased production of erythropoietin. Erythropoietin has been synthesized but is not commercially available at this time. Other drugs are ineffective in treating this type of anemia.

P: Obtain laboratory data and base treatment on the results.

CASE 13

CC: M.B. is a 40-year-old woman admitted to the hospital for surgical repair of a duodenal ulcer.

Past Medical History

M.B. has a 10-year history of peptic ulcer disease that has been managed with antacids and cimetidine. She also gives a long history of rheumatoid arthritis for which she has been treated with steroids off and on for the past 20 years. She also has a history of dysmenorrhea and dermatitis treated with various creams and ointments.

Problem List

1. Peptic ulcer disease
2. Rheumatoid arthritis (RA)
3. Dermatitis
3. Dysmenorrhea

Medication History

Mylanta 30 ml prn stomach pain
Cimetidine 300 mg q.i.d.
Naproxen 375 mg prn menstrual cramps
Prednisone 10 mg qd increase to t.i.d. with RA flare
0.5% Triamcinolone cream t.i.d. to q.i.d. prn rash and itching

Physical Examination

GEN: Nervous, frail appearing female of small stature in no apparent distress.

VS: BP 160/105 HR 100 RR 15 T 37 Wt 40 kg

HEENT: Moon facies; posterior subcapular cataract

CHEST: Within normal limits (WNL)

ABD: Soft, obese; rebound tenderness upper-right quadrant

EXT: Wasted-appearing with poor muscle tone; 2+ pitting edema to midcalf

SKIN: Transparent; striae over chest and abdomen; numerous excoriated patches and ecchymoses distributed over entire body

Results of Laboratory Tests

Na 148	Cr 1	FBS 240
K 2.9	Hct 47	Ca 7.5
Cl 96	Hgb 18	PO_4 3
HCO_3 40	RBC 5.5	Alb 4
BUN 12	WBC 12.3	LFT WNL

WBC differential: PMN 85, lym 10, mono 4
Chest x-ray: WNL
ABD x-ray: Evidence of early vertebral degeneration

Problem

S:

O:

A:

P:

Problem

S:

O:

A:

P:

Problem

S:

O:

A:

P:

Problem

S:

O:

A:

P:

Questions

1. Identify five adverse effects of steroid therapy found during the physical examination and five abnormal values due to steroids found on laboratory evaluation of this patient.
2. Identify any pharmacokinetic or pharmacologic drug interactions that may have been present in M.B. on admission.
3. Since M.B. is to undergo major surgery, what should her steroid regimen(s) be during the preoperative, perioperative, and postoperative, periods? Give drug, route, dose, duration and schedule.
4. After successful treatment and recovery from surgery, M.B. is to be discharged on prednisone 10 mg t.i.d. with the plan to taper her off steroids since her RA has been very stable. Design a steroid taper schedule for M.B.
5. List three monitoring parameters that you would follow to assure that M.B.'s steroids are not being tapered too rapidly.

CASE 14

CC: J.L. is a 48-year-old female who comes to acute care drop-in clinic with a 4-week history of fatigue, nervousness, nausea, and heartburn. She has lost 8 lb during this time despite an increased appetite and complaints of not having enough energy to do her work. If the room is hot, she is very uncomfortable and perspires a lot. She looks thin, nervous, and tired. She also complains of polyuria, polydipsia, and diarrhea.

Past Medical History

J.L. has had hypertension for 12 years; it was treated with furosemide and propranolol. She also has had type IIB diabetes for 3 years. Initially it was controlled with diet but oral hypoglycemic agents have been required for the last 6 months. Hyperthyroidism was diagnosed 1 year ago as Graves disease; this was initially treated with propylthiouracil 400 mg/day for 6 months. The dose has been gradually decreased to 100 mg/day 1 month ago. J.L. also has type IIB hypercholesterolemia and menopause.

Problem List

1. Hypertension
2. Type IIB diabetes
3. Hyperthyroidism
4. Type IIB hypercholesterolemia
5. Menopause

Medication History

Furosemide 40 mg q.d.
KCl 30 mEq/day
Propranolol 20 mg b.i.d.
Tolbutamide 500 mg b.i.d. x 6 months
PTU 100 mg q.d.
Clofibrate 500 mg b.i.d.
Mylanta II 30 ml 1 and 3 hours after meals and at bedtime
ASA 8–10/day for chronic headache
Conjugated estrogens 0.625 mg q.d. x 21 days per month
Generic cold capsule containing 50 mg phenylpropranolamine, 4 mg chlorpheniramine, 0.2 mg belladonna alkaloids and 500 mg acetaminophen 1 capsule b.i.d. x 2 weeks.

J.L. is a very compliant patient who takes her medications as prescribed, but she does not monitor her urine or blood glucose.

Physical Examination

VS: BP 148/98 HR 102 T 37.7 Wt 50 kg Ht 5'7"
HEENT: Prominent eyes with AV nicking, steady stare; neck thin; no JVD or HJR; thin, sparse hair; diffuse slight thyroid enlargement
CHEST: Normal breath sounds, no wheezes or rhonchi
COR: Heart prominent S1 and S2, no S3; ECG reveals sinus tachycardia
ABD: Soft without masses and without organomegaly
GU: WNL
RECT: WNL
NEURO/EXT: Deep tendon reflexes increased in upper and lower extremities (+3) bilaterally, increased pedal pulses bilaterally
SKIN: Warm and moist, WNL

Results of Laboratory Tests

Na 137	Hct 25	AST 15	FBG 340	Cholesterol 330
K 4.8	Hgb 8.5	ALT P	Ca 8.8	Triglycerides 120
Cl 98	WBC 4.8k	LDH 60	PO$_4$ 1.8	
HCO$_3$ 32	Plts 179k	Alk Phos 24	Mg 1.7	
BUN 28	MCV 90	Alb 3.8	PT 11.1	
Cr 1.6	MCHC 33.0	T Bili 1.4	PTT 37.8	

Thyroid function tests: T$_4$ 14.6, RT$_3$U 38, Anti-M 1:6400
Urinalysis: Glucose (−), ketones (−), protein (−), pH 6.5 (by Labstix)

Problem

S:

O:

A:

P:

Problem

S:

O:

A:

P:

Problem

S:

O:

A:

P:

Problem

S:

O:

A:

P:

```
┌─────────────────────────────────────┐
│  Problem ───────────────────────────│
│                                      │
│  S: ─────────────────────────────── │
│     ─────────────────────────────── │
│     ─────────────────────────────── │
│     ─────────────────────────────── │
│     ─────────────────────────────── │
│                                      │
│  O: ─────────────────────────────── │
│     ─────────────────────────────── │
│     ─────────────────────────────── │
│     ─────────────────────────────── │
│     ─────────────────────────────── │
│                                      │
│  A: ─────────────────────────────── │
│     ─────────────────────────────── │
│     ─────────────────────────────── │
│     ─────────────────────────────── │
│     ─────────────────────────────── │
│     ─────────────────────────────── │
│     ─────────────────────────────── │
│                                      │
│  P: ─────────────────────────────── │
│     ─────────────────────────────── │
│     ─────────────────────────────── │
│     ─────────────────────────────── │
│     ─────────────────────────────── │
└─────────────────────────────────────┘
```

Questions

1. J.L. does not monitor her blood or urine glucose. What method of glucose monitoring would you recommend? Select a product and state your reasons for this selection. Give instructions to the patient regarding how to use the product, how frequently to monitor her glucose under normal conditions and under special circumstances, and how to assess the control of her diabetes.
2. Assess her current therapy for her diabetes. Identify four subjective symptoms and two objective signs that support whether or not her diabetes is controlled. Recommend any appropriate changes in her total drug regimen that would affect her diabetic control. Be specific: give drug, dose, schedule, and dose titration if necessary. State your therapeutic endpoint for treating J.L.'s diabetes.
3. Evaluate J.L.'s current treatment for her hyperthyroidism. Give four subjective symptoms and six objective signs as evidence for your evaluation. Recommend any changes in drug therapy that are required. Be specific: give drug, dose, regimen, and duration.
4. J.L. is receiving clofibrate for her hypercholesterolemia. Is this the drug of choice for this condition in this patient? Is her cholesterol being adequately controlled? If not, recommend a new drug regimen for J.L. Give drug(s), schedule(s), and reasons for selection of this drug(s) in this patient.
5. List four important patient education tips that you would give J.L. concerning her new drug therapy that you recommended for her hypercholesterolemia.

CASE 15

CC: D.M., a 23-year-old male with an 11-year history of Type I diabetes mellitus, is followed in general medical clinic. He was brought to the emergency room with a 2-day history of nausea, vomiting, malaise, polydipsia, and polyuria. He was partying, drank a large amount of alcohol, and woke up 2 days prior to admission (PTA) feeling "sick to his stomach." He has vomited six times since then. He denies headache, chest pain, cough, fever, symptoms of an upper respiratory infection, or abdominal pain. The patient states that he last gave his insulin 2 days PTA.

Past Medical History

D.M. has had type I diabetes mellitus since age 12, with numerous hospital admissions for diabetic ketoacidosis (DKA).

Problem List

1. Diabetic ketoacidosis
2. Metabolic acidosis
3. Dehydration/hyponatremia
4. Hyperkalemia
5. Hypophosphatemia

Social History

D.M. works for his father. His mother died of suicide. He is a social drinker; he does not smoke nor is he an intravenous drug abuser (IVDA). D.M. has a very poor understanding of his disease.

Medication History

D.M.'s insulin regimen is a three-times-a-day sliding scale consisting of:

8 AM   15 U regular and 10 U NPH s.c.
12 noon   2–5 U regular s.c.
6 PM   5–10 U regular s.c.

Physical Examination

GEN: Well-developed, well-nourished 23-year-old male in mild distress, breathing rapidly
VS: BP 100/85 (supine), HR 120, BP 99/60 (sitting), HR 140, RR 34, T 36 Wt 53 kg (normal Wt 60 kg)
HEENT: Dry tongue and mucous membrane

CHEST: Clear to auscultation and percussion, negative rales, wheezing, rhonchi
COR: Tachycardia, regular rate and rhythm
ABD: Positive voluntary guarding, active bowel sounds
EXT: Poor skin turgor
NEURO: Alert and oriented x 3

Chest x-ray: Clear with no acute infiltrate
ECG: Sinus tachycardia, normal intervals

Results of Laboratory Tests

Na 125	Cr 2.1	Glu 670
K 6.0	Hct 45.7	Ca 8.7
Cl 89	Hgb 15.2	PO_4 2.0
HCO_3 13	WBC 25.5k	Mg 1.8
BUN 45	Plts 200k	

Arterial blood gases (room air): PO_2 82, PCO_2 24, pH 7
Urinalysis: Sp Gr. 1.033, pH=6, trace protein, 2% glucose, positive ketones, 0–3 WBC, 0–2 RBC
Blood cultures: x 2 pending
Urine culture: pending

Problem _____

S: _____

O: _____

A: _____

P: _____

Problem _____

S: _____

O: _____

A: _____

P: _____

Problem _____

S: _____

O: _____

A: _____

P: _____

Problem

S:

O:

A:

P:

Problem

S:

O:

A:

P:

CASE 16

CC: P.C. is a 44-year-old male who is employed as a computer marketing expert—a job he describes as "very high stress". He returns to the clinic today for further workup; he reports severe constipation for the past 30 days, polydipsia, polyuria, a "thick" neck, nausea, lack of energy, and a weight gain of 20 lb (over the past year) without an increase in appetite. Test results from his last visit, 10 days ago, are now available.

Problem List

1. Hypothyroidism, newly diagnosed today
2. Diabetes mellitus, insulin dependent since age 18
3. Type IIa Hypercholesterolemia, diagnosed 6 months ago, treated with dietary restrictions that have failed.
4. Pulmonary embolism on January 30, 1988
5. Iron deficiency anemia
6. HTN for 8 years

Medication History

Current medications:

Beef insulin NPH 15 U q 5 PM along with regular insulin 5 U q 8 AM & 10 U q 5 PM since last clinic visit

Warfarin 5 mg q AM since January 31, 1988

Fe SO$_4$ 300 mg p.o. t.i.d. since June 1987

HCTZ 100 mg qd × 8 years

Verapamil 80 mg t.i.d. × 1 month

Acetaminophen 325 mg with codeine 60 mg 1–2 tablets q 4–6 h prn abdominal pain (4 tablets per day)

Diazepam 10 mg q.i.d. prn nervousness. Takes 30 mg/day

P.C. is a very compliant person who always takes his medication. He does have a very difficult time with his insulin therapy; he has had five hospital admissions for ketoacidosis and frequent cases of fainting from hypoglycemia.

Allergies

None known.

Social History

P.C. smokes one pack per day of cigarettes and occasionally uses marijuana and cocaine; he does not use i.v. drugs.

Family History

Father died from myocardial infarction and alcoholism. Mother committed suicide 1 year after father's death.

Physical Examination

GEN: Overweight, tired looking, stressed man

VS: BP 150/92, HR 80, T 36.6, RR 16, Wt 103 kg, Ht 6'0"

HEENT: Decreased range of motion (ROM), mild ptosis, grade I AV nicking, enlarged thyroid gland

COR: WNL

CHEST: Clear, no rhonchi or wheezes

ABD: Pain on palpation in right lower quadrant and in mid-gastric region; (+) BS

GU: WNL

RECT: WNL guaiac trace (+)

EXT: Skin dry and cool, lipoatrophy on both thighs

NEURO: Decreased deep tendon reflexes (+) bilaterally with decreased pedal pulses bilaterally

Results of Laboratory Tests

Na 146	Hct 44	AST 36	FBS 360	PT 20.6
K 4.6	Hgb 14.8	ALT 28	Ca 9.2	PTT 45
Cl 116	WBC 6.3k	LDH P	PO$_4$ 3.7	
HCO$_3$ 21	Plts 198k	Alk Phos P	Mg 1.9	
BUN 18	MCV 90	Alb 3.2	Chol 380	
Cr 1	MCHC 34	T Bili 1.2		

Trigyclerides: P
Urinalysis: WNL

Problem

S:

O:

A:

P:

Problem

S:

O:

A:

P:

Problem

S:

O:

A:

P:

Problem

S: _____

O: _____

A: _____

P: _____

Problem

S: _____

O: _____

A: _____

P: _____

Problem

S: _____

O: _____

A: _____

P: _____

Renal Disease

CASE 17

CC: A.D., a 40 year-old-male, presents to the emergency room with complaints of sudden weakness, a single fainting episode 30 minutes ago, hematemesis, and flank pain. The patient reports abdominal pain for the past week that subsided about 4 hours prior to onset of the other symptoms.

Past Medical History

The patient has an 18-year history of analgesic abuse secondary to chronic pain resulting from a motor vehicle accident. The description of the pain has always been nebulous; the pain reportedly moves from one anatomical region to another. Mild, transient decreases in renal function have been noted in the past. The patient has carried a diagnosis of Addison's disease for 10 years and is currently being treated with hydrocortisone. A.D. has had gastric ulcers twice and was treated with cimetidine for 4 months, but it was discontinued 6 months ago. A.D. has been treated for mild hypertension for 6 years.

Problem List

1. Renal failure secondary to Problem 2
2. Analgesic abuse for chronic pain
3. Anemia
4. Addison's disease
5. Hypertension
6. Bleeding gastric ulcer

Medication History

Hydrocortisone 30 mg p.o. qd (20 mg q AM and 10 mg q PM)

Acetaminophen/codeine (325 mg/15 mg) tablets; the patient reports taking about 20 tablets per day

ASA 325 mg, 2 tablets q 2–3 h prn

Generic pain capsules (acetaminophen 325 mg, salicylamide 200 mg/capsule) 2–3 capsules as needed

HCTZ 50 mg p.o. qd

Cimetidine 300 mg one p.o. pc and hs (discontinued 6 months ago)

Allergies

None known.

Physical Examination

GEN: Well developed, well-nourished, pale male looks to be in moderate distress. The patient appears lethargic but responds appropriately to commands and questions.

VS: BP 105/65 HR 117 T 37 RR 22 Wt 72 kg Ht 5'10"

HEENT: Dry mucous membranes; pupils equal, round, react to light and accommodation (PERRLA); extraocular muscles intact

COR: Sinus tachycardia

CHEST: Unremarkable, without rales, rhonchi, wheezes or rubs

ABD: Guarding with pain on palpation, mild distension

GU: Deferred

RECTAL: Guaiac-positive

EXT: Pale

Results of Laboratory Tests

Na 138	Hct 33	AST 15
K 3.6	Hgb 11	ALT 12
Cl 98	WBC 8k	Alk phos 54
HCO$_3$ 25	Plts 160k	Alb 3.4
BUN 32	MCV 93	Ca 9.7
Cr 3.6	MCHC 32	PO$_4$ 4

Urinalysis: pH 6, SG 1.003, protein-positive, glucose-negative, RBC 10/HPF, WBC 6/HPF, bacteria smear negative, hyaline casts and granular casts present.

Endoscopy reveals a small bleeding ulceration on the gastric mucosa.

History of Present Illness

A nasogastric tube is placed and the stomach is lavaged with saline. The patient is started on intravenous normal saline at 500 ml/hour. One hour after admission the bleeding stops (i.e., no return blood with saline lavage) and the patient's blood pressure has increased by 123/85.

Problem 6. Blood Loss and Peptic Ulcer Disease

S: A.D. complains of fainting, lethargy, sudden weakness, and abdominal cramps.

O: Guaiac-positive, hematemesis, hypotension, tachycardia, Hct 33, Hgb 10, dry mucous membranes, history of gastric ulcer, bleeding verified by endoscopy.

A: The patient has blood loss secondary to a bleeding gastric ulcer. The bleeding has stopped, but there is a high potential for rebleeding. The gastric ulcer is probably secondary to analgesic abuse. Transfusion of blood products may be withheld for now, because the Hct is greater than 30 but it may decline with rehydration, the bleeding has stopped, and the blood pressure and heart rate are stable. The dose of ranitidine must be adjusted for renal failure.

Ranitidine dosage determination:

1. Calculate creatinine clearance:
$$Cl\ Cr = \frac{(140-40)72}{(72)3.6} = 27.77\ ml/min$$

2. $Fx = \dfrac{Cl\ Cr\ (patient)}{Cl\ Cr\ (normal)} = 27.77/100 = 0.28$

3. Normal parameters:
   $Vd = 1.8$ liter/kg $= 129.6$ liters
   $f = 0.69$
   $t_{1/2} = 2.1$ hour
   $k = 0.693/2.1 = 0.33$

(see Chapter 10, Appendix A for normal parameters)

4. K failure $= k(fFx - 1) =$
   $0.33\ (0.69(0.28 - 1) + 1) = 0.166$

5. Calculate desired peak and trough concentrations. The normal ranitidine dose is 150 mg p.o. q12h. Since the normal $t_{1/2}$ is 2.1 hour and the normal interval is q 12 (i.e., about 6 times $t_{1/2}$) very little ranitidine would be expected to accumulate.

Estimated normal peak $= D/V$
$\qquad = 150$ mg/129.6 liters
$\qquad = 1.15$ mg/liter
Estimated normal trough $= Co\ e^{-kt}$
$\qquad = 1.15\ e^{-(0.33)(12)}$
$\qquad = 0.02$ mg/liter

Given a K failure of 0.166 the $t_{1/2} = 0.693/0.166 = 4.1$ hour or about 2 times the normal $t_{1/2}$. Next calculate a peak and trough based on an interval twice as long as the usual:

Estimated peak $= D/V$
$\qquad = 150$ mg/129.6 liters
$\qquad = 1.15$ mg/liter
Estimated trough $= Co\ e^{-kt}$
$\qquad = 1.15\ e^{-(0.166)(24)}$
$\qquad = 0.021$ mg/liter

The appropriate dose is ranitidine 150 mg p.o. qd.

P: Type and cross match blood in case of rebleeding. Continue to re-expand volume with D5½ NS at 250 ml/hour. Monitor Hgb/Hct, HR, BP, and nasogastric tube return. Hold HCTZ. Begin ranitidine with dose adjusted for renal failure. Discontinue current analgesics; may use low-dose codeine if tolerated. Change the route of administration and dose of the steroid. See Addison's disease (Problem 4).

Problem 1. Renal Failure

S: A.D. complains of flank pain.
O: Cr 3.6; BUN 32; urinalysis reveals hyaline and granular casts; hematuria, leukocyturia, proteinuria, albumin 3.4
A: The renal failure is secondary analgesic abuse and has been worsened by hypovolemia. The hyaline casts are indicative of dehydration. Hypoalbuminemia, hematuria, leukocyturia, and proteinuria suggest analgesic nephropathy.

$$Cl\ Cr = \frac{(140-40)(72)}{72(3.6)} = 27.8\ ml$$

P: Replenish volume. Monitor U/A, creatinine, BUN, urinary intake and output. Discontinue acetaminophen, ASA, and salicylamide. Reassess renal function daily until stable.

Problem 3. Anemia

S: A.D. complains of fainting and weakness.
O: HR 115, RR 22, Hct 33, HGB 11. RBCs are normocytic and normochromic
A: Anemia is probably secondary to blood loss but may be due in part to chronic renal failure.
P: Parenteral iron replacement should be considered since A.D. would be an inappropriate candidate for oral iron at this time because of the bleeding ulcer.

Problem 4. Addison's disease

S: A.D. complains of weakness.
O: Hypovolemia (probably due to blood loss)
A: It is difficult to assess his Addison's disease at this time due to acute blood loss. An increased dose of steroid is needed now due to the stress of his bleeding ulceration.
P: Reassess the signs and symptoms of Addison's disease once the patient is stable. Monitor Na, K, Glu, and BP. Increase the dose of hydrocortisone to 50 mg b.i.d. and change the route to i.v. for now. Dexamethasone 4 mg i.v. qd is an acceptable alternative. If the serum Na drops below 135, fludrocortisone will be required. After the patient's condition is stable, the previous oral dose may be reinstituted but A.D. should take the hydrocortisone with 30 ml of antacid or after meals (Mg^{2+} containing antacids are generally contraindicated in renal failure).

Problem 2. Analgesic Abuse

S: A.D. complains of an 18 year history of chronic pain that is nebulous in nature.
O: The patient reports taking high doses of multiple analgesics. A.D. has gastric ulcer disease, and according to old chart the renal failure is due to chronic tubulointerstitial disease.
A: A.D. is a patient with a long history of analgesic abuse by report, from the chart, and by his symptoms.
P: Provide patient education; discuss the consequences of renal failure with A.D. and set up an appropriate counseling program.

Treat any pain for now with oral codeine (although there is a possibility of addiction/withdrawal. Eventually try to discontinue all analgesics.

Problem 5. Hypertension

S: No symptoms.

O: History of HTN; BP is now 140/95.

A: The patient has either essential HTN or HTN secondary to chronic renal disease. Treatment is needed in order to avoid the complications of HTN.

P: Begin a sodium-restricted diet. Since Cl Cr is less than 30 ml/minute, change HCTZ to furosemide 40–80 mg p.o. q.d. and continue to monitor BP. Monitor potassium (steroids and furosemide may both cause a decrease in potassium levels).

CASE 18

O.A. is a 36-year-old male with a chief complaint of a high fever, chills, and lethargy for 12 hours. O.A. has been on maintenance hemodialysis three times per week for the last 2 years due to renal failure secondary to idiopathic rapidly progressive glomerulonephritis. The patient was treated for Gram-positive sepsis 9 months ago with complete recovery after 2 weeks of antibiotic therapy.

Problem List

1. Sepsis
2. Chronic renal failure

Medication History

Multivitamin with minerals, 1 tablet daily.
Folic acid 1 mg, 1 tablet daily

Allergies

None known.

Physical Examination

GEN: Ill-appearing male, lethargic, with intermittent chills.

VS: BP 110/79 HR 102 T 39.8 RR 19 Wt 60 kg

HEENT: Pupils equal, round, react to light and accommodation, extraocular muscles intact

COR: Normal sinus rhythm

CHEST: Without rales, rhonchi, wheezes or, rubs

ABD: No organomegaly, without guarding

GU: Deferred

RECTAL: Guaiac-negative

EXT: Right-sided radial arteriovenous fistula in place

Results of Laboratory Tests

Na 140	HCO_3 27	Glu 159	Hct 49
K-3.9	BUN 40	Hgb 17	WBC-17k
Cl 101	Cr 3.8		with shift to left
			Plts 165k

Blood cultures and sensitivities: Gram-positive cocci, resistant to penicillin, cefazolin, nafcillin, and vancomycin; sensitive to AB 77.

Problem

S:

O:

A:

P:

Problem

S:

O:

A:

P:

Questions

1.a. The house officer contacts pharmaceutical services for assistance in dosing the antibiotic AB 77 in O.A. The only information available on this medication is as follows:

Molecular weight	189
Protein binding	14%
Highly water soluble	1.3 g/1 ml H_2O
Vd	0.3 liter/kg
Distribution after dose	Occurs rapidly (within 10 minutes)
Cl	Elimination by the kidneys is in a first-order fashion
Toxic effects	Peaks >70 mg/liter have been associated with grand mal seizures; troughs >20 mg/liter have been associated with irreversible retinal damage
Minimum concentration	Break-through growth occurs with troughs <5 mg/liter.
Recommended levels	Peaks 55–60 mg/liter, troughs 8–15 mg/liter
Usual dosage	1250 mg i.v. q8h (given via i.v. bolus or by infusion)

The hospital laboratory has the ability to do a quantitative assay of AB 77

1b. Recommend a loading dose for this patient to achieve a level of 60 mg/liter.
2. The patient is given a 1080 mg i.v. bolus and a level is drawn 10 minutes later (64 mg/liter). Sixteen hours later, the AB 77 level just prior to dialysis is 45 mg/liter. The patient is then hemodialyzed for 4 hours and the AB 77 level at the end of dialysis is 6 mg/liter. Calculate a patient-specific Vd.
3. The patient will be dialyzed q 72 hours, and each session will be 4 hours in duration. What maintenance dose and dosing interval would you recommend to yield peaks of 55–60 mg/liter and troughs of 8–15 mg/liter?
4. Calculate the expected serum concentration after 4 hours of hemodialysis.
5. A trough level of 1.55 mg/liter is unacceptable. Calculate the infusion rate required to maintain a level of 11.45 mg/liter during dialysis.
6. Without the aid of predialysis and postdialysis levels would you have predicted that AB 77 would be dialyzed? Why?
7. How should the order for AB 77 be written in this particular case?

CASE 19

CC: K.B. is a 53-year-old female who presents to the emergency room with complaints of weakness, nausea, and confusion for 2 days. The patient also complains of constipation for the last 7 days.

Past Medical History

K.B. has a 42-year history of diabetes. K.B.'s insulin regimen was changed from beef/pork insulin to human insulin 10 days ago. The patient has had a history of mild renal failure (with proteinuria, Cl Cr = 30–50 ml/minute) for 2 years. K.B. has had signs and symptoms of peripheral neuropathy for the last 20 months. Symptomatic treatment of her peripheral neuropathy was begun with amitriptyline 1 week ago. The patient has a long history of hypertension.

Problem List

1. Hyperkalemia
2. Diabetes (hypoglycemia, peripheral neuropathy)
3. Renal failure
4. Hyperphosphatemia
5. Hypocalcemia
6. Hypertension

Allergies

No known drug allergies.

Medication History

Insulin 20/10 NPH/Reg q AM, 8/8 NPH/Reg q PM (was changed from beef/pork to human insulin 10 days ago)
Amitriptyline 75 mg p.o. q hs.
Hydrochlorothiazide/Triamterine, 25 mg and 50 mg, 1 p.o. qd × 2 weeks (was previously on HCTZ 50 mg qd)
KCL 10 mEq, 2 tablets daily

Physical Examination

GEN: K.B. is a thin female who appears lethargic and has difficulty responding to commands and questions.
VS: BP 135/88 HR 59, T 37, RR 21, Wt 45 kg, Ht 5'3"
HEENT: Pupils equal, round, react to light and accommodation, extra ocular muscles intact
COR: Bradycardic
CHEST: WNL
ABD: No organomegaly
GU: WNL
RECTAL: Guaiac-negative
EXT: Decreased muscle strength, diminished reflexes

Results of Laboratory Tests

Na 140	Cr 3.0	MCV 98	Alb 3.5
K 6.2	Hct 40	MCHC 34	Glu 87
Cl 101	Hgb 13	AST 30	Ca 7.9
HCO_3 28	WBC 8k	ALT 29	PO_4 4.7
BUN 87	Plts 170k	Alk Phos 49	Hgb glyco 12.8

ECG: Spiked T-waves, widened QRS complex
Urinanalysis: Protein-positive, bili negative, Glucose-negative, pH = 6.7

Problem _____

S: _____

O: _____

A: _____

P: _____

Problem _____

S: _____

O: _____

A: _____

P: _____

Problem _____

S: _____

O: _____

A: _____

P: _____

Problem _____

S: _____

O: _____

A: _____

P: _____

Problem

S:

O:

A:

P:

Problem

S:

O:

A:

P:

Gastrointestinal Diseases

CASE 20

CC: L.V. is a 48-year-old bank executive who comes to clinic today with the chief complaint of gnawing abdominal pain. The discomfort has been waking him up around 2 A.M. every day, and eating something usually relieves it.

Past Medical History

L.V. had Crohn's disease but it is currently in remission. The last attack was 1 year ago. Sigmoidoscopy showed colonic, rectal, and terminal ileal involvement. L.V. also has type II diabetes mellitus; onset was in 1982. Attempts at weight reduction and dietary control have failed. L.V. monitors his urine glucose daily. Readings have been consistently 2% by Diastix for 1 month. His angina is stable; he has had no attacks within the last 6 months. L.V. suffers chronic renal failure due to diabetes but it is now stable. His hypothyroidism was diagnosed in 1984. L.V. has type IIB hypercholesterolemia; attempts at reducing dietary cholesterol have failed.

Problem List

1. Peptic ulcer disease
2. Crohn's disease
3. Type II diabetes mellitus
4. Angina
5. Chronic renal failure
6. Hypothyroidism
7. Type IIB hypercholesterolemia
8. Hypokalemia
9. Depression
10. Constipation

Medication History

L.V. is a compliant patient and knows the purpose and adverse effects of his medications. He is currently taking:

Prednisone 20 mg b.i.d. for 1 year
Sulfasalazine 1 g q.i.d. for 1 year
Hydrocortisone enemas 100 mg b.i.d. for 1 year
Glyburide 10 mg b.i.d. for 1 month, previously not well-controlled on Tolazamide 1.5 g/day
Isosorbide dinitrate 60 mg q6h since 1984
Propranolol 40 mg q.i.d. since 1984
Levothyroxine 0.1 mg qd since 1984

Percodan 2 tablets p.o. q4–6h prn pain. L.V. takes 4 tablets/day for leg pain. Began about 2 weeks ago.
Diazepam 10 mg p.o. q6h prn anxiety

Allergies

None known.

Social History

L.V. smokes one pack per day; he drinks three to four martinis per day.

Review of Systems

L.V. complains of constipation. He now has only two bowel movements per week; previously he had two bowel movements each day. L.V. also complains of feeling depressed and that with all his medical problems is likely to die soon. The burning pain in his legs is most bothersome since the rest of his body is always cold. He is always tired and is having difficulty concentrating.

Physical Examination

GEN: L.V. is an obese man who appears to be in mild distress.
VS: BP 120/80 HR 60 reg T 37.2 RR 12 Wt 90 kg (60 kg a year ago) Ht 5'10"
HEENT: WNL
COR: NL S1 and S2; no murmurs, rubs, or gallops
CHEST: WNL
ABD: Epigastric tenderness
RECT: Guaiac-positive
EXT: Reduced reflexes, reduced sensation in both lower extremities, dry skin

Results of Laboratory Tests

Na 140	Hct 37	FBG 400
K 3.1	Hgb 12.3	Ca 9
Cl 100	WBC 12k	PO_4 4.1
HCO_3 26	Plts 208k	Mg 2.2
BUN 45	Chol 300	
Cr 3.3	Triglycerides: 140	
HgbA1C 13%	TSH >15	

Urinalysis: WNL
Endoscopy showed three small pyloric channel ulcers.

Problem 1. Peptic Ulcer Disease

S: L.V. complains of a gnawing abdominal pain that awakens him every morning about 2 AM and that is relieved by food.

O: Endoscopy revealed three small pyloric channel ulcers. His stool is guaiac-positive, and Hct = 37, Hgb = 12.3

A: L.V. has active peptic ulcer disease (PUD) that may have been precipitated by ethanol, smoking, corticosteroids, and the aspirin in Percodan. While all currently available therapeutic regimens are equally effective, certain drugs are preferred in L.V. Sucralfate and aluminum-containing antacids would worsen his constipation. Magnesium antacids would result in elevated Mg levels because of his impaired renal function and therefore should only be used occasionally for pain relief. Cimetidine would impair the clearance of propranolol and diazepam and, while these interactions can be managed with dose reductions, they are easily avoided. Either ranitidine or famotidine could be used because the dose does not have to be decreased in moderate renal failure. Patients who continue to smoke do not heal their ulcers as rapidly as those who do not smoke. A bland diet has not been shown to be superior to a regular diet.

P: Discontinue Percodan. Begin ranitidine 300 mg qhs for 6–8 weeks. Encourage L.V. to discontinue smoking and decrease his alcohol consumption. Advise L.V. to avoid aspirin-containing products and foods that irritate or upset his stomach. Monitor pain relief (although not correlated with healing), guaiac, Hgb, and Hct, and side effects of ranitidine including mental confusion and hepatotoxicity.

Problem 2. Crohn's Disease

S: No complaints.

O: Sigmoidoscopy 1 year ago showed colonic, rectal, and terminal ileal involvement. His stool is guaiac-positive but he has active PUD.

A: Crohn's disease appears to be in remission. While drug therapy is effective in inducing remissions, it is ineffective in maintaining them. Sulfasalazine is most effective for colonic disease, and steroid enemas are most useful for localized rectal disease; L.V. also has ileal involvement. Steroid enemas can be up to 95% absorbed depending upon the condition of the mucosa and retention time. Single daily doses of prednisone have fewer side effects than multiple daily doses and are effective. It is not necessary to increase the prednisone dose to include the hydrocortisone enema dose when the enemas are discontinued; L.V. is already on pharmacologic doses of steroid. L.V. probably has HPA suppression due to long-term steroid treatment.

P: Discontinue the hydrocortisone enemas and sulfasalazine. Obtain an 8-AM cortisol level; if>10, discontinue prednisone. Otherwise, consolidate prednisone to a single daily dose and decrease by 2.5–5 mg/day/week until the dose is 7.5 mg/day. Thereafter decrease the dose by 1 mg/day/week until the AM cortisol is >10 or L.V. is off prednisone. Provide increased steroid coverage during times of stress until the cortrosyn stimulation test is normal (6–9 months). Monitor for an exacerbation of the Crohn's disease (bloody diarrhea, cramping abdominal pain) and for signs and symptoms of adrenal insufficiency (flu-like syndrome, orthostatic hypotension, decreased glucose, and altered electrolytes). Counsel L.V. about compliance with the steroid taper, the signs and symptoms of adrenal insufficiency, reporting any flare of his Crohn's disease, how to obtain a Medi-Alert bracelet, and the need for steroid stress coverage.

Problem 3. Type II Diabetes Mellitus

S: Patient complains of feeling tired and burning pain in his legs.

O: FBS 400, HgbA$_{1c}$ 13%, reduced sensation in both lower extremities, urine glucose 2%.

A: L.V.'s diabetes is not well-controlled, and he has failed maximum doses of two oral hypoglycemic agents. His diabetes is being aggravated by the steroid therapy, but the magnitude of the elevation is greater than that usually seen. ASA interferes with the glucose oxidase method of urine testing. Human insulin is less antigenic than other forms of insulin. Propranolol, which can mask the signs and symptoms of hypoglycemia, may become a problem once L.V. is started on insulin therapy. Diabetic neuropathy is very difficult to treat but better control of his diabetes may prevent progression. Aldose reductase inhibitors are agents for preventing neuropathy but are still investigational. Tricyclic antidepressants and their anticholinergic side effects may be a problem in L.V.

P: Hospitalize L.V. for initiation of insulin therapy and intensive teaching. Begin insulin therapy with human insulin; give 5 U regular now and adjust the dose with a sliding scale based on blood glucose monitoring q4h for 1 day. Tomorrow give one-half of today's regular insulin dose as NPH in the AM and one-fourth as NPH in the evening and continue with sliding scale regular insulin. Continue the process until a stable regimen is obtained and the dose is split with two-thirds being administered in the morning and one-third in the evening and the ratio between NPH: Regular is 2:1. Monitor blood glucose and keep between 80 and 140 mg/100 ml. Monitor for fatigue, signs and symptoms of hyperglycemia (polyuria, polydipsia, blurred vision) and of hypoglycemia (irritability, difficulty concentrating, feeling hungry, tremors, sweating or tachycardia). Begin teaching regarding insulin therapy. This includes how to measure and mix doses, injection technique, rotation of sites, insulin storage (keep bottles that you are using at room temperature, others in the refrigerator, keep insulin out of direct sunlight and away from heat). Teach blood glucose monitoring with increased frequency of monitoring during times of stress. Discuss the need for a balanced diet containing no concentrated sugars with 50% of calories from complex carbohydrates, 30% from fats, and 20% from protein in 3 meals per day taken at the same time each day. Keep the amount of exercise constant each day. Teach L.V. how to recognize and treat hypoglycemia (five Lifesavers or two packets sugar). Begin amitriptyline 75 mg qhs for neuropathy. Monitor for anticholinergic side effects (prevent constipation per Problem 10) including orthostatic hypotension and tachycardia; these may precipitate an anginal attack although unlikely because of the propranolol.

Problem 4. Angina

S: None.

O: History.

A: L.V.'s angina is well-controlled. Propranolol is no longer the best drug for L.V. because of his insulin therapy and the availability of alternatives. Nifedipine impairs endogenous insulin secretion, but this would not be a problem in L.V. who is receiving insulin. Verapamil is very constipating. Abrupt withdrawal of β-blockers may precipitate angina or myocardial infarction.

P: Taper propranolol to 20 mg q.i.d. for 2 days then discontinue. Begin diltiazem 30 mg q.i.d. and monitor for angina attacks. Give NTG 0.4 mg s.l. prn chest pain, may repeat q 5 minutes until three doses are given. Teach L.V. about the proper use and storage of the NTG.

Problem 5. Chronic Renal Failure

S: None.

O: BUN 45, Cr 3.3

A: L.V.'s chronic renal failure is probably secondary to diabetes. Drug therapy for this problem is unavailable.

P: Control any other factors that may also worsen renal function. Avoid nephrotoxic drugs if possible. Adjust the dose of drugs that are eliminated by the kidneys.

Problem 6. Hypothyroidism

S: Patient complains of constipation, depression, feeling cold, fatigue, and difficulty concentrating.

O: TSH >15, lowered DTRs, dry skin, weight gain, depression.

A: L.V.'s thyroid replacement dose is too low. His requirement is probably between 150 and 200

μg/day. The increase must be made slowly because of his angina. As T_4 has a long half-life, dose adjustments should not be made until steady state is reached, i.e., no more often than every 2 weeks.

P: Increase levothyroxine dose 0.025 mg/day every month until TSH <10 and TFTs are within normal limits. Expect cold intolerance, difficulty concentrating, dry skin, lowered DTRs, weight gain and depression to resolve and energy to increase. Monitor for tachycardia, anginal attacks, and signs and symptoms of hyperthyroidism.

Problem 7. Type IIb Hypercholesterolemia

S: None.

O: Cholesterol = 300

A: L.V. already has coronary artery disease and angina and has numerous risk factors for atherosclerosis such as smoking, diabetes, obesity, and ethanol abuse. The elevated cholesterol is also due to his uncontrolled DM and hypothyroidism. As L.V. has failed dietary therapy and his cholesterol level is above the 95th percentile for his age, he requires drug treatment. Niacin is a drug of choice, but would be difficult to use in L.V. because it increases blood glucose. ASA could not be used to prevent the flushing caused by niacin, it is contraindicated in PUD. Ethanol may also worsen flushing. Bile acid binding resins would worsen his constipation and bind thyroxine if administered together, but this can be managed. Neomycin is potentially nephrotoxic and probucol is not very effective. Colestipol is cheaper and may taste better than cholestyramine as well as require less frequent dosing. Lovastatin is effective, but the long-term side effects are unknown at this time.

P: Begin colestipol 5 g b.i.d. and increase the dose if necessary in 1 month. Each packet should be mixed in a full 8 oz of juice or liquid. Allow the mixture to become well hydrated; doses may be prepared ahead of time and refrigerated. After each dose, another 8 oz of liquid should be taken. Cold liquids improve palatability. The dose should be taken 1 hour before meals. Medications should be taken 1–2 hours after the colestipol. GI discomfort usually lessens with time. Constipation can be treated (see Problem 10). Monitor cholesterol and triglycerides in 1 month.

Problem 8. Hypokalemia

S: L.V. complains of feeling tired.

O: K = 3.1

A: L.V. has hypokalemia secondary to steroid therapy. Because of his renal failure, K^+ replacement must be done cautiously.

P: KCl 30 mEq p.o. now, repeat K^+ level tomorrow.

Problem 9. Depression

S: L.V. complains of feeling depressed.

O: L.V. talks about dying.

A: L.V. is depressed because many of his medical problems are not being controlled. Prednisone, propranolol, and hypothyroidism can cause depression and many patients in chronic pain become depressed. L.V. is talking about dying, not about suicide; his depression needs to be taken seriously. During his hospitalization for diabetes control, health care providers can evaluate his depression and provide support. L.V. does not have a personal or family history of depression. Drug therapy is not warranted at this time and treating his hypothyroidism, diabetic neuropathy, uncontrolled diabetes and tapering the steroids may improve his mood.

P: Provide psychological support and reassessment after other problems are controlled.

Problem 10. Constipation

S: L.V. complains of constipation.

O: L.V. has two bowel movements per week.

A: L.V. is constipated as evidenced by the decrease in frequency from his normal pattern. The oxycodone in the Percodan is probably causing the constipation, and two drugs begun today will also aggravate the problem. Large doses of magnesium cathartics should be avoided, as should phosphate-containing enemas due to his renal dysfunction. A physician needs to rule out medical causes of his constipation, particularly in relation to his Crohn's disease.

P: Ask L.V. which laxative he would prefer for immediate relief; let him choose among a glycerin suppository, 30 ml of lactulose, or a tap water enema. Increase fluid and fiber in his diet. Begin a sugar-free, low-sodium, and low-potassium bulk laxative 1 tsp t.i.d.

CASE 21

CC: B.B. is a 38-year-old, 150-lb female who comes to the pharmacy to purchase 10 Fleet's enemas and requests a refill of her sucralfate prescription. In a hoarse voice, she asks for your recommendation for severe menstrual cramps. She goes on to tell you how depressed she is because she can't seem to lose weight and she has been missing work because of her depression. Your technician tells you this is the third time B.B. has been in this week to buy Fleet's.

Past Medical History

The diagnosis of Hashimoto's thyroiditis was made in 1978. Since that time, B.B. has been well controlled on levothyroxine 0.15 mg p.o. qd. A major depressive disorder was diagnosed in 1977 but B.B. has not experienced any major depression since that time. Peptic ulcer disease was diagnosed in 1982;

since then she has had frequent acute exacerbations. In the last year, she has had three episodes of confirmed duodenal ulcers. The first was treated with cimetidine 600 mg b.i.d., the last two with sucralfate 1 g p.o. q.i.d. (last refill 8 weeks ago). In association with the ulcers, B.B. has had iron deficiency anemia; each time this has been treated with ferrous gluconate 325 mg p.o. q.d. for 1 month.

Problem List

1. Hypothyroidism
2. Peptic ulcer disease
3. Constipation
4. Iron deficiency anemia

Medication History

Sucralfate 1 g p.o. q.i.d.
Ferrous Gluconate 325 mg q.d.
Levothyroxine 100 μg p.o. q.d. decreased 1 month ago
Aluminum hydroxide suspension 30 ml prn

Allergies

None known.

Problem 1. Hypothyroidism

S: Patient complains of mood disorder (note: first occurred prior to the diagnosis/treatment of the thyroid disorder), constipation, dysmenorrhea.

O: L.V. has gained weight and speaks with a hoarse voice.

A: Current hypothyroid condition may be due to the decrease in dose.

P: As the patient had been well-controlled on levothyoxine 0.15 mg, the dose should be increased to this level. Before a change in therapy is initiated however, the diagnosis must be confirmed with laboratory tests for thyroid function (e.g., TSH, T_4, T_3) and other signs and symptoms of hypothyroidism identified (e.g., skin, ocular, and neuromuscular effects). The goal of therapy is to maintain the patient in a euthyroid state. Check TSH 2 weeks after changing therapy, T_4 and T_3 in 4–6 weeks, and for signs and symptoms of hyperthyroidism and hypothyroidism. The patient should be told the life-long nature of the treatment and how to identify the signs and symptoms of hyperthyroidism and hypothyroidism.

Problem 2. Peptic Ulcer Disease

S: None.

O: History

A: The duration of therapy (8 weeks) has been adequate for treatment (in fact, 4–6 weeks may be sufficient); refilling the prescription is not appropriate. If the symptoms of PUD were still present, the diagnosis would have to be confirmed by endoscopy and the ulcers treated with a full therapeutic course of a drug other than sucralfate (e.g., H2-receptor antagonist, antacids). Sucralfate and aluminum hydroxide are contributing to the patient's constipation. Smoking is a contributing factor to the disease. This patient is a candidate for maintenance therapy. Appropriate regimens include ranitidine 150 mg p.o. qhs or cimetidine 400 mg p.o. qhs for 1 year or more.

P: Begin ranitidine 150 mg qhs. The goal in this patient is to prevent recurrence of the disease. Monitor for signs and symptoms of PUD (abdominal pain, dark stools) and side effects of ranitidine (headache, dizziness, confusion, rash, increases in LFTs). The patient should be told to discontinue smoking, minimize alcohol consumption, and avoid aspirin-containing drug products.

Problem 3. Constipation

S: Complaints.

O: Patient purchased Fleet's enemas.

A: Contributing factors include sucralfate, hypothyroidism and ferrous gluconate.

P: Discontinue Fleet's enemas and sucralfate, treat hypothyroidism, encourage increased fluid and fiber intake. A bulk laxative may be tried if other measures fail. The goal is to restore bowel movements to normal (for this patient). Monitor frequency and consistency of BMs. The patient needs to be advised that BMs every day are not necessary for normal intestinal function.

Problem 4. Iron deficiency Anemia

S: None.

O: History

A: Contributing factors include PUD and menstruation. The dose and duration of ferrous gluconate were inadequate. Each 325-mg tablet contains 38 mg elemental iron versus 65 mg for ferrous sulfate. When dosed correctly, it is more expensive than the sulfate salt and does not offer any additional benefit. Treatment should be 200 mg elemental iron per day for about 6 months. Iron therapy may contribute to the patient's constipation.

P: The following laboratory tests should be obtained prior to iron therapy and should also be monitored if therapy is indicated: Hgb/Hct, Fe, MCV, MCHC, MCH and reticulocyte count. If therapy is warranted, ferrous sulfate 325 mg p.o. t.i.d. should be given for a duration of 6 months. The reticulocyte count will increase at about 1 week; the Hgb/Hct will increase in 4–6 weeks. Patient instructions: (a) the iron should be taken without food, but if GI upset occurs it can be taken with with food or antacids, (b) expect to see dark stools while taking the iron, (c) keep out of reach of children (d) iron can cause constipation, and (e) compliance for a 6-month course is necessary.

CASE 22

CC: D.B. is a 60-year-old female admitted to the university hospital for craniotomy secondary to trigeminal neuralgia unrelieved by conventional pain management and biofeedback techniques. Postoperatively, she complains of nausea and vomiting secondary to the morphine shots she requires for pain relief. D.B. also complains of feeling tired all the time and says she is constantly falling asleep after her shots for pain and nausea.

Past Medical History

D.B. has trigeminal neuralgia. D.B. suffers coronary artery disease (CAD), and has occasional exercise-induced angina. She also has peptic ulcer disease (PUD) which was treated with 6 weeks of cimetidine. D.B. has chronic constipation secondary to narcotics; she also has a history of asthma.

Problem List

1. Nausea and vomiting
2. Constipation
3. Peptic ulcer disease
4. Asthma
5. CAD, angina

Medication History

Percocet 1–2 tablets p.o. q 3–4 h prn pain
Amitriptyline 75 mg p.o. qhs for trigeminal pain
Cimetidine 800 mg p.o. qhs
Dexamethasone 4 mg p.o./i.v. q6h
Alternagel 30 ml p.o. with dexamethasone
Cimetidine 300 mg i.v./p.o. q6h with dexamethasone
Acetaminophen 650 mg p.o./p.r. q 4–6 h prn pain, T>38.5, or headache
Phenytoin 300 mg p.o. qhs for seizure prophylaxis
s.l. NTG 1/150 one s.l. q5 minutes × 3 prn chest pain
Prochlorperazine 5 mg p.o./i.v. q6h prn nausea and vomiting
Morphine 5–10 mg s.c./i.m. q 3–4 h prn pain
Theodur 200 mg p.o. b.i.d. when taking p.o.

Allergies

None known.

Physical Examination

GEN: Patient is a withdrawn female who looks her stated age.
VS: BP 120/78 HR 85 T 37 RR 20
HEENT: Craniotomy scar along posterior fossa
COR: WNL
CHEST: Negative wheezes, decreased breath sounds bilaterally
ABD: Nontender, full abdomen, bowel sounds present but diminished, (−) rebound, (−) pain
RECT: Guaiac-negative, no stool × 5 days

Results of Laboratory Tests

Within normal limits.

Problem 1. Nausea and Vomiting

S: Patient complains of nausea and vomiting secondary to morphine and postoperative pain.

O: None

A: Vomiting is secondary to emetogenic properties of narcotics (morphine). Prochlorperazine dose may be too low; dose needs to be increased to 10 mg p.o./i.v. or 25 mg p.r. q6h prn. Since the patient has a history of CAD and asthma, avoid antiemetics that potentiate hypotension or respiratory depression when given with narcotics (e.g., phenothiazines). The patient also complains of excessive sedation, contributed to in part by antiemetics. Change to a nonphenothiazine antiemetic such as benzquinamide. In general, benzquinamide does not potentiate respiratory depression or hypotension associated with narcotics. Less sedative properties are good for neurosurgical patients to allow for accurate neurological checks.

P: Discontinue prochlorperazine. Change to benzquinamide (Emete-Con) 25–50 mg i.m./i.v. q6h prn nausea and vomiting. Give slowly i.v. to avoid possible hypotension that occurs if it is given by rapid i.v. bolus. Monitor for continued emesis, nausea, sedation, blood pressure changes and respiratory rate.

Problem 2. Constipation

S: The patient complains of constipation.

O: D.S. had not had a stool for 5 days, her abdomen is distended and bowel sounds are diminished.

A: An accurate history of the patient's regular bowel habits is needed to assess if no stool for 5 days is unusual. However, normals usually have a bowel movement at least every 3 days. Percocet and anticholinergic properties of amitriptyline have contributed to the constipation preoperatively. Currently, morphine and Alternagel (aluminum-containing antacid) are contributing to constipation. She needs a laxative safe for long-term use since she may be on long-term narcotics for pain control. Avoid saline and stimulant laxatives for long-term use.

P: Inpatient Regimen: Give bisacodyl 10 mg p.r. now; repeat prn stool. Discontinue Alternagel and change to Mylanta or Maalox 30 ml p.o. with dexamethasone; or may alternate Mylanta and Alternagel every other dexamethasone dose. Ensure adequate hydration and ambulate t.i.d. Outpatient Regimen: Drink plenty of fluids; 6–8 8 oz glasses of water a day. Exercise regularly and increase fiber in diet. Metamucil 1 tbsp in large glass of juice qd, stir well. May add docusate 250 mg p.o. b.i.d. for 1 week when patient first goes home if still taking pain medications.

Problem 3. Peptic Ulcer Disease

S: Patient has history of peptic ulcer disease; it was treated for 6 weeks with cimetidine.

O: Guaiac negative; no complaints of stomach pain.

A: D.S. is asymptomatic at present, however, she will be on steroids for 3 weeks after the craniotomy for trigeminal neuralgia. Steroids may be ulcerogenic. Use antacids only for stress-ulcer prophylaxis; possibly more effective than H_2-blockers, cheaper, and no rationale for use of both agents prophylactically. Cimetidine has many drug interactions (phenytoin, theophylline) and is associated with CNS side effects, especially in elderly patients. Since her episode of PUD was a first episode, no long-term prophylaxis with H_2-blockers is necessary.

P: Discontinue cimetidine. Continue antacids while on dexamethasone then discontinue. Monitor theophylline, phenytoin levels when cimetidine has been discontinued; cimetidine inhibits the metabolism of both drugs.

Problem 4. Asthma

S: No complaints; by history only

O: No wheezes, decreased breath sounds bilaterally.

A: Morphine decreases respiration. Histamine release by narcotics is common, may cause respiratory depression and CO_2 retention. When cimetidine is discontinued, her current dose of theophylline may not be enough to maintain therapeutic serum levels (10–20 mg/liter).

P: Continue theophylline when taking oral medications. Check a theophylline level 24 hours after discontinuing cimetidine and adjust dose if needed.

Problem 5. Coronary Artery Disease and Angina

S: No complaints; by history only.

O: None.

A: Patient is presently asymptomatic.

P: Continue sublingual nitroglycerin 1/150 prn chest pain. Provide the following patient education upon discharge: keep nitroglycerin tablets in original container. Place one under the tongue prn chest pain; may repeat × 3 every 5 minutes. If pain is unrelieved by 3 tablets, contact your physician or go to the ER immediately. Take 1 tablet before activities known to provoke chest pain.

CASE 23

CC: D.M. is a 42-year-old male with polycystic kidney disease; he had a cadaver renal transplant (CRT) 2 years ago. Patient comes to clinic today complaining of nausea, frequent emesis, malaise, headache, pruritis, and a fever. Yesterday, D.M. noticed that his urine had become very dark.

Past Medical History

D.M. is status post cadaver renal transplant for end stage renal disease 2 years ago and is currently having an episode of moderate rejection. He has anemia, which required repeated transfusions because of shortness of breath and chest pain. The last transfusion was 6 weeks ago. He has had recurrent urinary tract infections (UTIs). He also has coronary artery disease (CAD) with angina and atrial fibrillation.

Problem List

1. Acute hepatitis
2. Nausea and vomiting
3. Pruritis
4. Pseudomonas UTI
5. Anemia
6. Cadaver renal transplant (CRT), moderate rejection episode
7. CAD with angina
8. Atrial fibrillation

Medication History

Digoxin 0.125 mg p.o. qd
Quinidine SO_4 300 mg p.o. q6h
Azathioprine 50 mg p.o. q.d.
Prednisone 40 mg p.o. qd
$FeSO_4$ 325 mg p.o. t.i.d.
Cyclosporine 80 mg p.o. q.d.

Physical Examination

GEN: Thin, ill appearing male who looks older than stated age.
VS: BP 130/90 HR 100 T 38.5 RR 25 Wt 60 Kg
HEENT: (+) moon facies, truncal striae, markedly icteric sclera, scratch marks on forearm
ABD: Full abdomen, RUQ tenderness, (−) rebound, liver slightly enlarged, (−) shifting dullness
RECT: Guaiac-negative

Results of Laboratory Tests

Na 132	Hct 25	AST 1250	Glu 78	PT 13.6
K 3.5	Hgb 8.5	ALT 1500	Ca P	PTT 35
Cl 92	WBC 13k	LDH 750	PO_4 P	Digoxin 2.5
HCO_3 30	Plts 120k	Alk Phos 40		Quinidine 3
BUN 65	MCV 85	Alb 3		Acetaminophen
Cr 6.0	MCHC 10	T bili 10		<10 mg/dl
		D bili 8		

24 hr CrCl = 10 ml/min
WBC differential: 70 polys, 10 baso, 12 lymph, 8 mono
Hepatitis screen: HbsAg(−), Anti-HB(−), HAV(−)
ECG: Normal sinus rhythm without sinus tachycardia. No prolongation of QT_c interval.
Urinalysis: WBC esterase (+); Gram stain: GNR; Culture: *Pseudomonas aeruginosa*

Problem 1. Acute Hepatitis (Probably Viral)

S: Patient has nausea, vomiting, malaise, decreased appetite, pruritis, headache, and reports of dark urine
O: Positive scleral icterus and jaundice, T Bili = 10.5 mg/dl, D Bili = 8.5 mg/dl, HAV(−), HBsAg(−), anti-HB(−). Increased AST and ALT; AST > ALT. Negative exposure to known hepatotoxins.
A: Acute viral hepatitis, probable non-A/non-B, secondary to blood transfusions required for anemia. Last transfusion was 6 weeks ago which is consistent with an incubation period of 15–150 days. There are no diagnostic tests or treatment for non-A/non-B hepatitis, except to treat the nausea, vomiting and pruritis symptomatically. LFTs should decrease over 15–20 weeks; bilirubin will decrease sooner. Monitor indicators of liver failure, which are mild now with the PT only slightly elevated and glucose WNL. The albumin is slightly decreased; DM may develop third spacing, therefore, do not give the patient a large sodium load. If PT prolongation is due to a nutritional vitamin K deficiency, PT will respond rapidly (within 24 hours). If PT does not respond to vitamin K, the patient's synthetic capabilities may be compromized; a PT unresponsive to vitamin K is a very poor prognostic sign.
P: Treat nausea and vomiting and pruritis (see Problem 2); gently rehydrate. Educate the patient regarding the risks of recurrent transfusions. Monitor LFTs, bilirubin, scleral icterus, hepatitis serology, bleeding. Give vitamin K 10 mg s.c. now.

Problem 2. Nausea and Vomiting

S: Patient complains of nausea and frequent vomiting.
O: D.M. has mild hyponatremia and contraction alkalosis. Patient is vomiting and therefore is losing K^+ and H^+.
A: Nausea and vomiting are secondary to acute viral hepatitis, uremia, or both. Need to treat to avoid further electrolyte imbalances and dehydration. An oral agent may not be the best choice due to frequent vomiting, and the i.m. route should be avoided because of abnormal coagulation tests.
P: Prochlorperazine 5–10 mg i.v. q6h or 25 mg p.r. q6h prn nausea and vomiting. Suppositories may be the best choice in this patient and will minimize side effects that occur when giving prochlorperazine i.v. Can change to prochlorperazine 10 mg p.o. q6h prn nausea and vomiting when the acute event has subsided. Monitor for sedation, orthostatic hypotension, and extrapyramidal side effects.

Problem 3. Pruritis

S: Patient complains of itching.
O: Scratch marks are evident on patient's forearms.
A: Pruritis is secondary to hepatitis which results in accumulation and deposition of bile salts in

subcutaneous tissues. Uremia may be contributing to the pruritis as well, by an unknown mechanism. If the pruritis is mild, Burow's solution or calamine lotion may be used topically. If itching is severe, systemic antihistamines or cholestyramine may be useful. Cholestyramine binds bile salts; the onset of action is approximately 1 week. Cholestyramine may bind digoxin; separate doses by giving the digoxin 1 *hour* prior to the cholestyramine. The goal is to prevent scratching and skin ulcerations in an immunosuppressed patient predisposed to staphylococcal infections.

P: Hydroxyzine or diphenhydramine 25–50 mg p.o. q6h prn. Calamine lotion to arms prn. If itching continues despite antihistamines: cholestyramine 1 p.o. q.i.d. in 8 oz water. Separate cholestyramine by 1 hour before or 2 hours after the digoxin dose. Cut nails, wear cotton gloves to decrease skin damage. Monitor for constipation and bloating with cholestyramine. Monitor for decreased itching or excessive sedation with antihistamines.

Problem 4. *Pseudomonas* Urinary Tract Infection

S: Patient reports burning on urination and fever.

O: (+) WBC esterase, (+) urine culture, increased WBC, increased bands, left shift, history of recurrent UTIs.

A: WBC and temperature are difficult to interpret in a patient on prednisone and azathioprine. The fever could be viral or bacterial in origin. Since the patient is immunosuppressed, he must be treated empirically as if it were a systemic infection. D.M.'s CrCl is 10 ml/minute with minimal urine output; an oral agent will not concentrate in the urine. Give antibiotics which achieve adequate tissue levels such as an aminoglycoside (tobramycin) plus an antipseudomonal penicillin (ticarcillin, mezlocillin, piperacillin).

P: Tobramycin LD: 2 mg/kg=(120 mg) i.v. × 1 followed by a daily dose to achieve peaks of 4–6 mg/liter; t ½ = 24–48 hours in CRF patient, therefore, conventional aminoglycoside dosing does not apply.[a] Add mezlocillin 3 g i.v. q8h (decrease dose when CrCl < 30 ml/min) and treat for 14 days. Repeat urinalysis and blood cultures. Monitor for ototoxicity and nephrotoxicity in CRF patient. Monitor for in vivo inactivation of tobramycin by penicillins resulting in decreased tobramycin levels and decreased efficacy.

Problem 5. Anemia

S: D.M. has had shortness of breath and chest pain in the past.

O: D.M. has decreased Hgb and Hct. His MCV is within normal limits. He is guaiac-negative.

A: D.M. most likely has anemia of chronic disease secondary to ESRD. CRF causes decreased production of erythropoietin in the kidney resulting in decreased formation of Hgb. Anemia of chronic disease will not respond to iron. Iron therapy contributes to constipation in CRF patients. Erythropoietin is not commercially available now.

P: Discontinue FeSO$_4$. Monitor Hgb, Hct, indices, SOB; transfuse prn to keep Hct >25 as he has CAD and angina.

Problem 6. Cadaver Renal Transplant With Moderate Rejection

S: D.M. complains of malaise.

O: D.M. has elevated BUN, Cr, and WBC.

A: Is the patient undergoing moderate rejection vs. cyclosporine (CSA) nephrotoxicity? Renal biopsy may be indicated to make the diagnosis. Pulse steroids are probably the best choice if D.M. is in rejection; muromonao-CD3 (OKT$_3$) and anti-thymocyte globulin (ATGAM) are not indicated in moderate rejection 2 years after transplant. Azathioprine and cyclosporine are not useful in treating a rejection episode; they are only useful as a prophylaxis for rejection.

P: Obtain a cyclosporine level. Give methylprednisolone 1 g i.v. q.d. for 3 days; continue CSA and azathioprine at the current doses if the CSA is within therapeutic limits. Resume prednisone 40 mg p.o. q.d. after the course of high-dose methylprednisolone. Alternative treatment is prednisone 2 mg/kg/day (120 mg/qd) × 3 days and taper by 10 mg q 3 days down to lowest possible maintenance dose. Monitor K$^+$, glucose, signs of rejection, mental status changes and GI bleeding. Monitor BUN, Cr, graft tenderness, and cyclosporine levels.

Problem 7. Coronary Artery Disease/Angina

S: None.

O: History.

A: This is not an active problem.

P: Begin nitroglycerin (NTG) 0.4 mg s.l. prn chest pain. Call the house officer after NTG is administered. Prior to discharge, begin patient education concerning the proper use of NTG.

Problem 8. Atrial Fibrillation

S: None.

O: ECG shows normal sinus rhythm without tachycardia. No prolongation of QT$_c$ interval. Digoxin level=2.5 mg/liter. Quinidine=3 mg/dl.

A: Atrial fibrillation is well controlled. Quinidine increases digoxin levels by two mechanisms: (a) decreases the volume of distribution of digoxin and (b) decreases digoxin clearance. Higher digoxin levels may be necessary to treat

---

[a]This patient has a t$_{1/2}$ of 12 hours; 60 mg i.v. q24h of tobramycin will achieve C peak=5.5 mg/liter and C min ~1.5 mg/liter.

atrial fibrillation. Digoxin levels will decrease by ~50% if quinidine is discontinued.

P: Continue current digoxin and quinidine doses.

CASE 24

CC: A.L. is a 53-year-old male who presents to the clinic today complaining of abdominal cramping, mild thirst, and watery diarrhea. He denies any recent travel outside the United States and has not eaten in a restaurant in over 2 weeks.

Problem List

1. Diarrhea: approximately six watery stools per day, onset about 3 days ago
2. Chronic sinusitis: originally treated with cefaclor, A.L. was changed to clindamycin 3 weeks ago after developing a *Proprionobacterium acnes* superinfection
3. Status post pulmonary embolism 3 months ago
4. Status post splenectomy 20 years ago secondary to Problem 5
5. Status post Hodgkins lymphoma 20 years ago

Medication History

Clindamycin 150 mg p.o. q6h
Warfarin 7.5 mg p.o. qhs
Acetaminophen 650 mg p.o. prn headache
Multivitamin 1 tablet p.o. q.d.

Allergies

None known.

Physical Examination

GEN: Thin male in mild distress
VS: BP 130/85 (lying) 125/78 (sitting) HR 82 (lying) HR 87 (sitting) T 38.5
HEENT: (−) lymphadenopathy
COR: WNL
CHEST: WNL
ABD: Diffuse tenderness in lower abdomen, (−) rebound, (−) RUQ pain
GU: WNL
RECT: Guaiac-negative
EXT: WNL
NEURO: WNL

Results of Laboratory Tests

Na 143	BUN 23	WBC 24.7	Alk Phos WNL	PT 18.6
K 3.3	Cr 1	AST WNL	Alb WNL	PTT 39
Cl 105	Hct 43	ALT WNL	T Bili WNL	
HCO$_3$ 23	Hgb 16	LDH WNL	Glu 110	

Urinalysis: WNL
Cultures and sensitivity: Stool positive for *Clostridium difficile* toxin
Sigmoidoscopy: Green-yellow raised lesions on the mucosal surface consistent with pseudomembranous colitis.

Problem ____

S: ____

O: ____

A: ____

P: ____

Problem ____

S: ____

O: ____

A: ____

P: ____

Problem

S:

O:

A:

P:

Problem

S:

O:

A:

P:

Problem

S:

O:

A:

P:

Problem

S:

O:

A:

P:

Questions

1. How would you treat A.L.'s pseudomembranous colitis (PMC)? List drug, dose, route, and duration of therapy. Explain why you chose this drug over others for this patient.
2. What would you tell this patient regarding fluid replacement and its importance in the treatment of severe diarrhea?
3. Would you recommend monitoring this patient for ototoxicity as a side effect of vancomycin therapy? Why or why not?

CASE 25

CC: F.A. is a 28-year-old female physician at a large university hospital. During her last night on call in the intensive care unit, she accidentally stuck herself with a needle while placing a central line in one of her patients. While reviewing the medical record, F.A. discovers that the patient has recent serologies positive for HBsAg. She is married and is 6 months pregnant with her first child.

Problem

S:
O:
A:
P:

Problem

S:
O:
A:
P:

Questions

1. What treatment do you recommend for F.A. at this time? List drug, dose, route, and duration of therapy.
2. Would you treat F.A.'s husband with HBIG? Why or why not?
3. If F.A. is HBsAg positive at the time of delivery, what are your recommendations for her child? List drug(s), dose, route and duration of therapy.

CASE 26

CC: M.P. is a 62-year-old woman who is transferred to university hospital with a complaint of recent onset bloody diarrhea (up to 12 stools per day).

Problem List

1. Type I diabetes of 18 years duration
2. Chronic bronchitis

3. Hypothyroidism secondary to iodine-131 treatment of hyperthyroidism 15 years ago
4. Status post myocardial infarction (MI) in 1985
5. Status post cerebral vascular accident (CVA) in 1984 with resulting focal seizures
6. Vaginal infection with *Candida albicans*
7. Newly diagnosed ulcerative colitis

Medication History

NPH/regular insulin 15/10 U q 8 AM; 10/5 U 5 PM
Theophylline 400 mg b.i.d. for 1 yr
Prednisone 20 mg b.i.d. for 1 yr
Terbutaline 5 mg q.i.d. for 1 yr
Metaproterenol inhaler 2 puffs q 4–6 h prn for 3 yrs
Phenytoin 100 mg t.i.d. since 1984
Nifedipine 20 mg t.i.d.
Isosorbide dinitrate 40 mg q.i.d.
NTG paste 2 inches qhs
ASA 650 mg b.i.d.
Levothyroxine 0.1 mg q.d.

Allergies

None known.

Social History

M.P. stopped smoking 1 year ago; she had previously smoked ½ pack per day.

Physical Examination

GEN: Acutely ill-appearing woman
VS: BP 152/74 HR 96 T 37.6 RR 18 Wt 45 kg
HEENT: No masses, PERRLA
COR: Distant S1 and S2
CHEST: Decreased breath sounds bilaterally, scattered wheezes and rhonchi
ABD: Soft, diffusely tender, hyperactive bowel sounds
GU: Deferred
EXT: 2+ DTRs symmetrical, thin, dry skin, bruise on LLE

ECG: NSR with no LVH, changes consistent with old inferior wall MI
Sigmoidoscopy: Ulcerated inflamed friable mucosa consistent with ulcerative colitis

Results of Laboratory Tests

Na 137	Hct 34.2	LDH 100	PO_4 2
K 4.3	Hgb 11.3	Alk Phos 60	Mg 1.8
Cl 96	WBC 10.1k	Alb 3.9	Chol 464
HCO_3 31	Plts 135k	T Bili 0.1	Trigycerides: 660
BUN 9	AST 19	FBG 279	
Cr 1.6	ALT 11	Ca 9.7	

TFTs: T_4 5.6, RT_3U 29, TSH <0.2
ABGs: PO_2 58, PCO_2 48, pH 7.44
Urinalysis: 2% glucose, 1+ protein, + ketones (by Labstix); yeast (+)

Problem _____
S: _____
O: _____
A: _____
P: _____

Problem _____
S: _____
O: _____
A: _____
P: _____

Problem

S:

O:

A:

P:

Problem

S:

O:

A:

P:

Problem

S:

O:

A:

P:

Problem

S:

O:

A:

P:

Problem

S:

O:

A:

P:

Questions

1. Recommend treatment for M.P.'s acute episode of ulcerative colitis. Be specific, list drug(s), dose(s), route(s), schedule(s), and duration. List five monitoring parameters that would detect adverse reactions of the recommended drug therapy.

2. Recommend an insulin regimen for M.P. while she is n.p.o. Include drug, dose, route, schedule and monitoring parameters.

3. Six weeks have passed and M.P. has not responded to her treatment for ulcerative colitis. The physician wishes to assess the extent of the disease by a barium enema. Recommend a bowel preparation for this test. Choose a product, dose, route, and schedule. State your reasons for choosing this preparation.

4. The barium enema shows pancolitis without resolution and it is decided to remove M.P.'s colon. Recommend steroid therapy for M.P. during and for 5 days after her surgery. Be specific, include drug, dose, route, schedule and duration.

5. Six hours after surgery, M.P. complains of severe nausea and has vomited three times. Recommend treatment for the anesthesia-induced nausea. Give the drug, dose, route, schedule, and reasons for your selection. What antiemetic drugs should be avoided in M.P. and why?

6. Now that M.P.'s colon has been removed, recommend a steroid taper that she can follow upon discharge from the hospital. List six monitoring parameters that you would follow during the taper.

7. M.P. is ready to go home and requires a new insulin regimen. Assume that she will be on the same diet that she received during her last week of hospitalization. Based upon the blood glucose data given below recommend an insulin regimen. Give reasons for any changes you make in the insulin regimen. Her insulin doses have been NPH/Reg 15/10 U at 8 AM and 10/5 U at 5 PM and her mean blood glucose: 7 AM 340 mg/100 ml, 12 noon 80 mg/100 ml, 4 PM 120 mg/100 ml, 10 PM 240 mg/100 ml.

8. M.P. is to be discharged on the same medications she took prior to admission except for the steroid taper and the new insulin regimen.
   a. Are there any drug interactions that would interfere with her glucose control? Identify the drug, the mechanism of the interaction and the significance of the interaction and state a plan for handling the drug interaction.
   b. Should her levothyroxine dose be altered? State your reasons for any recommended change in dose.

CASE 27

CC: C.C. is a 58-year-old female presenting with a 1-month history of "gnawing" epigastric pain, a 2-day history of vomiting coffeeground-like material, and soft, tarry stools. She is admitted to the hospital for workup and treatment of a probable bleeding peptic ulcer.

Past Medical History

C.C. has had peptic ulcer disease (PUD) for 20 years, it flares every 3–5 years. She has had primary hypothyroidism for 34 years. C.C. also has had chronic renal disease for 15 years and has been postmenopausal for 14 years. She had a deep venous thrombosis (DVT) 2 months ago. L.V. has had osteoarthritis for 2–5 years.

Problem List

1. Peptic ulcer disease
2. Primary hypothyroidism
3. Chronic renal disease
4. Menopause
5. DVT
6. Osteoarthritis

Medication History

Levothyroxine 0.15 mg p.o. q.d. × many years
Conjugated estrogen 0.625 mg p.o. q.d. × 13 years
Warfarin 5 mg p.o. q AM × 2 months
Ibuprofen 200 mg p.o. b.i.d. to q.i.d. (self-medicates for arthritis) × 1–2 months
Aluminum hydroxide capsules 475 mg p.o. t.i.d.
Sodium citrate mixture 10 ml p.o. t.i.d.
Multivitamin with folic acid 1 tablet p.o. q.d.

Allergies

None known.

Social History

C.C. does not smoke and drinks alcohol only occasionally. She is married and has two children.

Physical Examination

GEN: Woman with mild shortness of breath

VS: BP 146/88 (sitting) 132/64 (standing) HR 95 (sitting) 110 (standing) T 37.1 RR 28 Ht 5'7" Wt 126 lb (was 134 lb 4 weeks ago and 150 lb about 1 year ago)

HEENT: SL exophthalmos

COR: NL S1 and S2; (−) S3 or S4

CHEST: clear to auscultation and percussion

ABD: Epigastric pain, liver normal size, no splenomegaly

RECT: Guaiac-positive

SKIN: Hyperpigmentation on hands and arms

NEURO: WNL

Upper GI series: Duodenal ulcer

Results of Laboratory Tests

Na 141	Cr 3.2	MCV 68	Alk Phos P	PO_4 4
K 4.8	Hct 26	MCHC 26	Alb 3	Mg 2.2
Cl 104	Hgb 10	AST 40	T Bili 1	PT 27
HCO_3 22	WBC 7.2k	ALT 26	FBG 128	PTT P
BUN 38	Plts P	LDH P	Ca 9.2	

WBC differential: 47 polys, 39 lymph, 8 mono, 4 eos, 2 baso

TFTs: T_4 21, RT_3U 32

Urinalysis: WNL

Problem _____

S: _____

O: _____

A: _____

P: _____

Problem _____

S: _____

O: _____

A: _____

P: _____

Problem _____

S: _____

O: _____

A: _____

P: _____

Problem

S:

O:

A:

P:

Problem

S:

O:

A:

P:

Problem

S:

O:

A:

P:

CASE 28

CC: J.K. is a 36-year-old female with a 3-year history of alcoholic cirrhosis and had stopped drinking until 4 weeks ago. She is now drinking a fifth of vodka daily and is admitted for evaluation of chest pain and confusion of 24 hours duration.

Problem List

1. Alcoholism
2. Hemorrhoids
3. Esophageal varices
4. Ascites
5. Status post GI bleeding
6. Status post alcohol withdrawal seizures

Medication History

Spironolactone 100 mg p.o. t.i.d.
Acetaminophen extra strength 2 tablets p.o. q4h
Magnesium citrate 8 oz p.o. q6h for guaiac-positive stools
Cimetidine 400 mg p.o. q.i.d.
Diazepam 10 mg p.o. q6h prn ETOH withdrawal symptoms
Aspirin with codeine 60 mg p.o. q3h prn
Isoniazid 300 mg p.o. q.d.

Allergies

None known.

Physical Examination

VS: (supine) BP 100/60 HR 102 RR 24 T 38 Wt 60 kg Ht 5'6"

HEENT: Scleral icterus; ETOH on breath

COR: WNL

CHEST: No wheezes, few rhonchi that clear with coughing

ABD: Hepatomegaly, (+) fluid wave

GU: Deferred

RECT: Guaiac stool (+)

EXT: Cool to touch and pale nail beds. Bruises; + asterixis.

NEURO: Decreased sensation both lower extremities, normal DTRs, oriented × 1.

Results of Laboratory Tests

Na 138	Cr 1.4	MCV 106	Alb 2	Mg 4.8
K 6	Hct 26	MCHC 42	T Bili 5	PT 20
Cl 108	Hgb 11	AST 400	FBG 95	PTT 40
HCO_3 20	WBC 4.5k	ALT 340	Ca 9.5	Folate 0.7
BUN 32	Plts 60k	Alk Phos 180	PO_4 2.8	B_{12} 80

Urinalysis: WNL
ECG: Peaked T waves

Problem

S:

O:

A:

P:

Problem

S:

O:

A:

P:

Problem

S:

O:

A:

P:

Problem

S:_____

O:_____

A:_____

P:_____

Problem

S:_____

O:_____

A:_____

P:_____

Problem

S:_____

O:_____

A:_____

P:_____

Rheumatic Diseases

CASE 29

CC: M.M. is a 63-year-old-male with an 11-year history of seropositive rheumatoid arthritis who comes to clinic for evaluation. He complains of lethargy, fatigue, increased joint swelling, morning stiffness of greater than 2 hours duration, GI upset, constipation, headache, and dry skin.

Past Medical History

In 1977 M.M. was begun on gold therapy for his rheumatoid arthritis (RA). He received four injections each of 50-mg gold thiomalate at 1-week intervals. M.M. developed flushing and tachycardia after each injection, which required that he lie down for 30 minutes. He also developed a transient erythematous rash. The gold was discontinued after the fourth injection and prednisone was instituted at that time. M.M. was not treated with any other drugs for his RA until 1 month ago.

M.M. developed diabetes mellitus in 1980, which was classified as type IIb. He has been unable to lose weight despite extensive patient education. He is symptomatic (polyuria, polydipsia, fatigue) and requires drug treatment. Other medical problems include: hypothyroidism, diagnosed for 2 years; hypertension, diagnosed for 9 years; chronic liver disease, diagnosed for 5 years.

Problem List

1. Rheumatoid arthritis
2. Type IIb diabetes
3. Hypothyroidism
4. Chronic alcoholic liver disease
5. Hypertension

Medication History

These medications were prescribed at last clinic visit 1 month ago:

Indomethacin 25 mg q.i.d.
Predinsone 10 mg q.d.
Chlorpropamide 500 mg q.d.
Enteric-coated aspirin 650 mg q 3–4 h prn pain
Levothyroxine 0.050 mg q.d.
HCTZ 25 mg q.d.
Metoprolol 50 mg q.d.

Allergies

None known.

Social History

M.M. has chronic alcoholism.

Physical Examination

GEN: Cushingnoid-appearing male in no apparent distress.
VS: BP 150/95 HR 79 regular T 36.8 RR 20 Wt 85 kg Ht 5'10"
HEENT: Cataract left eye
COR: WNL
CHEST: Clear to ausculation and percussion.
ABD: Striae, obese, mild ascites
GU: WNL
RECT: Guaiac-positive
EXT: Red, hot, swollen MTP joints, wrists, ankles, and knees
NEURO: WNL

Results of Laboratory Tests

Na 140	Hct 36	AST 122	FBG 70	PT 13.7
K 3.1	Hgb 12	ALT P	Ca 8.9	PTT 38.3
Cl 103	WBC 8.5k	LDH 191	PO_4 3.7	Prot 5.6
HCO_3 27	Plts 180k	Alk Phos P	Mg 2	Uric acid 9.6
BUN 29	MCV 91	Alb 2.8		
Cr 1.4	MCHC 32	T Bili 1.5		

TFTS: $T_4 = 2$, $RT_3U = 20$, TSH $= 13$
Urinalysis: 2% glu Clinitest: − ketone, + bili, − protein
Chest x-ray: Severe osteoporosis of spine

Problem 1. Rheumatoid Arthritis

S: M.M. complains of lethargy, fatigue, increased joint swelling, and morning stiffness of greater than 2 hours duration.

O: Red hot swollen MTPs, wrists, ankles and knees. Eleven-year history of seropositive rheumatoid arthritis.

A: M.M. has progressive, uncontrolled RA that has not been properly treated. Treatment should have begun in 1977 with an adequate (1-month) trial of aspirin or an NSAID such as ibuprofen or naproxen. The gold should not have been discontinued because of a transient erythematous rash. The gold should have been discontinued until the rash resolved and then reinstituted at a lower dose with close observation. The flushing and tachycardia are a nitratoid reaction that is common with water-soluble gold salt. While prednisone is effective in treating RA it carries a high risk for side effects as seen in this patient. The dose of indomethacin prescribed at the last clinic visit is below the therapeutic dose. Enteric-coated aspirin is slow in onset for pain relief and prn dosing will not achieve therapeutic salicylate levels. The steroids, indomethacin, ethanol, and aspirin could have caused gastric erosions or ulceration, (see Problem 7). Sulindac may have less nephrotoxicity than other NSAIDs. Acetaminophen should be confined to doses less than 3.6 g/day and occasional use because of the possible enhanced hepatotoxicity in chronic alcoholic liver disease.

P: Discontinue indomethacin and enteric-coated aspirin. Begin sulindac p.o. 150 mg b.i.d. Reassess response in 2 weeks. Monitor BUN/Cr and urine output. Begin gold auriothioglucose 10 mg i.m., administer the next two doses as 25 mg i.m. every week, and then 50 mg every week until response or a total dose of 1 g. Before each dose obtain a urinalysis and CBC; observe for skin rashes and stomatitis and inquire about diarrhea. Watch for hematoma formation at the injection site because of elevated prothrombin time. Taper steroids (see Problem 8).

Problem 2. Type IIb Diabetes

S: M.M. complains of polyuria, polydipsia, and fatigue.

O: Urine 2% glucose, but FBG = 70

A: Chlorpropamide is not the drug of choice in the patient because M.M. continues to drink and chlorpropamide can cause a disulfiram-like reaction. Chlorpropamide is excreted by the kidneys, and M.M. has mildly impaired renal function (CrCl = 56ml/min). The dose of 500 mg/day of chlorpropamide is high and M.M.'s FBG = 70 mg/100 ml. Oral hypoglycemics can cause profound hypoglycemia in patients with liver disease although M.M.'s liver disease is not severe at this time. When hypoglycemia occurs because of chlorpropamide, it is likely to be of prolonged duration because of the long half-life of the drug. M.M. has a low albumin that may reflect his liver disease as well as his nutritional status. Metoprolol should not mask all the signs of hypoglycemia since it is a B_1 selective beta-blocker. The 2% urine glucose reading is due to interference with the Clinitest method by aspirin. Both HCTZ and prednisone may be aggravating M.M. diabetes.

P: Discontinue chlorpropamide. Begin tolazamide 100 mg q AM and reassess in 1 week. Begin urine testing with Testape q.i.d. Read the Testape at the wet-dry border to avoid drug interference. Continue education about his disease, diet, and weight loss. Try to get M.M. to stop drinking; arrange for him to attend Alcoholic's Anonymous. Teach M.M. how to test

his urine and to avoid high-dose ASA and vitamin C, which can interfere with the test results. Monitor FBG with a target of between 140–180 mg/100 ml. Keep his urine glucose negative. Decrease the polyuria and polydipsia, and increase his energy level.

Problem 3. Hypothyroidism

S: M.M. complains of lethargy, constipation, and dry skin.

O: T_4 = 2, RT_3U = 20%, TSH = 13

A: M.M. is hypothyroid and his dose is too low for adequate replacement. His dose should be increased slowly because of his hypertension and the likelihood of atherosclerotic cardiovascular disease. T_4 has a long half-life so doses should be adjusted no more frequently than every 2 weeks. Levothyroxine is the thyroid replacement preparation of choice because it has the most reliable hormone content.

P: Begin levothyroxine 0.075 mg q.d., reassess in 2 weeks. Monitor signs and symptoms of hypothyroidism and hyperthyroidism and TFTs. M.M.s lethargy and constipation should improve. Suggest that M.M. purchase a lotion or baby oil to treat his dry skin.

Problem 4. Chronic Alcoholic Liver Disease

S: None.

O: Bili = 1.5, AST = 122, Alb = 2.8, PT = 13.7, mild ascites

A: M.M. has chronic liver disease secondary to alcohol ingestion. There is no drug therapy to reverse the process. M.M. should avoid potentially hepatotoxic drugs so as not to aggravate his condition. Mild ascites does not necessarily require drug treatment and spironolactone has several troublesome side effects including hyperkalemia and gynecomastia.

P: Give menadiol 10 mg p.o. q.d. × 3 doses to rule out a nutritional basis for the elevated PT. Restrict M.M.'s sodium intake in order to promote a gentle diuresis. If this is ineffective and treatment is warranted, begin spironolactone 50 mg q.d. and increase the dose no more frequently than every 3 days to a maximum of 400 mg/day. Try to get M.M. to discontinue his ethanol intake. Monitor weight loss (want 0.5–1 lb/day), serum electrolytes, liver function tests and PT.

Problem 5. Hypertension

S: None.

O: BP 150/95, HR 79

A: BP is not well controlled although this is a single reading. HCTZ is not more effective in higher doses so there is no need to increase the dose. M.M. is not on an adequate dose of beta-blocker.

P: Increase metoprolol to 100 mg qd; reassess in 2 weeks. Monitor BP and serum electrolytes.

Problem 6. Hyperuricemia

S: None.

O: Uric acid = 9.6

A: M.M. has multiple risk factors for an elevated uric acid level including obesity, hydrochlorthiazide, low-dose aspirin, ethanol ingestion, and decreased renal function. There is no history of a gouty attack and drug treatment is not required at this time. A uric acid level > 10 or two acute attacks of gout are usually required to initiate long-term therapy.

P: Discontinue ASA and try to get M.M. to lose weight and stop drinking. Monitor uric acid levels and signs and symptoms of gout and urate nephropathy.

Problem 7. Guaiac-Positive Stool

S: M.M. complains of GI upset.

O: Guaiac-positive stool, Hgb = 12, Hct = 36

A: M.M. has GI bleeding of undetermined origin and will need a workup to determine the source. The most likely source is gastritis or peptic ulcer disease from his indomethacin, aspirin, prednisone, and ethanol. However, all other sources must be excluded. M.M. may also have iron deficiency anemia secondary to GI bleeding.

P: Wait for the diagnosis of the source of bleeding. Discontinue GI irritants as above and taper prednisone per Problem 8. Begin antacid of choice prn GI upset. Avoid the few antacids that contain considerable amounts of sodium such as Alka Seltzer.

Problem 8. Prednisone Toxicity

S: None.

O: M.M. is a cushingnoid-appearing male with striae, obesity, osteoporosis, elevated blood glucose, hypertension, cataract, and his K = 3.1.

A: M.M.'s steroid therapy has caused adverse reactions and is aggravating some of his other medical problems. Although M.M.'s prednisone dose is relatively low, he has many adverse effects due to steroids; this may be due to his decreased albumin leading to a higher amount of free steroid. Drug therapy is not available to slow osteoporosis in a male nor to treat his cataract.

P: Taper prednisone slowly by 1 mg every 2 weeks to 1 month until M.M. is off steroids or his AM cortisol is > 10. In 9 or 12 months perform a cortrosyn stimulation test to assess adrenal reserve. Monitor for signs and symptoms of worsening arthritis as well as signs and symptoms of adrenal insufficiency. Begin KCl 15 mEq b.i.d. for 1 week. Monitor serum K. Discuss the reasons for the taper with M.M. and

teach him to contact the clinic in case of a flu-like illness. Obtain a Medi-Alert bracelet. Tell health care providers about his history of taking steroids.

Problem 9. Constipation

S: M.M. complains of constipation.

O: None.

A: There are no drug-induced causes for his constipation. It is not clear if this is an acute or a chronic problem. Constipation can be a symptom caused by numerous diseases so if this is a severe or chronic problem, an evaluation is required. This may be due to his hypothyroidism. Simple constipation can be safely treated with drugs.

P: Obtain more information about the nature of the complaint. If acute, offer M.M. his choice of 30 ml milk of magnesia, a glycerin suppository, or a small dose of a stimulant laxative. A tap water enema is also an acceptable alternative. If the problem is chronic, begin a sugar-free, low-sodium bulk laxative such as carboxymethylcellulose or psyllium. Teach M.M. to increase his fluid intake and the amount of fiber in his diet.

CASE 30

CC: T.P. is a 73-year-old obese female who comes for follow-up in hypertension (HTN) clinic. She states that she feels fair; she has no chief complaint except for some mild swelling and pain in both knees. She has experienced morning stiffness in both hips and knees for several months, which has recently become increasingly painful on ambulation. She denies any nausea, vomiting, diarrhea, shortness of breath, chest pain, headaches, blurred vision, light headedness, heat or cold intolerance, and muscle weakness, but admits to occasional fatigue.

Past Medical History

CVA 3 years ago; trauma secondary to motor vehicle accident 15 years ago, in which she sustained several rib and right tibial fractures.

Problem List

1. HTN × 30 years
2. Mild right-sided hemiparesis
3. DJD × 20 years
4. Hypothyroidism, s/p thyroidectomy 17 years ago

Current Medications

HCTZ 25 mg p.o. qd
Nadolol 4 mg p.o. qd
Dipyridamole 75 mg p.o. t.i.d.
Enteric-coated aspirin 325 mg p.o. qd
Levothyroxine 0.15 mg p.o. qd

Physical Examination

GEN: Pleasant elderly female with mild right-sided weakness, mild swelling and tenderness in both knees.

VS: BP 154/82 (supine) 158/78 (sitting) HR 66 regular Wt 73 kg Ht 5'3" T 37.2.
HEENT: Hair thinning and dry, PERRLA, (−) goiter
COR: Regular rate and rhythm, normal S1 and S2, (−) S3, S4
CHEST: Lungs clear on auscultation and percussion
ABD: Liver and spleen WNL on palpation
EXT: Heberden's nodes on both hands, knees warm and tender to touch

Results of Laboratory Tests

Na 141   Cr 1.1   ESR 47
K 3.8   Hct 38.7 T_4(D) 8.7
Cl 99   Hgb 12.9 TSH 0.35
HCO_3 24   WBC 6.1   RF (−)
BUN 11   RBC 4.3

X-rays Bilateral Knees: Narrowed joint spaces consistent with DJD.

Problem 3. Degenerative Joint Disease

S: T.P. complains of morning stiffness with pain on initiating ambulation.

O: T.P. has Heberden's nodes on both hands. Her knees are warm and tender to touch. X-rays of bilateral knees show narrowed joint spaces consistent with DJD. She has elevated ESR; note RF (−).

A: The pain and inflammation is due to DJD and requires drug therapy to decrease both the pain and inflammation. Aspirin is a good choice in this patient. Acetaminophen is effective only for the pain but not for the inflammation. An NSAIA will be considered if the patient experiences side effects with ASA.

P: Begin enteric-coated ASA 650 mg q 4–6 h. Dose on a regular schedule until pain and inflammation are controlled. Increase the dose by 2 tablets every 2 weeks until relief. If tinnitus occurs, decrease the total daily dose by 2 tablets. Monitor pain and inflammation as a response to therapy, GI irritation, GI blood loss (Hct, stool guaiac if indicated), tinnitus, salicylate levels if no response or side effects (anti-inflammatory levels: 200–300 μ/ml). Patient education: Counsel patient that ASA can be taken with food, milk, or full glass of water to minimize GI upset. Ask patient to report any symptoms of GI upset or bleeding.

Problem 1. Hypertension

S: T.P. does not complain of headaches, chest pain, shortness of breath, blurred vision, muscle weakness, or fatigue.

O: BP 154/82 (supine) 158/78 (sitting) HR 66 regular

A: Her systolic pressure is mildly elevated most likely secondary to atherosclerotic cardiovascular disease (ASCVD). Her blood pressure may be decreased with a low-sodium diet and weight reduction. Presently she is stable on her current HTN therapy.

P: Continue HCTZ 25 mg p.o. qd and Nadolol 40 mg p.o. qd. Monitor BP, electrolytes (K^+), glucose, uric acid, renal function, and for side effects for HCTZ (dehydration, muscle cramping, dizziness) and for nadolol (lightheadedness, dizziness, fatigue, shortness of breath). Patient education: Discuss a low-salt and cholesterol diet and appropriate weight reduction. Stress the importance of compliance to medications. Review potential side effects of nadolol and HCTZ.

Problem 4. Hypothyroidism

S: T.P. has no symptoms of hyperthyroidism or hypothyroidism. (heat or cold intolerance).

O: T_4 (D) = 8.7 TSH = 0.35

A: She is presently controlled on her current levothyroxine dose of 0.15 mg qd.

P: Continue levothyroxine 0.15 mg p.o. qd. Monitor TFTs (T_4, TSH). Patient Education: Review potential adverse effects of levothyroxine. Review symptoms of hyperthyroidism and hypothyroidism.

Problem 2. Mild Right-Sided Hemiparesis

S: None.

O: VS as above.

A: Dypyridamole is in subtherapeutic dose and its efficacy is questionable. Antiplatelet agents to reduce risk of strokes is controversial. Also aspirin reduces the prevalence of stroke and death in men only. Patients with previous MI and HTN respond poorly. This patient does not have a history of transient ischemic attacks, therefore dypyridamole is not indicated.

P: Discontinue dypyridamole. Stress importance of compliance to HTN medications, and a low-sodium and fat diet to reduce risk of MI or another CVA.

CASE 31

CC: G.M. is a 19-year-old female recently diagnosed with systemic lupus erythematosus (SLE) who comes to the clinic for follow-up. Today she states that she has experienced constant fatigue since being diagnosed with SLE, and now is feeling quite depressed. She feels that she is being punished for her "sinful past of intravenous drug abuse and prostitution". Currently she denies any shortness of breath, chest pain, blurred vision, bleeding from her nose or mouth, blood in her stool or urine, black tarry stools nor any bruising. She admits to occasional morning joint swelling and stiffness, and erythematous rash involving her face, shoulders and both arms, which becomes worse when exposed to sunlight. She also admits to occasional headaches which are relieved with acetaminophen.

Past Medical History

SLE was diagnosed 3 months ago. She had mitral valve replacement (MVR) performed (St. Judes valve) 3 years ago resulting from subacute bacterial endocarditis secondary to intravenous drug abuse at age 16. Began heroin abuse at age 15, but has not used heroin since valve replacement.

Problem List

1. SLE diagnosed for 3 months.
2. MVR (St. Judes) performed 3 years ago.

Medication History

Warfarin 2 mg 2 tablets p.o. qd
Acetaminophen 325 mg 2 tablets p.o. q4h prn
   headaches
Ibuprofen 400 mg 1 tablet p.o. q.i.d.

Physical Examination

GEN: Young, thin female appearing moderately depressed and crying.

VS: BP 108/62 (sitting) 108/66 (supine) HR 78 (reg) Wt 46.5 Kg Ht 5'5" T 37.4

HEENT: Hair thinning (mild alopecia); butterfly eruption over bridge of nose and malar region of the face.

COR: Regular rate and rhythm. Prosthetic valve heard. (−) S3, S4; no gallops or rubs

CHEST: Lungs clear on ascultation and percussion. Erythematous macular rash present involving both shoulders and upper chest and back.

ABD: Mildly tender, palpable spleen, liver WNL

EXT: Mild swelling and tenderness noted on both hands and feet

Results of Laboratory Tests

Na^+ 141	Cr 2.9	ESR 78	RF (−)
K^+ 3.9	Hct 33.6	AST 24	PT 27.4 (Baseline 10.7)
Cl^- 98	Hgb 11.6	ALT 27	PTT 26.6
HCO_3 26	WBC 4.7	Alk Phos 67	LE (+)
BUN 39	RBC 5.6	Chol 159	ANA (+)

Urinalysis: Sp Gr 1.018, 3+ protein.
Chest x-ray: Heart and lungs are WNL.

Problem 1. Systemic Lupus Erythematosus

S: G.M. complains of constant fatigue, occasional morning joint swelling and stiffness, erythematous rash involving face, shoulders, both arms, increased sensitivity to the sun, and headaches.

O: Mild alopecia, mild swelling and tenderness on both hands and feet, abdominal tenderness, and a palpable spleen are noted on physical examination. Cr 2.9, urinalysis 3+ protein; LE (+), ANA (+), RF (−), ESR = 78.

A: The patient is now showing signs of SLE-induced nephritis. Immunosuppressive therapy is now indicated to control the systemic manifestations of the disease. The agent of choice is prednisone at a dose 1 mg/kg/day p.o. given once daily. If no response is seen, the dose can be increased to 2 mg/kg/day in 2–3 divided doses. If the disease becomes life-threatening, consider using methylprednisolone 500 mg i.v. over 20 minutes q12h for 3–5 days. Oral prednisone (1–2 mg/kg/day) is then begun after completing the "pulse" therapy. After the disease is controlled, prednisone should be slowly tapered by reducing the dose by approximately 10% every 5–7 days until the lowest possible maintenance dose is reached, which is usually 10–20 mg p.o. qd. If no response to steroid therapy, consider cytotoxic agents. These must be carefully monitored since G.M. is currently taking warfarin. Either cyclophosphamide (dose 3 mg/kg/day) or azathioprine (dose 2.5 mg/kg/day) could be used in combination with steroid therapy but cyclophosphamide may cause hemorrhagic cystitis and should be avoided in this anticoagulated patient. Acetaminophen is preferred for joint pain and headaches. If the joint pain is accompanied by inflammation, ibuprofen is appropriate in this patient. The starting dose is 400 mg p.o. q.i.d. to a maximum dose of 3200 mg/day in 3–4 divided doses. Avoid using ASA. It is contraindicated in a patient currently taking warfarin.

P: Begin prednisone 45 mg p.o. q.d. Continue acetaminophen. Increase ibuprofen to 600 mg q.i.d. Monitor for response to the steroid therapy by assessing: renal function by Cr and urinalysis, skin manifestations by the rash, joint pain, stiffness, inflammation, and ESR. Monitor potential adverse effects of the steroids, BP, sodium and water retention; electrolytes (Na^+ K^+), mental status, hyperglycemia (serum glucose), and GI complaints.

Monitor prolonged steroid therapy by assessing: Cushingnoid symptoms, poor wound healing, increased risk of infection, and hPA suppression. Monitor pain relief and potential adverse effects resulting from NSAIA's such as gastric distress, nausea/vomiting/diarrhea, skin rashes, renal function (ClCr), LFTs, CBC and occult blood loss (check stool guaiac).

Patient Education: Take medications as prescribed. Steroid therapy: Take with food/milk to decrease irritation. Notify your physician if the following symptoms occur: Unusual weight gain, muscle weakness, sore throat, swelling, infection, or menstral irregularities. For prolonged steroid therapy: Do not discontinue therapy. Medi-Alert bracelet. Keep an emergency steroid dose.

Problem 2. Anticoagulation Therapy

S: None.

O: Mitral valve replacement (St. Judes) secondary to subacute bacterial endocarditis; PT = 27.4 (baseline 10.7)

A: Anticoagulation for valve replacement for this type of valve is required for life. Her PT is above the therapeutic range (1.5–2.5 × baseline). Need to hold dose until PT decreases to therapeutic range than restart warfarin at a new lower dose. Avoid ASA in patients taking warfarin. Avoid i.m. injections due to increased risk for hematoma.

P: Hold the warfarin dose × 1 day. Restart warfarin therapy at lower dose (2–3 mg/day). The goal is a PT within the therapeutic range (1.5–2.5 × baseline PT) For warfarin therapy monitor PT weekly until stabilized, then monthly; Hct/Hgb for blood loss; urinalysis for urinary blood loss; stool guaiac for GI blood loss; ecchymoses; hemoptysis; epistaxis; and gingival bleeding.

Patient Education: Advise the patient to take warfarin as prescribed. She should hold warfarin dose and report if any of the following symptoms occurs: unusual bruising or bleeding, black tarry stools, severe headaches, and blood in stool or urine. She should avoid ASA and OTC products containing aspirin. She should not increase leafy green vegetables in diet as these may decrease the warfarin effect. She should use a soft toothbrush to minimize gum bleeding. A Medi-Alert bracelet is recommended.

CASE 32

CC: J.C. is a 70-year-old obese female who presents to the clinic for evaluation of her arthritis. She complains of increased swelling and pain in her hands, ankles, and knees.

Past Medical History

J.C. has had rheumatoid arthritis for 10 years. She has had previous trials of ASA, ibuprofen, and naprosyn at maximal doses. J.C. also has had gout for 3 years. She has had multiple acute attacks in the past; the last acute attack occurred 1 month ago. J.C. has hyperuricemia with a history of uric acid stone formation, deep venous thrombosis (DVT) 2 months ago, congestive heart failure (CHF) for 1 year, hypertension, and renal insufficiency.

Problem List

1. Rheumatoid arthritis, progressive
2. Gout
3. Hyperuricemia with history of uric acid stone formation
4. Deep venous thrombosis, 2 months ago
5. Congestive heart failure
6. Hypertension
7. Renal insufficiency

Medication History

Piroxicam 20 mg p.o. q.d. × 4 months
Buffered ASA 325 mg p.o. prn
Furosemide 40 mg p.o. q AM
Probenecid 250 mg p.o. b.i.d.
Colchicine 0.5 mg p.o. qd
Warfarin 5 mg p.o. q.d.
Digoxin 0.0625 mg p.o. q.d. × 6 months

She has a history of good compliance with her medication.

Allergies

Chloroquine
Penicillamine (rash)

Social History

Ethanol: 1 pint of table wine per day
Tobacco: 1 pack per day for 50 years

Physical Examination

GEN: J.C. is a pale, obese female who appears to be in moderate distress.
VS: BP 140/90 HR 85 Wt 72 kg (ideal body weight 60 kg)
CHEST: Mild bilateral rales
COR: Positive S3 and S4

Results of Laboratory Tests

Na 140	Hct 27
K 4	Hgb 8.5
Cl 100	WBC 6.5
HCO₃ 26	Uric Acid 12
BUN 40	PT 18
Cr 2.5	Digoxin 0.6

Chest x-ray: Enlarged heart

Problem

S:

O:

A:

P:

Problem

S:

O:

A:

P:

Problem

S:

O:

A:

P:

Problem

S:

O:

A:

P:

Problem

S:_____

O:_____

A:_____

P:_____

Problem

S:_____

O:_____

A:_____

P:_____

Problem

S:_____

O:_____

A:_____

P:_____

Questions

1a. What remitting agent would you recommend for J.C.'s rheumatoid arthritis. Give two reasons to justify your choice. For the agent you recommend, give dose, route, and titration schedule. List four monitoring parameters specifically for that agent and how often they should be done.

1b. In addition, evaluate her current RA medication. Recommend any changes and give the reasons for the changes of her current RA medication therapy if necessary.

2. List four factors (drugs and/or disease) that may have contributed to the elevation of J.C.'s uric acid.

3. Evaluate J.C.'s current treatment regimen for gout/hyperuricemia. Make recommendations, if necessary, for any changes in J.C.'s therapy. Be specific, give dose, route, and duration. Give two reasons to support your answer.

4. While evaluating J.C.'s CHF, the intern noted that she still complains of dyspnea and fatigue. The digoxin level of 0.6 ng/dl was thought to be too low. The intern asked you to calculate a new maintenance dose to achieve a steady-state level of 1.2 mg/ml.

CASE 33

CC: T.B. is a 48-year-old male, Type I diabetic who comes to drop-in clinic with a chief complaint of a painful right great toe of 24 hours duration and the inability to walk. He has never had anything like this before.

Past Medical History

Type I diabetes was diagnosed since age 18; it has been difficult to control. He has had three episodes of diabetic ketoacidosis and many episodes of hypoglycemia. Migrane headaches have been a considerable problem for him at work. He has been placed on probation because of excessive absenteeism. He has had a seizure disorder since a motor vehicle accident that resulted from drunk driving. He has one seizure per week. He also has renal insufficiency secondary to diabetes. He has hypertension that has been fairly well-controlled, although he has suffered from numerous side effects of various antihypertensives. T.B. also has reflux esophagitis that has exacerbations and remissions and atopic dermatitis that tends to flare when he is stressed. A kidney stone was surgically removed in 1985.

Problem List

1. Acute gout
2. Type I diabetes mellitus
3. Migraines
4. Seizures
5. Renal insufficiency
6. Hypertension
7. Reflux esophagitis
8. Atopic dermatitis
9. S/P kidney stone (1985)

Medication History

NPH/regular insulin 15/15 at 7 AM and NPH/regular 10/10 at 6 PM
Phenytoin 300 mg p.o. hs × 3 months
Cafergot suppositories one q 30 min at onset of headache
HCTZ 50 mg b.i.d.
KCL 30 mEq qd
Captopril 25 mg t.i.d.
Clobetasol proprionate 0.05% ointment applied to elbows, backs of knees, trunk, and shins t.i.d. × 2 months

Allergies

None known.

Social History

T.B. is recently married and has two adopted teenage sons. He works as a stockbroker. He is a heavy user of ethanol and smokes two packs of cigarettes per day. He does not use recreational drugs.

Physical Examination

GEN: Well-developed male in moderate distress
VS: BP 190/90 HR 110 T 38.9 Wt 75 kg Ht 6'1"
HEENT: PEERLA, no AV nicking, normal thyroid
COR: NL S1 and S2, no S3 or S4, no murmurs or rubs
CHEST: Clear to ascultation and percussion, no rales, wheezes, or rhonchi
ABD: Soft, nontender, no organomegaly
GU: WNL
RECT: WNL, guaiac-negative
EXT: Red swollen, very painful right great toe
NEURO: Oriented ×3, normal DTRs, cranial nerves intact

Results of Laboratory Tests

Blood was drawn at 12 noon and tests were performed by autoanalyzer.

Na 139	Cr 2.6	AST 55	T Bili 1.1	Chol P
K 5.6	Hct 31.4	ALT P	FBG 50	PT 10.9
Cl 101	Hgb 10.8	LDH P	Ca 9	PTT 25.2
HCO₃ 24	WBC 20.9k	Alk Phos 120	PO₄ 3.1	Uric acid 12.6
BUN 76	Plts 202k	Alb 3.0	Mg 1.9	Triglycerides P

Urinalysis: pH=5.5, protein trace, glucose negative, ketones negative, crystals positive

Problem

S:

O:

A:

P:

Problem

S:

O:

A:

P:

Problem

S:

O:

A:

P:

Problem

S:

O:

A:

P:

Problem

S:

O:

A:

P:

Problem

S:

O:

:A

P:

Problem

S:

O:

A:

P:

Problem

S:

O:

A:

P:

Problem

S:

O:

A:

P:

Questions

1. The laboratory values are telephoned to the clinic. T.B. gave himself his usual insulin injection this morning, but he has eaten nothing. How should his hypoglycemia be treated in the clinic now? Be specific and give drug, dose, route of administration, and duration of treatment.
2. Recommend the best drug treatment for T.B.'s acute attack of gout. Be specific and give drug, dose, route, schedule, and duration of therapy. List two reasons why you would avoid other available alternatives.
3. Does T.B. require chronic or intermittent treatment for his gout and hyperuricemia? Why or why not? Give reasons for your choice. For the treatment he requires, give drug, dose, schedule, and reasons for your selection of this drug.
4. Three weeks later, T.B. returns to clinic with a diary of his blood glucose values. All values are consistent with the following representative values. He has been receiving the same doses of NPH and regular insulin as he was on at his last visit to the drop-in clinic which are NPH 15/regular 15 U at 7 AM and NPH/regular 10 at 6 PM.

7 AM	12 Noon	4 PM	10 PM	2AM
280	150	140	120	180

What changes would you make in his insulin regimen? Give your reasons for this change.

CASE 34

CC: F.I. is a 29-year-old female with a history of rheumatoid arthritis (RA), who comes to the clinic for her follow-up appointment. Today she states that her morning joint pain and fatigue have not decreased. She also has been experiencing several episodes of stomach "burning pain" after taking her doses of ASA. She wishes something stronger for the pain, claiming that the aspirin is not working to reduce her constant pain. She also states she takes her medications all the time, when she is able to remember. She denies nausea, vomiting, diarrhea, chest pain, and blurred vision and admits to occasional palpitations, which she attributes to her "irregular heart rate."

Past Medical History

RA was diagnosed 5 months ago; atrial fibrillation was diagnosed 3 years ago.

Problem List

1. Rheumatoid arthritis for 5 months
2. Atrial fibrillation for 3 years

Medication History

Digoxin 0.25 mg 1 tablet p.o. qd
Procainamide SR 500 mg 1 tablet p.o. t.i.d.
ASA 325 mg 2 tablets p.o. q.i.d.

Physical Examination

GEN: F.I. is a young female appearing in moderate pain and depressed.

VS: BP 112/68 (sitting) 112/70 (supine) HR 90 (irregular) T 37.2 Wt 120 lb Ht 5'6"

HEENT: (+) Scleritis in both eyes

COR: Irregular rate and rhythm, (−) S3, S4

CHEST: Lungs clear on auscultation and percussion

ABD: Palpable spleen, liver size WNL

RECT: Guaiac-negative

EXT: Bilateral swelling of MCP joints and the dorsum of both wrists; mild flexion contractures of both elbows

Results of Laboratory Tests

Na$^+$ 143	Cr 0.9	ESR 120	Procainamide
K$^+$ 4.7	Hct 34.6	Salicylic acid level 13	level 5.8
Cl$^-$ 102	Hgb 11.3	RF (+)	
HCO$_3$ 27	WBC 8.1	Dig level 1.2	
BUN 18	RBC 5.3	ANA (+) 1:320	

X-rays bilateral hands: Narrowed joint spaces at MCP spaces

Problem

S:

O:

A:

P:

Problem

S:—————————————————————
—————————————————————
—————————————————————
—————————————————————

O:—————————————————————
—————————————————————
—————————————————————
—————————————————————

A:—————————————————————
—————————————————————
—————————————————————
—————————————————————
—————————————————————

P:—————————————————————
—————————————————————
—————————————————————

Respiratory Disease

CASE 35

CC: J.F. is a 65-year-old retired man who comes to drop-in clinic today (2/5) with complaints of a "chest cold" that has worsened his chronic mild shortness of breath and has increased his sputum production. He complains of mild nausea, vomiting, a decreased appetite, and a severe headache that began February 4. J.F.'s wife states that he has been confused recently.

History of Present Illness

J.F. was seen in clinic on February 3 for a regular appointment. Transdermal nitroglycerin 20 mg/24 hour was added to his angina regimen because of increasing frequency of attacks despite therapy with NTG 0.4 mg s.l. prn.

Past Medical History

Chronic bronchitis secondary to 100-pack-year smoking; he still smokes 2 PPD. Angina.

Problem List

1. Chronic bronchitis
2. Angina

Medication History

Theodur 300 mg b.i.d. for 4 years
Metaproterenol 2 puffs q.i.d. and prn for years
Diazepam 5 mg q.i.d. "for nerves" × 2 weeks
NTG 0.4 mg s.l. prn
Prednisone taper. Prednisone 60 mg/day was begun last June and continued until last November when it was determined to be ineffective. The taper has been at the rate of 5 mg/day/week. The current dose is 5 mg/day, which began 2/3.

Social History

J.F. has a 100-pack-year history of tobacco; he currently smokes 2 packs per day. He does not use ethanol.

Allergies

None known.

Physical Examination

GEN: Cushingoid-appearing man in moderate distress.
VS: Lying BP 110/80 HR 80; sitting BP 100/60 HR 100 T 37 RR 34 Wt 95 kg Ht 5'8"
HEENT: PERRLA
COR: Normal S1 and S2, no S3 or S4, no murmurs

CHEST: Bilateral rales and rhonchi; few expiratory wheezes that clear with coughing
ABD: No masses or tenderness, protuberent
RECT/GU: Benign prostatic hypertrophy, Guaiac-negative
EXT: Numerous bruises
NEURO: WNL

Results of Laboratory Tests

Blood was drawn on February 3 at 8 AM:

Na 135	Hct 48	AST 36	Glu 60	PT 10
K 5.5	Hgb 15	ALT 24	Ca 9	PTT 32
C1 101	WBC 9.8 k	LDH 90	PO_4 2.7	Theophyl-
HCO_3 28	Plts 175 k	Alk Phos 84	Mg 2	line 15
BUN 24	MCV 96	Alb 3.8	Chol 190	Cortisol <5
Cr 1.2	MCHC 33.5	T.Bili 0.2	Tri 175	

Arterial blood gases: PO_2 60, PCO_2 45, pH 7.40
WBC differential: PMN 60%, lymphs 25%, bands 0%, eos 10%, monos 5%
Urinalysis: WNL
Prebronchodilator FEV_1 = 1200 ml
Postbronchodilator FEV_1 = 1550 ml
Chest x-ray: No evidence of pneumonia

Problem 3. Adrenal Insufficiency

S: Patient complains of nausea, vomiting, and anorexia.
O: Glu = 60, orthostatic hypotension, dehydration BUN/Cr = 10, K = 5.5, elevated eos, cortisol < 5.
A: J.F. has adrenal insufficiency that has been precipitated by the stress of his upper respiratory infection. J.F. has HPA axis suppression because of 5 months of prednisone 60 mg/day. His symptoms coincide with a decrease in his prednisone dose below that required for physiologic replacement. J.F.'s condition does not appear to be severe enough to require hospitalization.
P: Give 100 mg hydrocortisone Na succinate i.v. stat along with 1000 ml of D5NS over 2 hours. If stable and can take oral medication begin 50 mg hydrocortisone p.o. q6h × 1 day, then 25 mg hydrocortisone p.o. q6h × 1 day, then hydrocortisone 25 mg q12h × 1 day, then 30 mg hydrocortisone qd. Taper the hydrocortisone by 5 mg/day/week until J.F. is off hydrocortisone or his cortisol level measured prior to the AM dose is > 10. J.F. should be given steroid coverage for stress and educated about the signs and symptoms of adrenal insufficiency. In 9—

12 months perform a cortrosyn stimulation test to assess adrenal reserve. If normal, discontinue stress coverage by steroids. Monitor signs and symptoms of adrenal insufficiency: BP, HR, serum glucose, K, nausea, vomiting, arthralgias, and fatigue. J.F. needs a Medi-Alert bracelet.

Problem 1. Chronic Bronchitis

S: J.F. complains of shortness of breath, increased sputum production, and confusion.

O: J.F. has an increased respiratory rate, elevated heart rate, rales, rhonchi, wheezes, decreased O_2, increased CO_2, decreased FEV_1, increased Hct, no evidence of pneumonia on chest x-ray, and normal WBC with a normal differential except for eos.

A: J.F. has a moderate exacerbation of his chronic bronchitis that is probably due to the upper respiratory infection. J.F. has a reversible component as evidenced by the improvement in his FEV_1 after bronchodilator therapy. His theophylline level is within the therapeutic range and there is no reason to increase his dose. J.F. has no new factors that would alter his clearance of theophylline such as FEV_1 <1 liter, CHF, etc. Expectorants would not provide any therapeutic benefit, but adequate hydration may help. Nebulized β_2-agonists are not required unless J.F. is unable to use his metered dose inhaler correctly. The use of antibiotics in exacerbations of chronic bronchitis without evidence of pneumonia is controversial, but current evidence suggests that they are beneficial. The increased Hct and normal pH suggest long-term hypoxemia and hypercarbia. J.F. will need more evaluation to document if there is a need for chronic oxygen therapy. His elevated heart rate may be due to either his hypoxemia, dehydration, or his metaproterenol. Ipratropium is indicated for maintenance therapy for chronic bronchitis and is especially useful for increased sputum production. BPH is not a contraindication to ipratropium since the drug is minimally absorbed systemically, but J.F. should be monitored carefully. Steroids have been found to be ineffective in J.F. Diazepam can cause respiratory depression and should be avoided if possible.

P: Continue Theodur 300 mg b.i.d. and metaproterenol 2 puffs q.i.d. and prn. Assess J.F.'s ability to use the inhaler correctly. Begin cotrimoxazole 160/800 mg b.i.d. Discontinue diazepam. Administer a pneumococcal vaccine at the next regular clinic appointment and an influenza vaccine once a year. Monitor shortness of breath, sputum production, ABGs, RR, HR, chest auscultation, FEV_1, fever, and WBC. Instruct J.F. on the proper use and care of his inhaler.

Problem 2. Angina

S: J.F. reports an increasing frequency of attacks.

O: History

A: J.F.'s angina requires treatment but the nitroglycerin patch may be causing his severe headache and contributing to his hypotension. Tolerance usually develops to the patches. Nonselective β-blockers are contraindicated in this patient with bronchospastic pulmonary disease. Tachycardia from β_2-agonists and theophylline should be avoided so as not to precipitate an angina attack. A calcium channel blocker would be a good choice for the treatment of this patient's angina.

P: Remove the nitroglycerin patch now. Administer acetaminophen 650 mg p.o. After the symptoms of adrenal insufficiency have resolved and BP is normal, begin diltiazem 30 mg q8h. Increase the dose at 2–3 day intervals until the angina is controlled or a maximum daily dose of 360 mg is reached. Monitor frequency of anginal attacks and prn NTG use, BP, signs and symptoms of CHF, arrhythmias, and GI disturbances. Review patient education regarding proper storage and use of sublingual NTG.

CASE 36

CC: J.H. is a 49 year-old, 70-kg male admitted to the neurosurgical service for an anterior cervical discectomy for a herniated cervical disc. Just prior to induction of anesthesia, he became acutely short of breath, with chest tightness, cough, and wheezing. He was given methylprednisolone 125 mg i.v., a loading dose of aminophylline 750 mg i.v., and a metaproterenol treatment via a nebulizer, and the surgery was canceled.

History of Present Illness

J.H. has a 35-year history of asthma and was doing well prior to admission except for occasional exacerbations that were adequately controlled by Theodur and metaproterenol. However, J.H. ran out of both these medications 1 week prior to admission (PTA).

Past Medical History

J.H. has had a 3.5-year history of neck pain radiating to the right shoulder and upper arm with intermittent numbness. Two weeks PTA, his magnetic resonance imaging (MRI) scan showed a C4-5 herniated disc. J.H.'s BP has been mildly elevated for 3 months, so his metoprolol dose was increased 3 days PTA. J.H.'s duodenal ulcer was diagnosed 4 weeks PTA by endoscopic examination and although his abdominal pain and black tarry stools have diminished, he still has a positive stool guaiac. J.H. has mild degenerative joint disease (DJD), which has had the same intensity of pain over the past 5 years.

Problem List

1. Asthma diagnosed 35 years ago
2. Hypertension (HTN) diagnosed 10 years ago
3. Duodenal ulcer diagnosed 4 weeks ago
4. Mild DJD diagnosed 5 years ago
5. Herniated disc

Allergies

J.H. is allergic to aspirin (ASA).

Social History

J.H. has smoked 1.5 packs per day for 30 years and uses ethanol.

Medication History

Theodur 300 mg p.o. b.i.d.
Metaproterenol inhaler 2 puffs prn shortness of breath (SOB)
HCTZ 25 mg p.o. qd
Metoprolol 100 mg p.o. b.i.d.
Ranitidine 150 mg p.o. b.i.d.
Acetaminophen 650 mg p.o. q4h prn pain (takes about 3 doses/day)

Physical Examination

GEN: J.H. is a 49 year-old male in acute distress with wheezes on inspiration and expiration which resolved after treatment with metaproterenol and i.v. methylprednisolone.
VS: BP 150/95 HR 80 Temp. 37 RR 24 Wt. 70kg
HEENT: WNL
COR: Sinus rhythm
CHEST: Wheezes on inspiration and expiration
ABD: No pain, no guarding
GU: WNL
RECTAL: Guaiac—positive
EXT: Bilateral knee pain, no redness or swelling

Results of Laboratory Tests

Na 143	BUN 12	WBC 8.4	Alk Phos 76
K 4.3	Cr 1.0	RBC 4.89	AST 22
Cl 106	Hgb 14.7	MCV 92	Bili 0.6
HCO_3 25	Hct 44.2	MCH 30.1	

PFTs measured 3 months PTA: Prebronchodilator, FEV_1 1.5 liter; postbronchodilator FEV_1, 2 liter.

Problem 1. Asthma

S: Patient complains of shortness of breath, chest tightness, cough, and wheezing on inspiration and expiration.

O: RR 24, pre-bronchodilator FEV_1 1.5 liter, post-bronchodilator FEV_1 2.0 liter, WBC 8.4

A: The two factors that may have contributed to J.H.'s acute exacerbation of asthma include (a) The patient ran out of medications 1 week PTA (b) Metoprolol (a B_1 selective antagonist) dose was increased 3 days PTA to a dose that decreases its B_1 selectivity. The patient's acute distress resolved with the use of metaproterenol and methylprednisolone. The patient has been under stress secondary to anticipation of surgery. The patient has only been using his metaproterenol inhaler on an as needed basis.

Predicated average steady state theophylline levels based on Theodur maintenance dose = 5.6 mg/liter. Predicted change in concentration of theophylline due to aminophylline loading dose = 19 mg/liter. The patient has a 33% increase in FEV_1 with bronchodilators. The patient is afebrile with a normal WBC therefore is not likely to have an infection.

P: Increase Theodur dose to 400 mg p.o. t.i.d. Taper methylprednisolone as tolerated. Change metaproterenol to 2 puffs q.i.d. and prn SOB. Discontinue metoprolol. Provide patient education on smoking and compliance with medications. Monitor BP, HR, RR, PFTs, LFTs, ABGs in acute exacerbations, and chest x-ray.

Problem 2. Hypertension

S: J.H. has had mildly elevated BP for 3 months.

O: BP 150/95, HR 80, Electrolytes—normal

A: The patient is in acute respiratory distress, which can elevate BP and HR. J.H. is experiencing stress from anticipating the surgery, which can elevate BP and HR. Metoprolol may be exacerbating his asthma. HCTZ 25 mg is an appropriate dose that effectively lowers BP with minimal effects on electrolytes. Since hypertension is a chronic problem and the patient is in acute distress, the current BP and HR cannot be used to assess the efficacy of his current management.

P: Discontinue metoprolol. Continue HCTZ 25 mg p.o. qd. Start verapamil 80 mg p.o. t.i.d. Monitor BP, HR, and electrolytes.

Problem 3. Degenerative Joint Disease

S: J.H. has bilateral knee pain with no redness or swelling.

O: J.H. has allergy to ASA.

A: His pain has been about the same for 5 years and is controlled with about 3 doses of acetaminophen per day. ASA and NSAID should not be used because patient has an allergy, active duodenal ulcer, and acetaminophen is the drug of choice in mild DJD.

P: Continue acetaminophen 650 mg p.o. q4h prn pain. Monitor pain relief and LFTs.

Problem 4. Duodenal Ulcer

S: Patient reports no pain and there is no guarding.

O: Endoscopic examination shows duodenal ulcer; J.H. is guaiac-positive.

A: Patient is still having active disease but is improved.

P: Continue ranitidine for 2–4 more weeks. Monitor abdominal pain guaiac, and side effects.

CASE 37

CC: J.C. is a 25-year-old male who comes to clinic today (2/7) complaining of severe nausea, vomiting, anorexia, nervousness, palpitations, and insomnia of 1-day duration.

Past Medical History/Problem List

1. Asthma (mild) since childhood
2. Atopic dermatitis
3. Chronic daily tension headaches
4. Seizure disorder (generalized tonic clonic seizures, 3/month)
5. S/P Deep venous thrombosis (DVT) 1 month ago

Medication History

Theodur 600 mg 9 AM for 5 years
Albuterol inhaler 2 puffs q6h and prn for 5 years
Cafergot suppositories 1 q6h prn headache, uses 1–2 per day for 6 months
Carbamazepine 200 mg 9 AM, 1 PM, 5 PM, and 9 PM for 3 years
Valproic acid 500 mg 9 AM, 1 PM, 9 PM for 8 months
Warfarin 7.5 mg qd at 4 PM × 1 month
Erythromycin 500 mg q.i.d. × 7 days for chlamydia urethritis, he finished the course yesterday.

J.C. is compliant with all his medications.

Allergies

ASA causes bronchospasm. Phenytoin caused a severe skin rash 8 years ago.

Social History

J.C. does not smoke and occasionally drinks ethanol.

Review of Systems

J.C. complains of dizziness and paresthesias in his lower extremities of nearly 6 months duration.

Physical Examination

VS: BP 160/90 HR 105 T 37.5 RR 18 Wt 80 kg Ht 5'1"
HEENT: Within normal limits
COR: Normal
CHEST: Few expiratory wheezes bilaterally
ABD: No masses or tenderness, active bowel sounds
EXT: Fine hand tremor, decreased pedal pulses bilaterally, severe dermatitis on both lower extremities
NEURO: Within normal limits

Results of Laboratory Tests

Na 137	Hct 45.9	AST 159	FBG 110	Carbamazepine 12
K 4.4	Hgb 15.3	ALT 121	Ca 9.3	Theophylline 18
Cl 105	WBC 5.8k	LDH 88	PO_4 2.8	Valproic acid 70
HCO_3 21	Plts 200k	Alk Phos 53	Mg 2.4	
BUN 10	MCV 95	Alb 3.8	PT 18.0	
Cr 0.8	MCHC 33	T Bili 1.5	PTT 39	

Problem

S:

O:

A:

P:

Problem

S:

O:

A:

P:

Problem

S: _____
_____

O: _____
_____
_____

A: _____
_____
_____
_____

P: _____
_____
_____

Problem

S: _____
_____

O: _____
_____
_____

A: _____
_____
_____
_____

P: _____
_____
_____

Problem

S: _____
_____

O: _____
_____
_____

A: _____
_____
_____
_____

P: _____
_____
_____

Problem

S: _____
_____

O: _____
_____
_____

A: _____
_____
_____
_____

P: _____
_____
_____

Problem

S:

O:

A:

P:

(SOB), wheezing, and increased production of purulent green sputum.

Past Medical History

C.T. has had asthma and chronic obstructive pulmonary disease (COPD) for 40 years. He was diagnosed with hypertension (HTN) 20 years ago and has had (CHF) for 10 years (currently controlled). Additionally, he has had angina for 14 years.

Problem List

1. Acute exacerbation of asthma/chronic bronchitis
2. Hypertension
3. Congestive heart failure
4. Angina

Medication History

Albuterol inhaler 2 puffs q.i.d. and prn shortness of breath
Ipratropium bromide inhaler 2 puffs q.i.d.
Theodur 300 mg p.o. b.i.d.
Methylprednisolone 60 mg i.v. q6h
Digoxin .125 mg p.o. q.d.
HCTZ 25 mg p.o. q.d.
NTG 1/150 s.l. prn chest pain

Social History

Smoke: 45 pack years, still smokes
Ethanol: moderate

Allergies

C.T. is allergic to meperidine and penicillin.

Physical Examination

       VS: BP 130/85 HR 130 RR 30 Ht 6'0" Wt 78.3 kg
    HEENT: Mild AV nicking, no masses, no thyromegaly
      COR: S1, S2; no S3, no S4
    CHEST: Left lower lobe crackles, rales, and rhonchi, expiratory and inspiratory wheezes
      ABD: Diffusely tender throughout, especially midepigastrum
   RECTAL: Guaiac-negative, nontender, good tone
      EXT: Mild cyanosis, mild clubbing
    NEURO: Intact

Results of Laboratory Tests

Na 137	Hct 44.9
K 4.6	Hgb 15.0
Cl 98	WBC 16.8
HCO_3 27	Theo pending
BUN 10	Digoxin 1.6
Cr 0.8	

Pulmonary function tests: Prebronchodilator FEV_1 700 ml Postbronchodilator FEV_1 1000 ml
Arterial blood gases on room air: PO_2 45, PCO_2 54, pH 7.36

Questions

1. J.C.'s current chief complaint may be a drug-induced problem. Which drug is most likely causing his current complaints of severe nausea, vomiting, anorexia, tremor, nervousness, palpitations, and insomnia? Explain why his chief complaint may be drug induced. Give reasons and any supporting documentation. What would you recommend to treat his chief complaint?
2. There are abnormalities in his liver function tests. Identify the drug that may be causing this problem. Based on these abnormalities would you recommend a change in his drug therapy? Be specific and give reasons. If a new drug is indicated, give doses, schedule, and titration. Discuss your considerations involving his other drugs during initiation of the new drug.

CASE 38

CC: C.T. is a 71-year-old male admitted to the hospital with a 2-week history of progressive respiratory distress. He claims to have lung tightness, shortness of breath

Problem

S:

O:

A:

P:

Problem

S:

O:

A:

P:

Problem

S:

O:

A:

P:

Problem

S:

O:

A:

P:

Questions

1. Give patient education to C.T. regarding the use of his inhalers.
2. After the patient has been on oral prednisone for 3 months, 20 mg p.o. q.d., the physician asks you how to initiate beclomethasone inhaler therapy with the hope of tapering the prednisone. Give your recommendation on how the beclomethasone therapy should be initiated, include reasoning.
3. Should this patient be started on antibiotic therapy? Why or why not? If so, give drug, dose, route, frequency, and duration.
4. C.T. returns to clinic 2 weeks after discharge from the hospital. His theophylline level from that day comes back as 8 mg/liter. Calculate his Cl, V, P, $t_{1/2}$. Make a recommendation to achieve an average steady-state theophylline level of 13 mg/liter (include drug, dose, route, and frequency).

CASE 39

CC: H.P. is an 84-year-old male being seen in chest clinic for follow up of his COPD/emphysema/chronic bronchitis, with complaints of increased shortness of breath (SOB), increased sputum production, and increased cough for 1 week. He also states that his sputum has turned to a "greenish-brown" color.

History of Present Illness

H.P. has a 100-pack year smoking history and claims to have quite smoking 2 months ago. He has had a chronic cough for 20 years that is worse in the morning.

Past Medical History

H.P. has been widowed for 15 years and lives alone. Every time he comes into the clinic, he is wearing the same set of clothes, which are rather worn. His anemia was diagnosed 14 years ago, at which time his complaints of constipation began.

Problem List

1. Chronic obstructive pulmonary disease (COPD)/ emphysema/chronic bronchitis
2. Anemia
3. Constipation

Medication History

Metaproterenol 2 puffs q.i.d. and prn SOB
Theodur 300 mg p.o. b.i.d.
Prednisone 20 mg p.o. qd × 5 years
Cotrimoxazole 1 p.o. b.i.d. × 10 days start with change in sputum color
$FeSO_4$ 325 mg p.o. t.i.d. × 14 years

Physical Examination

GEN: H.P. is an obese cushingoid-appearing male in moderate respiratory distress.
VS: BP 170/85 HR 90 T 37 RR 24 Wt 80 kg
HEENT: Mild rosacea on face
COR: WNL
CHEST: Decreased breath sounds in both lung fields
ABD: Soft, nontender, positive bowel sounds, striae
GU: WNL
RECTAL: Guaiac-negative
EXT: Thin, muscle wasting, fractured wrist healing slowly after falling 2 months ago, many ecchymoses

Results of Laboratory Tests

Na 145   Cr 1   Plts 240k
K 3.2   Hct 35   Glu 300
Cl 98   Hgb 11   Theo 12
HCO_3 27   WBC 15k   TIBC WNL
BUN 12

Smear: macrocytic, hyperchromic cells
Pre-bronchodilator: FEV_1 0.9 liter
Postbronchodilator: FEV_1 1.0 liter
ABGs: PO_2 50 PCO_2 55
Chest x-ray: Hyperinflated lungs, no evidence of pneumonia

Problem

S:

O:

A:

P:

Problem

S:

O:

A:

P:

Problem

S:

O:

A:

P:

Problem

S:

O:

A:

P:

Cardiovascular Disorders

CASE 40

CC: J.G. is a 69-year-old man admitted to the hospital with a 1-day history of pain, tenderness, and swelling in his left thigh.

Past Medical History

J.G. had a left hip arthroplasty 6 weeks ago. He ambulates one to three times a day for 15 minutes. He has a history of chronic obstructive pulmonary disease (COPD) and has smoked 2 packs per day for 40 years. He also has a history of hypertension and congestive heart failure, which are fairly well controlled when J.G. remembers to take his medication.

Problem List

1. Rheumatoid arthritis × 18 years
2. COPD × 5 years
3. Congestive heart failure (CHF) × 2 years
4. Hypertension × 2 years
5. Left hip arthroplasty, 6 weeks ago
6. Deep Venous Thrombosis

Medication History

Aspirin 325 mg 3 tablets p.o. q.i.d. × 15 years
Metaproterenol inhaler 2 puffs prn × 5 years (1–2 times/day)
Theodur 300 mg p.o. b.i.d. × 4 years
Hydrochlorothiazide 25 mg p.o. q AM × 2 years
K tabs 2 p.o. b.i.d. × 2 years
Captopril 6.25 mg p.o. q.i.d. × 1.5 years
Aspirin with 30 mg codeine 2 tablets p.o. q4–6h prn pain × 6 weeks

Allergies

Acetaminophen

Physical Examination

GEN: J.G. is an obese, pale, elderly male complaining of tenderness and pain in his left thigh, worsening shortness of breath (SOB), paroxysmal nocturnal dyspnea (PND), 2–3 pillow orthopnea, stiffness, tiredness, and weakness.
VS: BP 150/95 HR 105 RR 24 T 37 Wt 90 kg Ht 5′8″
HEENT: WNL
COR: Sinus tachycardia, (+) S3, (+) S4
CHEST: bilateral rales, wheezing
ABD: (+) HJR
GU: Deferred
RECT: Guaiac-negative
EXT: Pale nail beds, swelling in MCP and PIP joints of hands, swelling in left thigh (L>R), (+) Homan's sign, 3+ pitting edema

Results of Laboratory Tests

Na 146	Cr 0.8	Fe 35
K 5	FBS 180	TIBC 500
Cl 104	Hgb 10	PT 11.5
HCO$_3$ 26	Hct 30	PTT 30
BUN 24	MCV 70	Theophylline 14

Arterial blood gases: PO$_2$ 60, PCO$_2$ 50
VQ Scan: Negative

Problem 6. Deep Venous Thrombosis

S: Patient complains of tenderness and pain in left thigh.
O: Swelling L>R, warm to touch, (+) Homan's sign, (−) VQ scan
A: Deep venous thrombosis in left thigh is probably secondary to recent surgery (left hip arthroplasty), decreased ambulation, and obesity.
P: Give heparin 6300 U (50–70 U/kg) bolus i.v. over 30 minutes. Follow with a maintenance continuous infusion of 1350 U/hour (10–15 U/kg/hour). The goal is to obtain a PTT between 60 and 80 seconds. Treatment should be continued for 7 to 10 days for stabilization of the clot. No i.m. injections and avoid drugs that inhibit platelet function, i.e., aspirin. Monitor CBC and platelet every other day, guaiac and urinalysis every third day. Examine all sites for bleeding every day. Begin oral anticoagulation with warfarin on day 1 or 2 of heparin therapy. Since he has no history of previous DVT, he should be treated for 6 weeks to 6 months with warfarin. The goal of warfarin therapy is a PT 1.2–1.5 times his baseline value.

Problem 1. Rheumatoid Arthritis

S: Patient complains of stiffness.
O: Patient has swelling in MCP and PIP joints of the hands.
A: Aspirin has been effective in decreasing the pain in J.G.'s hands. Since J.G. now has a DVT and aspirin irreversibly inhibits platelet function, begin ibuprofen, which is not as potent

as other NSAID in affecting platelet function and its effects on platelet function are reversible. However, ibuprofen is still a GI irritant and may cause gastric bleeding.

P: Discontinue aspirin. Begin ibuprofen 600 mg p.o. q.i.d. Ibuprofen may be increased up to 3200 mg/day if needed for pain relief and/or preservation of function.

Problem 3. Congestive Heart Failure

S: Patient has worsening SOB, PND, 2–3 pillow orthopnea, and weakness.

O: HR 105 (sinus tachycardia), RR 24, (+) S3, bilateral rales, (+) HJR, 3+ pitting edema

A: J.G. has symptoms of both right- and left-sided heart failure, which may be secondary to stress (recent surgery), anemia, diet, and poor compliance. His CHF may improve with an increased dose of captopril. However, patients are at an increased risk of renal impairment if captopril is used with an NSAID. Also NSAIDs will antagonize some of the pharmacologic effects of ACE inhibitors. Enalapril only requires once a day dosing and may increase compliance.

P: Begin enalapril 5 mg qd. Continue to titrate dose up to control symptoms of CHF. Monitor serum K^+ since J.G. is on a potassium supplement, has a K^+ level of 5, and is taking enalapril which can cause hyperkalemia. Discontinue hydrochlorothiazide and add furosemide 40 mg p.o. q.d. Consider adding digoxin to increase the force of contraction since J.G. has a + S3. Consider Hydralazine as an additional afterload reducer since J.G. is unlikely to develop more tachycardia. Monitor signs and symptoms of CHF and drug toxicity. Stress compliance with medications and counsel patient to restrict sodium intake in diet.

Problem 2. Chronic Obstructive Pulmonary Disease

S: Patient complains of worsening SOB.

O: Bilateral rales, wheezing, PO_2 60, PCO_2 50, RR 24, theophylline 14 mg/liter

A: His COPD is not well controlled on the current regimen. The metaproterenol inhaler should be scheduled and not just prn. The theophylline level is in the therapeutic range. Ipratropium may be indicated if improvement is not seen after optimizing the current regimen. Steroids would be the drug of last resort.

P: Give metaproterenol inhaler 2 puffs q.i.d. and prn. Check that FEV_1 increases >15% after therapy. Review proper technique of inhaler use with patient. Stress compliance.

Problem 4. Hypertension

S: No symptoms.

O: BP 150/95, (+) S4

A: J.G.'s BP is above the desired endpoint of <140/90.

P: Remind J.G. of the importance of losing weight to help lower his BP. Since enalapril and furosemide were added for his CHF, this may also help decrease his BP. Monitor BP.

Problem 7. Iron Deficiency Anemia

S: Patient complains of tiredness and weakness and appears pale.

O: Pale nail beds, Hgb 10, Hct 30, MCV 70, Fe 35, TIBC 500

A: His iron deficiency anemia is perhaps secondary to aspirin use (GI irritation and antiplatelet effect) although J.G. is guaiac-negative. J.G. should have cause of the iron deficiency worked up to exclude GI cancer. J.G. needs treatment to replace his iron stores and decrease his symptoms.

P: Check smear for macrocytes. Give ferrous sulfate 325 mg p.o. t.i.d. for 6 months. May take with food to decrease GI irritation. Monitor reticulocyte count (NL in 2 weeks), hemoglobin, and hematocrit (NL in 6 weeks). Note: Stools may turn black due to iron therapy and not bleeding from warfarin. Stress compliance.

CASE 41

CC: T.M. is a 46-year-old male who presents to the emergency room at 10 PM with a complaint of tightness and burning of the chest and pain under the jaw that radiates down the left arm. T.M. states that he was working in the garden this morning, when he noticed that he was feeling weak, and sweating more than usual. The pain became worse as the day progressed and was not relieved by antacids. T.M. comes to the ER now as he is concerned about the chest pain that he has had frequently in the past few weeks. Upon further questioning, T.M. states that for the past 2 months he has been having 15–20 attacks of chest pain per week that usually resolve within several minutes with rest.

Past Medical History

T.M. has a 20-year history of hypertension and a 10-year history of coronary artery disease, which have been poorly controlled secondary to poor patient compliance. T.M. also has diabetes and hyperlipidemia, which have been difficult to control with diet. Recently he has been complaining of polydipsia, polyphagia, and polyuria. T.M. has had numerous complaints of constipation.

Social History

T.M. has a smoking history of 1 ppd for 30 years. He drinks a six pack of beer nightly.

Family History

Father and brother died in their 40s of myocardial infarctions (MI).

Problem List

1. Hypertension (HTN) for 20 years
2. Coronary artery disease for 10 years
3. Type II Diabetes mellitus for 1 year
4. Type II hyperlipidemia for two years
5. Constipation

Medication History

Verapamil 80 mg p.o. t.i.d. × 6 months

Hydrochlorothiazide (HCTZ) 50 mg p.o. b.i.d. × 19 years

Clonidine 0.2 mg p.o. q day × 1 year

Nitroglycerin (NTG) 1/150 mg prn chest pain × 10 years

Maalox TC 30 ml p.o. prn stomach pain × 2 months

Physical Examination

On July 1, 10 PM, these are the findings from a physical examination:

GEN: T.M. is an anxious, diaphoretic, obese male appearing older than his stated age who complains of substernal chest pain that radiates to his jaw and down his left arm.

VS: BP 160/100 HR 110 T 37.4 RR 28 Wt 98 kg (IBW 70 kg)

HEENT: AV nicking and narrowing

COR: normal S_1 and S_2, $+S_4$

ABD: Obese

RECT: Guaiac-negative

EXT: WNL

ECG: ST segment elevation, 4-mm leads II, III, aVF; Q waves leads II, III, aVF; sinus tachycardia

T.M. is diagnosed as suffering an acute myocardial infarction and is admitted to the coronary care unit for observation. There he is started on O_2 at 3 liter/minute via nasal prongs and given morphine 4 mg i.v. every 2 hours as needed for pain and anxiety. He is also started on metoprolol 15 mg i.v. (5 mg every 5 minutes), then 50 mg p.o. every 6 hours × 48 hours, then 100 mg twice daily.

On July 2 at 7 AM these are T.M.'s vital signs

VS: BP 140/90 HR 85 T 37.2 RR 20

ECG: 10 PVCs/minute; one 16-beat run of V-Tach at 0655 hours; ST segment elevation, 4 mm leads II, III, aVF; Q waves leads II, III, aVF

Results of Laboratory Tests

Na 139	BUN 17	WBC 9.3k
K 4.1	Cr 1.0	Plts 220k
Cl 100	Hct 35	FBS 340
HCO_3 25	Hgb 10.8	$HgbA_{1c}$ 13.5%

Date	Time	AST	ALT	Alk Phos
7/1	2200	36		
7/2	0600	57	22	63

Date	Time	CK (88–230)	CK-MB (<16)	CK-MB% (<4% Tot CK)
7/1	2200	3316	199	6
7/2	0600	6060	405	7

Date	Time	LDH (88–230)	LDH$_1$ (17–27%)	LDH$_2$ (28–38%)
7/2	2200	920	49	33
7/3	0600	1290	45	29

Date	Triglycerides	Cholesterol
7/2	558 mg/dl	400 mg/dl

Problem 6. Myocardial Infarction

S: Patient reports tightness and burning of the chest, pain under the jaw, and down the left arm, and complains of weakness and sweating prior to the attack.

O: T.M. is a diaphoretic, anxious male. His ECG shows these changes: 4 mm ST segment elevation, abnormal Q waves leads II, III, aVF. He has sinus tachycardia, $+S_4$, elevated CK, CK-MB, increased LDH (more importantly $LDH_1 > LDH_2$), increased AST (nonspecific), and increased WBC secondary to acute myocardial infarction. Also, an increased glucose is observed.

A: T.M. is having a myocardial infarction, and there is a need to stabilize the patient to prevent further damage to the myocardium and/or sudden death. Relief of the chest pain is important, as the pain and the anxiety may generate tachycardia.

P: Admit to the CCU. Start oxygen 2–4 liters/minute by nasal prongs or mask. Give morphine 2–4 mg i.v. q 2–4 h to relieve the pain and decrease the anxiety; it will also act as a vasodilator. Give NTG s.l. If the chest pain does not subside, consider i.v. NTG if the patient's hemodynamics warrant this therapy (findings of CHF, i.e., decreased cardiac output and increased PCWP). If i.v. NTG is initiated start at 5–10 μg/minute and titrate to desired effect. Monitor ECG, CK, and LDH. Treat other problems as related to the MI. Because thrombolytic therapy (streptokinase or tissue plasminogen activator) needs to be initiated within 6 hours of the onset of chest pain T.M. is not a candidate. To possibly limit the infarct size and to prevent sudden death, start metoprolol 15 mg i.v. (5 mg i.v. q 5 minutes) followed by 50 mg p.o. every 6 hours × 48 hours then 100 mg twice daily.

To prevent recurrence of the MI, T.M. should be started on aspirin 325 mg p.o. q.d. There is some evidence that ASA and systemic heparinization are helpful in unstable angina. Start heparin 8000 U i.v. bolus followed by 1100 U/hour continuous infusion. Prior to the initiation of heparin, a baseline aPPT, PT, and platelet count must be obtained. Obtain a second aPPT 4–6 hours after the bolus dose. Increase or decrease the heparin infusion as necessary to keep the aPTT between 60–80 seconds. Continue heparin therapy for 5–7 days. T.M. does not need to be started on warfarin at this time.

Problem 7. Arrhythmias

S: None

O: 10 PVCs/minute, and one 16-beat run of V-Tach

A: Ventricular tachycardia can be life threatening. It occurs because of alterations in the electrophysiologic characteristics of the myocardial cells involved in the ischemic process.

PVCs are frequent in patients with an MI, the value of PVCs as a warning arrhythmia for malignant ventricular arrhythmias (VT or VF) is controversial. However, as there are >8 PVCs per minute they should be treated. The 16-beat run of V-Tach warrants therapy.

P: Treat with lidocaine. $V_d = 1.1$ liter/kg, $V_i = 0.5$ liter/kg, $Cl = 0.6$ 1/min/kg

Loading dose total = (98 kg) (1.1 liter/kg) (3 mg/liter) = 325 mg
Loading dose initial = (98 kg) (0.5 liter/kg) (3 mg/liter) = 150 mg
Maintenance dose = (70 kg) (0.6 liter/min/kg) (3 mg/liter) = 126 mg/hour = 2 mg/min

Therefore give a 150-mg loading dose and start a lidocaine infusion at 2 mg/min. If the PVCs or VT reappear within 5–10 minutes give another 75- to 150-mg bolus. Concurrent use of a beta blocker and lidocaine decreases the clearance of lidocaine, therefore observe T.M. for signs of lidocaine toxicity.

Problem 2. Coronary Artery Disease

S: Patient complains of chest pain (acute myocardial infarction). He has a history of uncontrolled angina in the past 2 months.

O: None.

A: Risk factors for coronary artery disease (CAD) include hyperlipidemia, diabetes, hypertension, smoking history, obesity, male sex, and family history.

P: Educate T.M. about the risk factors of CAD and stress the importance that T.M. stop smoking, control his weight, and comply with his medication regimen to decrease his risk factors. The verapamil can be a contributing factor for T.M.'s constipation. Change the verapamil to diltiazem 30 mg p.o. q6h and increase the dose to 60 mg p.o. q6h if T.M. tolerates it. Metoprolol has recently been added to his regimen, which will also be effective in controlling T.M.'s angina. If T.M.'s angina is not controlled with the combination of the beta blocker and calcium channel blocker (i.e., still having frequent anginal attacks) add isosorbide dinitrate 20 mg p.o. q6h and titrate up until the anginal attacks are under control. Monitor T.M.'s heart rate closely since an inferior wall MI may be associated with transient heart block.

Problem 4. Hyperlipidemia

S: None.

O: Triglycerides 558 mg/100 ml, cholesterol 400 mg/100 ml.

A: Hyperlipidemia is a risk factor for CAD. T.M. has failed diet therapy and now requires medical management. HCTZ and beta blockers can increase lipid levels.

P: Stress the importance of a diet low in calories, cholesterol, and fats and initiate medical therapy. Niacin is the drug of choice for the treatment of type II Hyperlipidemia. However, as T.M. has non-insulin-dependent diabetes mellitus, niacin is a relative contraindication as it has a potential to cause hyperglycemia. Niacin 100 mg three times daily and increase the dose as tolerated could be prescribed for T.M. Administration of aspirin 30 minutes prior to the niacin will help with the flushing effect of niacin.

A better choice for T.M. is lovastatin, which would be initiated at 20 mg once daily. Check T.M.'s LFTs every 4–6 weeks for the first 15 months of therapy and periodically thereafter. If the transaminase levels increase three times the upper limit of normal, discontinue the lovastatin. T.M. should have a baseline ophthalomology examination, another one shortly after starting lovastatin, and then yearly to look for opacities. CPKs should be monitored to detect myositis although lovastatin does not need to be discontinued unless the patient is symptomatic or the levels are very high.

The combination of lovastatin with a bile-acid resin has been demonstrated to produce additive effects in decreasing cholesterol and triglycerides. Therefore, add colestipol 5 g twice daily. However, colestipol can cause constipation and T.M. should receive docusate sodium 250 mg p.o. b.i.d. The colestipol should be mixed with at least 4 oz of water or juice before ingestion. Increase the doses of the medications at 3-month intervals—time to assure adequate treatment with the current dose—until the triglycerides are below 290 and the cholesterol is below 275.

Problem 3. Type II Diabetes Mellitus

S: T.M. complains of polyuria, polyphagia, and polydipsia.

O: Fasting blood glucose 340, HgbA$_{1c}$ 13.5%, Wt 98 kg

A: An AMI can exacerbate glucose intolerance. However, T.M.'s HgbA$_{1c}$ of 13.5 suggests that his diabetes is not controlled by diet and requires medical therapy.

P: While in the hospital, cover with a sliding scale of human regular insulin. Watch for possible changes in insulin requirements or an increase in glucose with concomitant use of calcium channel and beta blockers. For the following levels of blood sugar, give the indicated units of insulin:

Glu	U
≤200	0
200–240	3
240–280	5
280–340	7
>340	9 and call house officer

When the patient is stable, re-educate the patient regarding weight control and add an oral hypoglycemic. Consider glyburide 2.5 mg p.o. qd. If T.M.'s FBS is >180 mg/100 ml after 1 week, increase the glyburide dose by 2.5-mg increments until his FBS is <180 mg/100 ml or a maximum dose of 20 mg is reached.

Problem 1. Hypertension

S: No symptoms.
O: BP 140/90, AV nicking and narrowing.
A: AV nicking and narrowing indicate a long-standing process. HCTZ 50 mg b.i.d. is too high a dose, which has the same efficacy with a 25–50 mg p.o. qd dose. HCTZ can increase the triglyceride levels. Oral clonidine is not a good drug to use in a noncompliant patient.
P: Monitor the BP and discontinue the HCTZ. Change the clonidine to clonidine TTS2 to aid in compliance. T.M. is on metoprolol, which will help control his HTN. The metoprolol may increase T.M.'s lipids; however, the cardioselectivity is an advantage in light of his diabetes. Reassess the regimen when T.M. is stable and make changes if necessary. Add captopril if necessary as it will not affect the lipid profile.

Problem 5. Constipation

S: Frequent complaints.
O: None.
A: Straining at stool is undesirable in a patient with an MI. The morphine, verapamil, and colestipol can contribute to the constipation.
P: Initiate docusate sodium 250 mg p.o. b.i.d. and discontinue the verapamil. Increase the bulk in the diet; keep the patient well hydrated. Consider psyllium 2 tablespoons twice daily.

Problem 8. Anemia

S: None.
O: Hct 35, Hgb 10.8
A: Low hematocrit decreases oxygen-carrying capacity, which can exacerbate angina. If the anemia is secondary to blood loss, the cause must be found. The anemia does not warrant therapy at this time.
P: Check the blood smear; get TIBC and Fe levels if anemia does not correct over time. Get vitamin B_{12} and folate levels if the smear is abnormal. Do not start iron therapy now as iron can be constipating. Consider later if necessary.

CASE 42

CC: C.K. is a 60-year-old man who arrived at the emergency room accompanied by his wife. C.K.'s wife states that over the past 2 days C.K. has been confused, has had a decreased appetite, and has had diarrhea.

Past Medical History

C.K. has had an aortic valve replacement. He has a 1-year history of congestive heart failure for which he takes furosemide and digoxin. Over the past 5 days, C.K. has felt bloated so he doubled his furosemide dose. He also has a 2-year history of hypertension for which verapamil was added 10 days ago for better control. He has had one attack of gout every month for the past 4 months.

Problem List

1. Aortic valve replacement, 10 years ago
2. Hypertension x 2 years
3. Congestive heart failure x 1 year
4. Gout x 4 months
5. Urinary tract infection, 2 weeks ago

Medication History

Warfarin 5 mg p.o. qhs x 10 years
Furosemide 40 mg p.o. b.i.d. x 1.5 years (increased to 80 mg b.i.d. x 5 days)
Digoxin 0.25 mg p.o. qAM x 1 year
Verapamil 80 mg p.o. t.i.d. x 10 days
Allopurinol 300 mg p.o. q.d. x 2 months
Colchicine 0.6 mg p.o. q.d. x 2 months
Cotrimoxazole DS 1 tablet p.o. b.i.d. x 10 days (treatment ended yesterday)

Physical Examination

GEN: Pale man in distress, complaining of nausea, diarrhea, lethargy, and leg cramps.
VS: BP 140/95 HR 65 RR 20 T 37 Wt 60kg
HEENT: WNL
COR: Positive S3, positive S4
CHEST: WNL
ABD: Voluntary guarding
GU: Deferred
RECT: Guaiac-negative
EXT: Ecchymoses x 2 on right calf due to bumping into table,
NEURO: Oriented x 3

Results of Laboratory Tests

Na 132	SCr 1	UA 8
K 2.8	Hgb 13	Urinalysis heme (−)
Cl 100	Hct 36	FBS 200
HCO₃ 23	PT 25	Digoxin level 2.7
BUN 20	PTT 36	

PT 18–20 sec, for the past year (PT 18 sec, 2 mos ago)
ECG: Second-degree AV block, multifocal PVCs, flattened T wave

Problem

S:

O:

A:

P:

Problem

S:

O:

A:

P:

Problem

S:

O:

A:

P:

Problem

S:

O:

A:

P:

Problem

S:

O:

A:

P:

Problem

S:

O:

A:

P:

Problem

S:

O:

A:

P:

Questions

1. List the subjective and objective evidence for C.K.'s digoxin toxicity.
2. What factors contributed to C.K.'s digoxin toxicity?
3. What medication should C.K. take when he experiences an acute gout attack?
4. Why has C.K.'s protime increased from 2 months ago?
5. What type of patient education concerning warfarin would you review with C.K.?
6. Is verapamil an appropriate antihypertensive agent for C.K.?

CASE 43

CC: S.L. is a 71-year-old female who presents to clinic with complaints of frequent episodes of chest pain with minimal exertion relieved with sublingual nitroglycerin (NTG) and that her asthma seems to be out of control. She has also noticed a burning pain in her stomach which is worse 1–2 hours after meals.

Past Medical History

S.L. has a 35-year history of hypertension. In 1974 she had a myocardial infarction (MI). She has been in chronic atrial fibrillation since and is treated with digoxin. Two weeks ago she presented to the clinic with increasing chest pain and nifedipine was added to her regimen. S.L.'s asthma has been difficult to control, and she has been admitted to the hospital numerous times for acute exacerbations where she has required treatment with intravenous steroids. However, she has never been intubated.

Problem List

1. Coronary artery disease x 25 years
2. Angina, 2–3 attacks per day x 1 month
3. Hypertension (HTN) x 35 years
4. Suffered MI in 1974
5. Chronic atrial fibrillation
6. Asthma x 25 years (adult onset)
7. Constipation

Social History

S.L. has smoked one pack per day for 40 years; she stopped smoking 10 years ago. She occasionally drinks alcohol (ETOH).

Medication History

Digoxin 0.125 mg p.o. q AM x 8 years
Isosorbide dinitrate 5 mg s.l. q6h x 8 years
NTG 1/150 prn chest pain x 10 years
Propranolol 40 mg p.o. t.i.d. x 2 years
Nifedipine 10 mg t.i.d. x 2 weeks
Hydrochlorothiazide 50 mg p.o. b.i.d. x 35 years
KCl 20 mEq p.o. qd x 10 years
Theodur 200 mg p.o. b.i.d. x 15 years
Prednisone 15 mg p.o. qd x 1 year

Physical Examination

GEN:	S.L. is an elderly female in no apparent distress
VS:	BP 160/80 HR 85 irreg, irreg T 37.7 RR 21 Wt 48 kg
HEENT:	AV nicking and narrowing
CHEST:	Bibasilar rales, crackles, and wheezes
ABD:	WNL
RECTAL:	Guaiac-positive
EXT:	2+ pitting edema at the ankles.

Results of Laboratory Tests

Blood was drawn at 9 AM:

Na 146	HCT 37.1	Alb 3.6
K 5.4	Hgb 12.2	CPK 37
Cl 103	ALT 44	LDH 143
BUN 36	AST 29	Digoxin 5.2
Cr 1.6	Alk Phos 87	Theophylline 5.4

ECG: Atrial fibrillation, ventricular response 85/minute.

Endoscopy: A discrete crater in the proximal portion of the duodenal bulb

Problem

S: _____

O: _____

A: _____

P: _____

Problem

S:

O:

A:

P:

Problem

S:

O:

A:

P:

Problem

S:

O:

A:

P:

Problem

S:

O:

A:

P:

Problem

S:

O:

A:

P:

Problem

S:

O:

A:

P:

Problem

S:

O:

A:

P:

Questions

1. The medical resident wants to put S.L. on warfarin to prevent a stroke from her chronic atrial fibrillation, and the resident asks you for your opinion. Do you agree or disagree, and what are your reasons?
2. Upon further review, the medical student observes that the patient has a digoxin level of 5.2 ng/ml and suggests that S.L. receive digoxin antibody fragments. Do you agree or disagree and what are your reasons? Calculate the kinetics for her digoxin.
3. Assess S.L.'s current drug therapy for each of her problems. Recommend any changes and defend your reasons for them.
4. What patient education would you give S.L. regarding the proper use and storage of her nitroglycerin?

CASE 44

CC: M.M. is a 58-year-old female who is admitted to the coronary care unit for evaluation for chest pain of recent onset and mental confusion.

Problem List

1. Congestive heart failure x 4 years
2. Hypertension x 20 years

3. Angina
4. Arrhythmia

Medication History

Furosemide 20 mg p.o. daily
Milk of magnesia 30 ml p.o. qhs for constipation

Allergies

Penicillin (hives)

Physical Examination

GEN: Well-developed, well-nourished female, appearing older than stated age and in moderate distress

VS: BP 100/60 (160/100 3 days ago in clinic) HR 90-105 irreg/irreg R 32 Wt 70 kg Ht 5'6"

HEENT: AV nicking

COR: Jugular venous distention 9 cm, (+) S3 (+) S4, PMI diffuse sustained palpable AAL

CHEST: Rales, ⅓ way up both sides

ABD: Soft to palpation; (+) hepatojugular reflux

GU: Deferred

RECT: Deferred

EXT: Cool and clammy skin, 2+ sacral edema, 4+ ankle edema, pulses 2+

NEURO: Oriented x1, decreased DTRs bilaterally

Results of Laboratory Tests

Na 125	Cr 2.8	MCV 112	T. Bili 0.6	PT 13.1
K 4.6	Hct 29	AST 60	FBG 100	PTT 33.4
Cl 98	Hgb 10	ALT 30	Ca 9	Fe 30
HCO_3 28	WBC 6.4	LDH 140	PO_4 2.8	TIBC 240
BUN 36	Plts 180	Alb 2.8	Mg 3	CPK 510

Urinalysis: WNL
ECG showed evidence of old inferior wall MI with multifocal PVCs 10-14 minute. Voltage changes consistent with LVH. Swan-Ganz catheterization revealed RA 9, PA 42/28, PCWP 24, CO 2.9, SVR 1980, BP 100/70. Echocardiogram showed EF 25%.

Problem

S:

O:

A:

P:

Problem

S: _____
_____
_____

O: _____
_____
_____
_____

A: _____
_____
_____
_____
_____
_____

P: _____
_____
_____
_____

Problem

S: _____
_____
_____

O: _____
_____
_____
_____

A: _____
_____
_____
_____

P: _____
_____
_____
_____
_____

Problem

S: _____
_____
_____
_____

O: _____
_____
_____
_____

A: _____
_____
_____
_____
_____

P: _____
_____
_____
_____

Questions

1. Lidocaine is to be administered. What initial bolus dose would achieve a peak serum level between 4 and 5 μg/ml?
2. Calculate a maintenance infusion dose to keep this patient's serum lidocaine level at 4 μg/ml.
3. The medical student wants to treat this patient's CHF acutely with dopamine or dobutamine, and she asks you for advice. Which one of these two agents would you recommend and why?
4. For the above drug you have recommended, give an initial dosage regiment for this patient. Show results in micrograms per minute and drops per minute (base on 500-mg vial placed in 250 ml of D5W and use an i.v. set of 60 drops/ml).
5. Which one of the following agents (verapamil, isosorbide dinitrate, propranolol) would you use for this patient's angina after she is hemodynamically stable and has the following values: PCWP 14; SVR 1400; CI 3.2; ECHO, EF 28%?
6. Defend your reasoning for why you would or would not use each drug listed in Question 5.
7. For the drug you selected for use, give an initial dosage regimen.
8. Assuming that this patient is a slow acetylator, calculate an oral loading and maintenance dose

of procainamide HCl for this patient to achieve a steady-state procainamide peak concentration of 8 μg/ml and a trough concentration $\geq$ 4 μg/ml.

CASE 45

CC: D.C. is a 68-year-old male who presented to the emergency room with a chief complaint of dizziness and shortness of breath. He also complained of a "flu-like syndrome", which he has had for the last 5 days. Upon further questioning, he states that he started to cough up bloody sputum 2 days ago when the dizziness started.

Problem List

1. Hypertension x 20 years
2. Deep venous thrombosis 3 times in the last 5 years; most recently 1 year ago
3. Asthma x 40 years
4. Pulmonary embolism

Medication History

Slow-K (KCl) 8mEq p.o. t.i.d.
Hydrochlorothiazide 100 mg p.o. q AM
Hydralazine 25 mg p.o. q.i.d.
Propranolol 20 mg p.o. q.i.d.
Milk of magnesia 30 ml p.o. hs prn irregularity

Allergies

None known.

Physical Examination

GEN: Slightly obese male in acute distress
VS: BP 210/140 HR 98 T 38.7 RR 36 Wt 180 lb Ht 5'10"
HEENT: AV nicking, papilledema
COR: NL S1 and S2; + carotid bruits
CHEST: Decreased breath sounds in left lower lobe; pleural rubbing; expiratory wheezes
ABD: Obese, soft without masses
GU: Deferred
RECT: WNL
EXT: WNL
NEURO: Oriented x 3, NL DTRs

Results of Laboratory Tests

Na 140	BUN 36	WBC 12.9	Alb 4	PO_4 4.0
K 5.6	Cr 3.4	Plts 210k	T.Bili 2.0	Mg 2.0
Cl 95	Hct 46	AST 30	FBG 90	PT 10
HCO_3 22	Hgb 15.1	ALT 20	Ca 9.0	PTT 30

ABGs: PO_2 60, PCO_2 50, pH 7.3 (on 2 liters O_2 via nasal prongs)
Urinalysis: 1+ protein, RBC 10–20/HPF
ECG: Sinus tachycardia, LVH

Problem

S:

O:

A:

P:

Problem

S:—————————

O:—————————

A:—————————

P:—————————

Problem

S:—————————

O:—————————

A:—————————

P:—————————

Problem

S:—————————

O:—————————

A:—————————

P:—————————

CASE 46

CC: S.M. is a 51-year-old female who presents to clinic with the major complaint of increasing substernal chest pain that occurs at rest, usually in the middle of the night and early in the morning. The pain does not occur during the day and is usually relieved with 1–2 sublingual nitroglycerin (NTG) tablets.

Past Medical History

S.M. has a 26-year history of difficult-to-control type I diabetes mellitus. She is currently monitoring her blood glucose at home 3 times a week and reports that her fasting blood glucose ranges from 150–350 mg/100 ml. She had a right below-the-knee amputation in 1984 secondary to her diabetes. In 1979, she was diagnosed with hypertension. In 1983, she presented with a non-Q-wave myocardial infarction. She has had 1–2 attacks of angina per week prior to this clinic visit. She has been hospitalized twice for exacerbations of her chronic obstructive pulmonary disease (COPD; 1985 and 1986).

Problem List

1. Severe peripheral vascular disease
2. Severe inoperable coronary artery disease (100% right coronary artery; 85% left anterior descending artery; and 90% left circumflex artery)

3. Type I diabetes mellitus x 26 years
4. Chronic obstructive pulmonary disease
5. Hypertension
6. Degenerative joint disease

Social History

S.M. has smoked 1½ packs per day for 36 years. She continues to smoke. She denies ETOH and i.v. drug abuse.

Medication History

Insulin 10 U regular/15 U NPH q AM,
    5 U regular/5 U NPH q PM x 6 months
Theodur 500 mg q12h x 10 years
Albuterol 2 puffs q6h x 7 years
Beclomethasone 4 puffs q6h x 2 years
Propranolol 60 mg b.i.d. x 2 months
Isosorbide dinitrate 5 mg s.l. q6h x 1 year
Nitroglycerin 1/150 prn chest pain x 7 years
Hydrochlorothiazide 25 mg p.o. qd x 9 years
Naproxen 250 mg p.o. b.i.d. prn x 15 years

Physical Examination

GEN: S.M. is a female who is having some difficulty breathing.
VS: BP 150/90 HR 76 T 36.8 RR 25 Wt 55 kg
HEENT: AV nicking and narrowing
COR: NSR
CHEST: Bibasilar rales and ronchi, numerous expiratory wheezes
ABD: WNL
RECT: Guaiac-negative
EXT: Arthritic changes of hands and knees

Results of Laboratory Tests

Na 139	Hct 45.7	Alk Phos 65
K 5.1	Hgb 15.1	Alb 3.4
Cl 103	WBC 6	FBG 300
HCO_3 27	Plts 225	$HgbA_{1c}$ 12.8%
BUN 44	AST 18	ESR 35
Cr 1.9	ALT 27	Theophylline 15

Urinalysis (by dipstick): (+) protein, trace heme, (−) bili, 1% Glu, pH 6.3
Arterial blood gas (on room air): PO_2 85, PCO_2 45, pH 7.41
Pulmonary Function Tests: Pre–beta agonist, FEV_1 = 0.9, FVC = 1.5; Post–beta agonist: FEV_1 = 1.1, FVC = 1.65

Problem

S:

O:

A:

P:

Problem _____

S: _____
_____
_____

O: _____
_____
_____
_____

A: _____
_____
_____
_____
_____
_____

P: _____
_____
_____
_____

Problem _____

S: _____
_____
_____

O: _____
_____
_____
_____

A: _____
_____
_____
_____
_____
_____

P: _____
_____
_____
_____

Problem _____

S: _____
_____
_____

O: _____
_____
_____
_____

A: _____
_____
_____
_____
_____
_____

P: _____
_____
_____
_____

Problem _____

S: _____
_____
_____

O: _____
_____
_____
_____

A: _____
_____
_____
_____
_____
_____

P: _____
_____
_____
_____

Problem

S: _____

O: _____

A: _____

P: _____

Acetaminophen 325 mg 2 tablets p.o. q.i.d. x 4 years
Digoxin 0.25 mg p.o. q AM x 2 years
Warfarin 5 mg p.o. qhs x 1 year

Physical Examination

GEN: diaphoretic, confused woman in distress. She also complains of polydipsia, polyphagia, nocturia, orthopnea, and weakness.

VS: BP 205/130 HR 106 RR 24 T 37 Wt 86 kg Ht 5'2"

HEENT: (+) AV narrowing/nicking, (+) retinal hemorrhages, (+) papilledema

COR: NL S1, S2; (+) S3, S4; sinus tachycardia

CHEST: Bibasilar rales

ABD: (+) HJR

GU: Deferred

RECTAL: Guaiac-negative

EXT: 2+ pitting edema

Results of Laboratory Tests

Na 138	HgbA$_{1c}$ 11%
K 3.1	Hgb 14
Cl 95	Hct 43
HCO$_3$ 27	WBC 5
BUN 30	LFT WNL
Cr 2.4	PT 19
Glu (fasting) 340	PTT 30

CASE 47

CC: E.T. is a 45-year-old woman who presents to the ER with a 2-day history of severe headaches, nausea, blurred vision, and dizziness.

Past Medical History

E.T. has a 14-year history of essential hypertension, recently treated with hydrochlorothiazide and clonidine. She ran out of clonidine 1 week ago. E.T. also has a history of Type II diabetes mellitus with poor control (blood sugars in the 300s and complaints of hyperglycemic symptoms). She also has congestive heart failure and degenerative joint disease and had deep venous thrombosis.

Problem List

1. Hypertension x 14 years
2. Type II diabetes mellitus x 5 years
3. Degenerative joint disease x 4 years
4. Congestive heart failure x 2 years
5. Deep venous thrombosis, 1 year ago

Medication History

Hydrochlorothiazide 25 mg p.o. q AM x 14 years
Clonidine 0.1 mg p.o. b.i.d. x 6 months
Glyburide 10 mg p.o. q AM x 1 year (was previously on Tolazamide)

Problem

S: _____

O: _____

A: _____

P: _____

Problem

S:

O:

A:

P:

Problem

S:

O:

A:

P:

Problem

S:

O:

A:

P:

Problem

S:

O:

A:

P:

CASE 48

CC: L.C. is a 59-year-old female with recurrent ventricular tachycardia and severe coronary artery disease who is admitted for a two-vessel coronary artery bypass graft (left anterior descending artery and right circumflex artery). Two days after surgery, the nurse finds L.C. unresponsive and apneic. A cardiac arrest is called, and L.C. is found to be in ventricular tachycardia (VT).

Past Medical History

L.C. was diagnosed with hypertension (HTN) in 1976. In 1983, she presented with new-onset angina and ruled in for an inferior wall myocardial infarction. In 1985, she presented with an increase in fatigue secondary to ventricular tachycardia (heart rate of 180/minute, SBP 80). During electrophysiologic studies, the VT was inducible on quinidine, but not on procainamide. In 1986, L.C. presented with an acute GI bleed secondary to peptic ulcer disease, which has been stable on ranitidine. Prior to admission for her coronary artery bypass graft, L.C. has had complaints of fatigue, malaise, fever, arthralgias and myalgias, and anorexia with a 10-kg weight loss in the past 5 months.

Social History

L.C. denies i.v. drug abuse. She has a smoking history of 1 pack per day for 33 years and rarely drinks alcohol.

Problem List

1. Recurrent ventricular tachycardia x 3 years.
2. Coronary artery disease x 5 years
3. Hypertension x 11 years
4. Peptic ulcer disease x 1 year
5. Coronary artery bypass graft
6. Cardiac arrest

Medication History

Hydrochlorothiazide 25 mg p.o. q day x 11 years
Metoprolol 50 mg p.o. b.i.d. x 8 years
Isosorbide dinitrate 20 mg p.o. q6h x 5 years
Ranitidine 150 mg p.o. qhs x 6 months
Procan SR 750 mg p.o. q6h x 2 years
Cefazolin 500 mg i.v. q8h x 2 days
Nitroglycerin 1/150 prn chest pain x 8 years

Physical Examination

GEN: L.C. is a cachectic-appearing female in severe distress.
VS: BP 60/palp HR 220 T 37.3 RR 0 Wt 46 kg

HEENT: Raised erythematous rash over the cheeks and nose
COR: Ventricular tachycardia at 220 beats/minute
ABD: WNL
GU: WNL
RECT: Guaiac-positive
EXT: Swelling of proximal interphalangeal (PIP) and metacarpophalangeal (MCP) joints of both hands and wrists, swelling of feet and knees.

Results of Laboratory Tests

Na 138	Cr 1.3	MCV 80	Alb 2.9
K 2.7	Hct 33	MCH 30	ESR 45
Cl 92	Hgb 10.3	AST 85	ANA (+)
HCO_3 33	WBC 3	ALT 74	Anti-DS ANA (−)
BUN 28	Plts 420	Alk Phos 76	

Chest x-ray: Bilateral inflammation of the pleural membrane, with bilateral interstitial fibrosis.

Problem

S:

O:

A:

P:

Problem

S:

O:

A:

P:

Problem

S:

O:

A:

P:

Problem

S:

O:

A:

P:

Problem

S:

O:

A:

P:

Problem

S:

O:

A:

P:

Skin and Eye Diseases

CASE 49

CC: P.A. is a 26-year-old female who presents to the clinic with multiple complaints. She complains of crampy, lower abdominal pain that has been bothering her for the past 2 years. The pain is usually relieved with the passage of flatus or stool. Her stools are hard, "pencil-like", and pasty looking. At other times she will have diarrhea, which is usually worse in the morning. She has no energy and feels tired all the time. Occasionally she has heartburn, which she treats with antacids. She also complains that the acne on her face, back, and neck has not gotten better even with the use of Clearasil and the Buf-Puf with Fostex soap. Lately, she has noticed a lot of flaking from her scalp, despite daily shampooing. In the last couple of days, she has noticed the appearance of a very itchy, fine, red rash that now covers her legs and lower trunk.

Problem List

1. Irritable bowel syndrome
2. Adverse drug reaction
3. Acne
4. Dandruff
5. Hypertension

Allergies

None known.

Medication History

Clearasil (8% sulfur, 1% resorcinol)
Fostex Soap (2% salicylic acid)
Cotrimoxazole DS x 5 days for urinary tract infection
Mylanta II prn
Demulen 1/35

Physical Examination

GEN: Slightly anxious 26-year-old female complaining of crampy abdominal pain, a bloated feeling, decreased energy, and multiple dermatological problems.

VS: BP 140/90 HR 80-regular RR 18 T 37.2 Wt 85 Kg

HEENT: Flaky, dry scalp with patches of easily loosened skin. Erythematous facial skin with grade II acne (comedones, papules, and occasional pustules) involving face, neck and back.

CHEST: WNL

ABD: Soft, tender, RUQ pain

RECTAL: Guaiac-negative

SKIN: Fine maculopapular erythematous rash covering legs and lower abdomen

Results of Laboratory Tests

Na 140	RBC 5.5	AST 23
K 4	Hct 42	ALT 20
Cl 103	Hgb 16	Alk Phos 35
HCO$_3$ 27	WBC 7	Alb 4.2
BUN 18	MCH 30	FBG 85
Cr 0.9	MCV 90	

Urinalysis: WNL
Stool: negative ova and parasites
Sigmoidoscopy: WNL

Problem 1. Irritable Bowel Syndrome

S: Patient has chronic crampy abdominal pain, right upper quadrant pain, pain relieved by defecation, intermittent constipation alternating with diarrhea that is worse in the morning, "pencil-like" pasty stool, bloated sensation and "heartburn"; she complains of feeling tired all the time and having no energy.

O: Negative guaiac, negative ova and parasites, WNL sigmoidoscopy.

A: This patient has classic symptoms of irritable bowel syndrome. This diagnosis is supported by the chronic intermittent nature of the symptoms without obvious signs of physical deterioration.

P: Reassure the patient that this condition does not lead to the development of inflammatory bowel disease or colonic cancer. It is important for the patient to understand that this is a chronic condition and can be alleviated but not necessarily cured. Teach the patient about the relationship between psychological stress and the disease. Life-style changes may be necessary. The constipation may respond to increased dietary bulk such as unprocessed bran or psyllium, 1–2 tablespoons b.i.d. to q.i.d.

Problem 2. Adverse Drug Reaction/Hypersensitivity

S: Patient has itchy, red rash.

O: P.A. has a fine, maculopular rash covering her legs and lower trunk; she has been taking cotrimoxazole tablets for the past 5 days.

A: The rash is most likely due to a hypersensitive reaction against this drug. The rash is irritating the patient and could worsen. The patient requires symptomatic relief.

P: Discontinue the cotrimoxazole. Begin diphenhydramine 25–50 mg p.o. q 4–6 h as needed for itchiness. Monitor clearing of the rash and decreased itchiness.

Problem 3. Acne Vulgaris

S: Nonimproving acne

O: Erythematous skin with comedones, papules, and pustules involving face, neck, and back. Currently using Clearasil and Fostex (medicated soap) with the Buf-Puf sponge.

A: The patient has grade II acne. Her current regimen has not produced an adequate response. These medications are not potent enough for her degree of acne. The patient is also using an oral contraceptive that contains a relatively high-potency progestin. The progestin effect created by the oral contraceptive is not adequately balanced by the amount of estrogen in this contraceptive. The excess progestin effect is probably contributing to her acne. Another oral contraceptive that will achieve a better hormonal balance between the progestin and estrogen should be initiated.

P: Discontinue Demulen 1/35.
Begin Brevicon. Discontinue Clearasil, Fostex, and Buf-Puf. Begin benzoyl peroxide 5% gel. Monitor for response, decrease in comedones, papules, pustules. Monitor for dry, irritated, and peeling skin. Advise patient to avoid contact with hair or colored fabric (because of bleaching effect of benzoyl peroxide). Apply to clean, dry skin. If excessive irritation occurs, temporarily stop use and resume after irritation has decreased. The patient should avoid direct sunlight because of increased sensitivity to the sun.

Problem 4. Dandruff

S: Patient has flaky, itchy, dry scalp.

O: Dry scalp with patches of easily loosened skin.

A: This problem is bothersome to the patient, cosmetically unappealing, and should be treated. The patient currently shampoos everyday but may not be doing it appropriately.

P: Use any antidandruff shampoo; tar-containing shampoos are more potent. Wash with shampoo several times a week. Patient education: advise P.A. that the benefit of the shampoo lasts about 2–3 days, so she needs to wash at least that frequently. The medication in the shampoo must be in contact with scalp long enough to work, so leave the shampoo on scalp for several minutes. The longer it is left on, the more effective it will be. Severe flare-ups can occur despite shampoo use since shampoos are not strong enough to suppress all natural fluctuations of disease. If she does not like the way the antidandruff shampoo makes her hair feel and smell, she may use a conditioner or rinse. These products will not decrease the potency of the antidandruff shampoo.

Problem 5. Mild Hypertension

S: None

O: BP 140/90

A: Patient has borderline hypertension, which may be controlled by weight loss and diet alone. Attempts should be made to control by non-drug measures before instituting antihypertensive agents.

P: Emphasize importance of weight loss and exercise. Initiate low sodium diet. Monitor blood pressure.

CASE 50

C.C.: M. H. is a 60-year-old male who presents to the emergency room complaining of shortness of breath and blurred vision.

Past Medical History

M.H. has a history of asthma controlled with bronchodilators and steroids. He had an episode of ventricular tachycardia 6 months prior to this admission. M.H., 3 days prior to admission, had an ophthalmic examination for his blurred vision. The ophthalmologist diagnosed primary open-angle glaucoma (POAG) and began treatment.

Social History

M.H. denies smoking, alcohol, or drug abuse.

Problem List

1. Acute exacerbation of asthma
2. History of ventricular tachycardia
3. Primary open-angle glaucoma

Medication History

Flecainide 400 mg 1 p.o. q12h
Ipratropium bromide inhaler 2 puffs t.i.d.
Albuterol inhaler 2 puffs q.i.d.
Theophylline (sustained release) 400 mg p.o. b.i.d.
Beclomethasone dipropionate inhaler 2 puffs b.i.d.
Levobunolol hydrochloride ophthalmic solution 0.5% 1 gtt ou b.i.d.

Physical Examination

GEN: Nervous, cyanotic appearing male complaining of blurred vision, wheezing, coughing, and nausea.

VS: BP 150/90 HR 95 R 30 T 37.8 Wt 80 kg

HEENT: Visual acuity without correction 20/80 OD and 20/60 OS. Tonometry measured intraocular pressure (IOP) of 34 mm Hg OU. Visual field examination revealed changes in the nerve fiber bundle consistent with glaucoma. Gonioscopy showed anterior angle chambers were open in each eye.

COR: WNL

CHEST: Patient using accessory muscles to breath. Numerous
inspiratory and expiratory wheezes.
ABD: WNL
GU: WNL
RECTAL: Guaiac-negative
EXT: WNL

Results of Laboratory Tests

Na 139	Hct 49	Alb 4
K 4.5	Hgb 14	T Bili 1
Cl 102	WBC 7k	Serum flecainide trough 1.3
HCO_3 24	Plts 160k	Serum theophylline pending
BUN 20	AST 25	
Cr 1	Alk Phos 55	

Arterial blood gases: PO_2 62, PCO_2 30, pH 7.34

Problem 1. Exacerbation of Asthma

S: Wheezing, shortness of breath, coughing
O: R = 30. The patient is using accessory muscles to breathe, has both inspiratory and expiratory wheezes, is cyanotic appearing, and is nervous. ABGs: PO_2=62, PCO_2=30, pH=7.34. Levobunolol hydrochloride ophthalmic solution 0.5% 1 gtt ou b.i.d. begun 3 days prior to admission.
A: The predicted serum theophylline level at steady state is 21 μg/ml. Therefore, M.H.'s bronchospasm is not due to a subtherapeutic theophylline level. Levobunolol is a nonselective β-adrenergic blocking agent that can be absorbed into the systemic circulation and precipitate bronchospasm in predisposed patients
P: Discontinue levobunolol and substitute pilocarpine hydrochloride ophthalmic solution 1% 1 gtt OU b.i.d. Give O_2 via nasal canula. Begin nebulized metaproterenol q1h until symptoms improve. Discontinue beclomethasone and begin methylprednisolone 40 mg i.v. q6h x 24 hours.

Problem 2. Nausea

S: Patient complaint.
O: BP 150/90, HR 95. M.H. appears nervous.
A: The predicted theophylline level of 21 mg/liter suggests nausea may be due to local and central nervous system effects seen with high theophylline levels.
P: Once the patient's respiratory status has improved, decrease the theophylline dose to achieve a serum concentration of 15 mg/liter. While waiting for the patient's respiratory status to improve, antacids can be used to relieve the patient's GI complaints. Monitor theophylline, nausea, emesis, and guaiac stools.

Problem 3. Blurred Vision

S: Patient complaint.
O: Visual acuity without correction 20/80 OD and 20/60 OS. Tonometry measured IOP of 34 mm Hg OU. Visual field examination showed

changes consistent with glaucoma. The trough serum flecainide concentration is 1.3 μg/ml. Gonioscopy showed anterior angle chambers were open in both eyes. Ipratropium bromide inhaler is being used.
A: Blurred vision is a common side effect associated with flecainide, especially at higher doses. Make sure that the patient is closing his eyes during inhalations of ipratropium as this agent will cause blurred vision if it gets in the patient's eyes, although the blurred vision is probably not related to ipratropium use.
P: Decrease the dose of flecainide to produce lower plasma levels or consider using an alternate antiarrhythmic. Monitor for arrhythmias, a decrease in blurred vision, and IOP.

Problem 4. History of Ventricular Tachycardia

S: Patient had ventricular tachycardia 6 months prior to admission.
O: Theophylline level. Flecainide 400 mg p.o. q12h. BP 150/90, HR 95, K 45. Trough flecainide concentration 1.3 μg/ml.
A: The trough flecainide concentration is in the range where proarrhythmic effect could be seen.
P: Decrease the flecainide dose or use an alternate antiarrhythmic agent. Question the patient about compliance with theophylline dosing regimen. Monitor blurred vision, ECG, occurrence of arrhythmias, flecainide, and theophylline concentrations.

Problem 5. Primary Open-Angle Glaucoma

S: Patient complains of blurred vision.
O: As mentioned in problem 3, the patient has findings consistent with POAG. M.H. is using ipratropium and beclomethasone inhalers.
A: Ipratropium and beclomethasone are probably not contributing to increased IOP. Short-term intravenous steroids should not contribute to an increase in IOP.
P: Use pilocarpine to control IOP. Monitor IOP, visual field, and blurred vision.

CASE 51

CC: H.S. is a 36-year-old female admitted for depression, increased fatigue, loss of appetite, shortness of breath, constipation, and weight gain of 13 kg over past month. She also has a 6-month history of a rash not attributed to her usual eczema. Six months ago she noticed the onset of rashes on her lips and upper arms, which spread to her neck and back over a 1-month period. She complains that the hydrocortisone ointment her private physician gave her has not helped much, and the itching is driving her crazy. Three days ago, she noticed the appearance of a new rash under her breasts and around her belt line. She complains that the itching is worse at night.

Past Medical History

H.S. has had eczema for 10 years. She has had a seizure disorder since being in a motor vehicle accident 20 years ago.

Social History

H.S. lives with husband and two children. She smoked tobacco (1 ppd x 20 year) and drinks alcohol (occasional glass of wine with dinner). She denies intravenous drug abuse (IVDA).

Problem List

1. Hypothyroidism
2. Eczema
3. Seizure disorder
4. Psoriasis
5. Scabies

Allergies

None known.

Medication History

Hydrocortisone ointment 1% prn
Triphasil-28
Phenytoin 300 mg qhs
Psyllium prn
Phenolphthalein prn

Physical Examination

GEN   H.S. is a pale 36-year-old female who appears in mild distress.

VS: BP 130/85 HR 70 R RR 20 R T 37.5 Wt 73 kg ($\uparrow$ 13 kg)

HEENT: Ptosis, palpable thyroid, enlarged tongue

CHEST: Few rales

GI: Decreased bowel sounds, guaiac-negative

SKIN: Diffuse, patchy, erythematous areas with raised silver, shiny, scaly plaques. Few excoriations over arms, neck and back. Consistent with psoriasis.
Tiny papules, with vesicles, and small burrows under breasts and around belt line consistent with scabies.

NEURO: Muscle weakness and pain, tingling sensations in extremities, decreased DTR, no seizures for past 15 years

Results of Laboratory Tests

Na 130	BUN 19	WBC 9k	Phenytoin 4
K 4.2	Cr 0.8	AST 21	Alb 4.3
Cl 96	Hct 35.1	ALT 24	
HCO$_3$ 32	Hgb 12.2	Glu 140	

Thyroid function tests: T$_4$ 3.0, TSH 11, FTI 0.9

Problem _____

S: _____

O: _____

A: _____

P: _____

Problem

S:

O:

A:

P:

Problem

S:

O:

A:

P:

Problem

S:

O:

A:

P:

Problem

S:

O:

A:

P:

Questions

1. Evaluate H.S.'s thyroid status. List subjective and objective findings that support your evaluation.
2. Discuss the treatment H.S. should receive. Evaluate the thyroid products available and determine which is best for H.S.
3. Identify and discuss potential drug interactions with H.S.'s thyroid therapy.
4. Prednisone 40 mg p.o. q.d. is ordered to treat H.S.'s psoriasis. Do you agree? Give one reason why prednisone should or should not be used to treat her psoriasis.
5. Outline a regimen for treating H.S.'s psoriasis. State the drugs, dose, route, and schedule that should be used. For the drug recommended, give one reason for its use in psoriasis.
6. List four items of patient information that should be given to the patient with regard to the regimen you recommended.
7. How should H.S.'s scabies be treated? Recommend a drug, route, and schedule for her.
8. List four items of patient information that should be given to this patient regarding the treatment of scabies.

CASE 52

CC: B.B.L. is a 52-year-old female with total body psoriasis and moderately severe arthritis who comes to the clinic today for follow-up.

Past Medical History

B.B.L. has rheumatoid arthritis, which was diagnosed 4 years ago. It has been somewhat difficult to control and has been progressive over the last 12 months. Mild deformities are noted in her hands. She was first started on ASA but developed an allergy, so acetaminophen 650 mg q6h prn pain was begun. Penicillamine 250 mg q.i.d. was then added 6 months ago. B.B.L. also has asthma, which is currently stable on Theodur 400 mg b.i.d. and albuterol 2 puffs q.i.d. B.B.L. has psoriasis of 10 years duration, which has been treated with various regimens of topical steroids. Current therapy is hydrocortisone cream 0.5% q.i.d. with occlusion and diphenhydramine 50 mg p.o. q6h prn itching.

Social History

B.B.L. smokes 2 packs per day of cigarettes. She drinks 1 pint vodka per day.

Problem List

1. Psoriasis
2. Rheumatoid arthritis
3. Asthma
4. Hypothyroidism (x 15 years)
5. S/P menopause

Medication History

Hydrocortisone cream 0.5% q.i.d.
Diphenhydramine 50 mg p.o. q6h
Theodur 400 mg b.i.d.
Albuterol 2 puffs q.i.d.
Penicillamine 250 mg q.i.d.
Acetaminophen 650 mg q6h
Conjugated estrogens 1.25 mg qd
Levothyroxine 100 μg qd

Allergies

ASA (bronchospasm)

Review of Systems

B.B.L. has fatigue, decreased appetite, constipation (last bowel movement 5 days ago), cold intolerance, morning joint stiffness of 1 hour duration, and burning after application of hydrocortisone cream.

Physical Examination

GEN: B.B.L. is a middle-aged woman who is in no apparent distress.
VS: BP 120/68 HR 68 T 37 RR 18 Wt 65 kg
HEENT: WNL
COR: Decreased S1 and S2
CHEST: No rales or rhonchi, with a few expiratory wheezes
ABD: Soft, nontender, no masses, decreased bowel sounds
GU: Deferred
RECT: Guaiac negative
EXT: Decreased DTRs, swelling and tenderness of MCP joints, wrists, knees, and ankles
NEURO: WNL

Results of Laboratory Tests

Na 140	Hct 31.6	AST 112	Glu 150	Uric Acid 6.5
K 3.3	Hgb 10.5	ALT 60	Ca 7.6	Fe 29
Cl 102	WBC 2.6k	LDH 330	PO$_4$ 4.2	Transferrin 279
HCO$_3$ 29	Plts 76k	Alk Phos 160	Mg 2.6	Iron Sat 11%
BUN 34	MCV 101	Alb 2.3	PT 13.5	Theophylline
Cr 1.2	MCHC 36	T.Bili 2.6	PTT 42.3	15

TFTs: T$_4$ 5.4, R$_3$TU 15, TSH 12
Urinalysis: Glu (−), ketones (−), WBC 2–5/HPF, protein 4$^+$ bili (+), RBC (−)

Problem

S:

O:

A:

P:

Problem

S:

O:

A:

P:

Problem

S:

O:

A:

P:

Problem

S:

O:

A:

P:

Problem

S:

O:

A:

P:

Problem

S:

O:

A:

P:

Questions

1. Assess the treatment of B.B.L.'s psoriasis. What recommendations for treatment of her psoriasis would you make? What other forms of psoriasis therapy are contraindicated in this patient? Why?
2. Evaluate the current treatment of B.B.L.'s rheumatoid arthritis. What therapy would you recommend? State drug, drug dosage form and product, dose, schedule, and reasons.
3. Evaluate the treatment of B.B.L.'s hypothyroidism. Is her current regimen adequate? Why or why not? What subjective and objective evidence supports your assessment? What treatment would you recommend?
4. How would you recommend that her constipation be treated?

CASE 53

CC: T.V. is a 72-year-old female who is admitted to the hospital for complaints of severe upper GI pain. Her GI symptoms started about 6 months ago when her husband became severely ill. She forgot to eat as she was busy caring for him. The pain usually was relieved by eating. Over the past few months, the pain worsened. She tolerated the pain fairly well until today, when it became unbearable. T.V. also has a history of mild psoriasis, which was controlled until the past 3 months by steroid creams. She presents now with a severe flare of the psoriasis over her scalp, back, and buttocks. She complains that her legs have been itching more, and seems to be relieved only when she is in the shower. As a result, she has been taking two to three showers every day.

Past Medical History

T.V. has psoriasis, degenerative joint disease, hypertension, and osteoporosis.

Social History

T.V.'s husband died 4 months ago. She smokes tobacco, ½–1 pack per day for 40 years.

Problem List

1. Peptic ulcer disease
2. Psoriasis
3. Degenerative joint disease
4. Hypertension
5. Osteoporosis

Allergies

Penicillin

Medication History

Triamcinolone cream 0.1%, apply topically to involved skin, prn
Piroxicam 20 mg q.d.
Conjugated estrogen 0.625 mg q.d.
Calcium carbonate 500 mg q.d.
Hydrochlorothiazide 50 mg q.d.

Physical Examination

GEN:	T.V. is a 72-year-old female in mild distress.
VS:	BP 160/95 HR 75 T 37 RR 16 Wt 47 kg
COR:	WNL
CHEST:	Clear
ABD:	Epigastric tenderness
RECTAL:	Guaiac-positive
NEURO:	Intact
SKIN:	Sharply demarcated erythematous papules, with raised silver, shiny, scaly plaques on scalp, back, and buttocks. Dry, cracking skin covering both legs.

Results of Laboratory Tests

Na 137	Cr 0.8	MCH 27	Ca 9.6
K 3.3	Hct 31.6	AST 25	PO$_4$ 2.0
Cl 105	Hgb 9.8	ALT 20	
HCO$_3$ 26	WBC 8k	Protein 7.3	
BUN 22	MCV 72	Alb 3.8	

Problem _____

S: _____

O: _____

A: _____

P: _____

Problem _____

S: _____

O: _____

A: _____

P: _____

Problem _____

S: _____

O: _____

A: _____

P: _____

Problem

S:

O:

A:

P:

Problem

S:

O:

A:

P:

Neurological Disorders

CASE 54

CC: G.K. is a 39-year-old stockbroker who comes to clinic today (February 3) complaining of increasing shortness of breath that began three days ago on January 31. She also complains that her headaches are increasing in frequency so that she now has one headache every week.

Past Medical History

G.K. has had asthma since childhood; theophylline level on January 27 was 12. She has chronic migraine headaches and peptic ulcer disease. The PUD was treated with cimetidine 300 mg q.i.d. for 6 weeks; it was discontinued at last clinic visit (January 27) because the ulcer had healed. G.K. also has mild hypertension; her BP during last three visits was 170–180/95–105. She has mild to moderate acne on face, chest, and back. She had a total abdominal hysterectomy and bilateral salpingoophorectomy in 1978.

History of Present Illness

G.K. has a history of steroid-dependent asthma for 4 years, but since she had been stable for over 6 months, it was decided to taper her steroid at her last clinical visit (January 27).

Problem List

1. Acute exacerbation of asthma
2. Chronic migraine
3. Status post healed PUD
4. Mild hypertension
5. Acne
6. Status post hysterectomy
7. Steroid toxicity

Medication History

G.K. is compliant with all her medications. Prednisone was tapered from qd 60 mg × 6 months in the following manner:

1/28	1/29	1/30	1/31	2/1	2/2	2/3
60	50	40	30	20	15	10

Theodur 400 mg b.i.d. for 3 years
Terbutaline inhaler 2 puffs b.i.d. began 1/27 in lieu of albuterol 2 puffs q.i.d.
Hydrochlorothiazide 150 mg qd for hypertension
Estrogen conjugated 1.25 mg qd × 21 days per month since 1978

Fluocinonide cream being used for acne although originally prescribed for another condition

Allergies

None known.

Physical Examination

GEN: G.K. is cushingoid-appearing young female in moderate respiratory distress.
VS: BP 175/95 HR 75 T 37 RR 30 Wt 55 kg Ht 5′7″
HEENT: PERRLA, comedones on face around nose and mouth
COR: Normal S1 and S2, no murmurs or gallops
CHEST: Moderate expiratory and inspiratory wheezes and rhonchi bilaterally, comedones on chest and back
ABD: No masses, tenderness or ascites, mildly obese, few striae
GU: WNL
RECT: WNL
EXT: Few ecchymoses
NEURO: Reflexes bilaterally equal

Results of Laboratory Tests

Na 140	BUN 20	WBC 12k	T Bili 0.8
K 3.1	Cr 1.0	Plts 180k	Glu (random) 155
Cl 101	Hct 39.7	AST 28	
HCO_3 22	Hgb 13.1	Alb 4.0	

Urinanalysis: WNL
Arterial blood gases: PO_2 60 PCO_2 25

Problem 1. Acute Exacerbation of Asthma

S: Patient complains of shortness of breath.
O: PO_2, PCO_2, wheezes, rhonchi, RR = 30, respiratory distress
A: G.K. has a history of steroid-dependent asthma for 4 years, but her dose of prednisone has been very rapidly tapered over the last 7 days. In addition, her β_2 agonist inhaler was recently changed, and terbutaline does not have a 12-hour duration. Her theophylline level is probably below 10 because her cimetidine was recently discontinued. Cimetidine decreases the clearance of theophylline, and the effect usually lasts for 3 days after the drug is discontinued. Her clearance should be close to normal now. All of these may be contributing to this acute exacerbation of her asthma. Moderate distress indicates that G.K. needs treatment,

but that she is not likely to develop respiratory failure and therefore does not require hospitalization at this time.

P: Administer the β_2 agonist albuterol 2–4 puffs q1h until improved. If G.K. is unable to use the inhaler correctly, a spacer may help in administration. A nebulized treatment of albuterol or metaproterenol is an alternative. Begin prednisone 60 mg every day for 1 week until G.K. is stable, then taper more slowly with a decrease of 5 mg/week until physiologic doses are reached then taper more slowly until G.K. is off steroids or her AM cortisol is >10. If G.K. is unable to be tapered off steroids, initiate inhaled steroids as triamcinolone 2–4 puffs t.i.d.–q.i.d. depending on the oral steroid dose at time of initiation. Keep G.K. on both oral and inhaled steroids for 1 week until she is stable, then resume the taper as above. Avoid the use of inhaled steroids during an acute exacerbation. Give G.K. a loading dose of 200 mg theophylline as a rapid release tablet. This should increase her level to approximately 11. Calculate a new maintenance dose for G.K. based on the level obtained. Monitor FEV_1, ABGs, FEV_1/FVC, RR, chest ascultation, SOB, and cough. For adverse effects, monitor nausea, vomiting, HR, tremors, nervousness, insomnia, and palpitations. During the steroid taper, monitor for an exacerbation of the asthma, as well as signs and symptoms of adrenal insufficiency. Teach G.K. how to use her inhaler correctly if her technique is incorrect. Suggest that G.K. keep extra inhalers in convenient locations such as at work. If G.K. is started on a steroid inhaler, provide specific information about using after the β_2 agonist inhaler and rinsing her mouth to decrease the risk of candidiasis. Teach G.K. how to recognize adrenal insufficiency, that health care providers will need to know about her steroid use, and how to obtain a Medi-Alert bracelet if she does not already have one.

Problem 2. Chronic Migraine

S: Complaint.

O: Patient has one headache per week

A: G.K. has headaches of such frequency that it is likely interfering with her life and she requires prophylactic treatment. Propranolol, amitriptyline, and verapamil would all likely be effective agents. However, propranolol is contraindicated in this patient with asthma. Atenolol a β_1 selective agent may be an alternative. Veraparmil is preferred to amitriptyline since it will also treat her hypertension. Ergots should be avoided if possible because they will aggravate her hypertension.

P: Begin verapamil 80 mg t.i.d. Monitor headache frequency, BP, HR, dizziness and constipation.

Have G.K. increase her fiber intake to avoid the constipation.

Problem 3. Status Post Healed Peptic Ulcer Disease

S: None.

O: Healed ulcer confirmed at last clinic visit.

A: G.K. has only had one episode of PUD that has been adequately treated. Maintenance therapy is not indicated in this patient. Her steroid therapy may have contributed to her PUD.

P: Monitor for signs and symptoms of recurrent PUD such as midepigastric burning pain, pain relieved by food or antacids, and dark tarry stools. Avoid foods that irritate her stomach and ulcerogenic substances such as aspirin and ethanol.

Problem 4. Mild Hypertension

S: None

O: BP 175/95

A: G.K.'s hypertension is not well controlled and this reading is consistent with the previous three BP measurements. The previous three readings were taken when G.K. was not in respiratory distress. Both the prednisone and the estrogens may be contributing to her HTN, and the doses of these medications should be decreased. The 150 mg dose of HCTZ is not more effective than a lower dose and is causing her hypokalemia.

P: Decrease estrogen dose as per Problem 6. Eventually, taper the prednisone per Problem 1. Begin verapamil as per Problem 2. Decrease the HCTZ to 25 mg qd. Replace K with 30 mEq/day for 1 week and remeasure serum K.

Problem 5. Acne

S: None

O: Patient has comedones on chest, back, and face.

A: Both estrogen and prednisone may be aggravating her acne. Topical steroids are not appropriate for the treatment of acne, and fluocinonide is too potent to be used on the face for long-term therapy. The acne should be treated since it is a cosmetic problem, but it is not severe enough at this point to require isotretinoin. Systemic antibiotics are not indicated since topical therapy has not been adequately tried.

P: Discontinue fluocinonide. Begin benzoyl peroxide 5% cream applied to face, back, and chest b.i.d. 30 minutes after washing with a nondrying soap such as Dove. The benzoyl peroxide can be titrated up to a 10% cream, 5% gel, and finally 10% gel if the acne does not respond. Redness, irritation, and dryness are used as endpoints, as well as a decrease in the number of lesions. G.K. should avoid contact of the benzoyl peroxide with her eyes, clothing, and hair. Her acne is likely to worsen for 3–4 weeks but should improve later. If the redness and irritation are severe, decrease the frequency of application. G.K. should use water-based cosmetics and avoid picking or squeezing the lesions.

Problem 6. Status Post Hysterectomy

S: None

O: History

A: G.K. needs estrogen replacement to prevent osteoporosis since she is prematurely post-menopausal. However, the dose required to maintain bone density is between 0.3 and 0.625 mg/day. The estrogens may be contributing to her HTN as above. Supplemental calcium may not be of additional benefit, but it will not interfere with her verapamil therapy.

P: Decrease the dose of conjugated estrogens to 0.625 mg qd. Monitor signs and symptoms of estrogen deficiency such as hot flushes, vaginal atrophy, and painful intercourse. Also monitor BP and signs or symptoms of DVT. Make sure that G.K. has a yearly pelvic examination and performs monthly breast self-examination.

Problem 7. Steroid Toxicity

S: None

O: Cushingoid appearance, hypertension, acne, striae, hypokalemia, hyperglycemia, ecchymoses, increased WBC.

A: Steroids are causing problems for G.K., but they should be tapered soon per Problem 1. Since G.K. has been on prednisone 60 mg/day for 6 months, she probably has HPA axis suppression and is at risk for adrenal insufficiency and will require steroid coverage in stress situations for up to one year. Estrogens may decrease the clearance of corticosteroids and thus may have contributed to the side effects seen in G.K. G.K. is at increased risk of osteoporosis because of her early menopause.

P: Taper prednisone as per Problem 1. In 9–12 months perform a cortrosyn stimulation test to assess adrenal reserve. Monitor for signs and symptoms of adrenal insufficiency.

CASE 55

CC: C.L. is a 56-year-old female who presents to clinic with chief complaints of recent seizures, diarrhea, and night sweats.

Past Medical History

C.L. has a 30-year-history of complex partial seizures that have been occurring 4–5 times yearly for the past several years despite compliance with her phenytoin therapy. She describes these seizures as starting with a tingling sensation in her abdomen

followed by a period of unresponsiveness. She has been told that she stares, picks at her clothes, and mumbles for 1–2 minutes after which she regains alertness but is drowsy and confused. Common migraines were diagnosed 3 years ago, and C.L. has recently been experiencing two headaches monthly without an obvious precipitating cause. She continues to use ergotamine with modest relief but is unable to tolerate the nausea associated with this medication. C.L. also complains of nightmares and has noticed that when she wakes her bed-clothes are soaked with perspiration. Morning fingersticks have been running near 180 mg/dl; PM fingersticks consistently measure about 320 mg/dl.

Problem List

1. Complex partial seizures × 30 years
2. Mitral valve replacement (mechanical valve), 1972
3. Type II diabetes mellitus, insulin dependent × 5 years
4. Classical migraine × 3 years
5. Duodenal ulcer, diagnosed by endoscopy 1 week ago
6. Diarrhea

Current Medications

Phenytoin 300 mg p.o. q hs × 30 years
Warfarin 7.5 mg p.o. qd
Insulin Reg/NPH 5 U/20 U q AM, 5 U/20 U q PM
Ergotamine tartrate 2 mg s.l. @ HA onset; MR in 30 minutes to a maximum of 3 tabs/HA or 5 tabs/week
Cimetidine 800 mg p.o. qhs (started this week)
Mylanta II 30 ml p.o. 1 and 3 hours p.c. and h.s.

Social History

C.L. smokes cigarettes, 22 packs years.

Review of Symptoms

She experiences GI pain with coffee, which is relieved by food.

Physical Examination

GEN: Overweight female; somewhat withdrawn.
VS: BP 130/78 HR 78 T 37 RR 16 Wt 80 kg
COR: Increased S1, S2; no S3, S4; prosthetic sound heard
RECT: Guaiac-positive
EXT: No ecchymoses, petechiae
NEURO: Decreased ankle jerk reflexes; otherwise WNL

Results of Laboratory Tests

Na 136	Hgb 14.5	Hgb A$_{1c}$ 9
K 3.4	Hct 44.0	Pt 19.8,
Cl 98	WBC 8.0 k	19.5 (3 months ago)
HCO$_3$ 23	Plts 270 k	Phenytoin 6.0
BUN 12	Alb 4.0	
Cr 1.0	Glu (random) 210	

Urinalysis: pH 6.0, protein (−), bili (−), Glu (−), ketones (−), blood (−)

Problem 1. Complex Partial Seizures

S: Patient has had recent increase in seizures: (+) aura; impaired consciousness for 1–2 min; abnormal speech and movements; postictal sedation and confusion. She previously had 4–5 seizures yearly. She is compliant with phenytoin.

O: Phenytoin = 6.0 μg/ml

A: C.L.'s phenytoin level is subtherapeutic. Her seizures may be rapidly controlled by giving an oral loading dose. Increase the maintenance dose (according to patient-specific pharmacokinetic parameters) to maintain a level within the therapeutic range. Cimetidine interacts with phenytoin.

P: Give phenytoin 300 mg p.o. stat; give 300 mg p.o. 2 hours later (will raise phenytoin level by 10 μg/ml). Increase phenytoin maintenance dose to 400 mg p.o. qhs. (est Cp_{ss} = 15 μg/ml). Monitor drowsiness, GI upset, visual changes, ataxia, nystagmus decreased mentation, slurred speech, phenytoin level, and seizure control. Advise C.L. to return to clinic if she shows signs and symptoms of phenytoin toxicity.

Problem 2. Peptic Ulcer Disease

S: GI pain after coffee that is relieved by food.

O: (+) duodenal ulcer by endoscopy; guaiac-positive

A: The ulcer requires treatment, however, drug interactions make cimetidine a poor choice because cimetidine leads to increased phenytoin levels and warfarin effect. There is no reason to use high-dose antacids concomitantly with H_2-antagonist because of increased cost. There is no benefit from a bland diet. Antacids may reduce phenytoin bioavailability.

P: Discontinue cimetidine. Start ranitidine 150 mg p.o. b.i.d. (or 300 mg p.o. qhs) × 8 weeks. Decrease antacid use to 30 ml p.o. prn pain. Space by 2 hours from phenytoin dose. Avoid coffee and irritating foods. Encourage patient to quit smoking.

Problem 3. Type II Insulin-dependent Diabetes Mellitus

S: AM fingersticks 320, PM fingersticks 180; nightmares; nightsweats.

O: Glu (random) 210, urine glu (−), protein (−), ketones (−), HgbA$_1$c 9

A: Reactive AM hyperglycemia (Somogyi effect) vs. Dawn phenomenon

P: Check early AM fingersticks (0200 or during symptoms). Adjust insulin accordingly: (a) If hypoglycemic, reduce NPH insulin in PM. (b) If hyperglycemic, increase PM regular and/or NPH insulin. Patient education: Advise C.L. to continue AM and PM fingersticks. Teach her to recognize signs and symptoms of hypoglycemia and hyperglycemia and to treat hypoglycemia with snack (4 oz juice followed by complex carbohydrate or protein).

Problem 4. Mitral Valve Replacement

S: No symptoms.

O: Prosthetic sound on heart examination; recent PT = 19.8; hematuria (−); no ecchymoses or petechiae

A: Appropriately anticoagulated for indication (1.5–2.0 × control). Cimetidine interacts with warfarin, therefore avoid. Phenytoin may increase warfarin metabolism but this is not important since the patient has been on both drugs for many years and the PT is stable.

P: Continue Warfarin 7.5 mg qd. Monitor PT, guaiac, CBC, and signs of bleeding.

Problem 5. Classical Migraine

S: Patient has two headaches per month. She gets modest relief with ergotamine but it causes nausea.

O: No objective data.

A: GI side effects of ergotamine are unacceptable to patient. Other abortive treatment options: NSAID's—caution with ulcer and warfarin. Acetaminophen is OK for analgesia. Headache frequency makes this patient an appropriate candidate for prophylaxis, however: Beta-blockers are relatively contraindicated in IDDM. Antidepressants may reduce seizure threshold in high doses; avoid if possible since alternatives are available.

P: Give acetaminophen 325–650 mg p.o. q 4–6 h prn HA. Start verapamil 80 mg p.o. t.i.d. Titrate up to 480 mg/day maximum. Allow 6 weeks for maximal effect. Monitor HR, BP, dizziness, constipation, and headache severity and frequency.

Problem 6. Diarrhea

S: Patient complains of diarrhea.

O: K = 3.4

A: Diarrhea most likely due to Mg/Al–containing antacid (Mylanta II). Ergotamine and cimetidine may also contribute.

P: Decrease antacid use as per PUD. If diarrhea persists, alternated Mylanta II with Al only antacid (e.g. Amphogel).

CASE 56

CC: S.S. is a 67-year-old female who presents to clinic for her scheduled appointment. Her chief complaints today include persistent itching of the scalp, increased difficulty walking, a disabling hand tremor, and vivid dreams that she feels may be causing her daytime anxiety.

Past Medical History

S.S. was diagnosed with Parkinson's disease 2 years ago. She was initially treated with trihexyphenidyl but levodopa was soon required. Levodopa was increased at her last clinic visit to her present dose. Last week, S.S. called the clinic because of nausea and vomiting. She received a prescription for metoclopramide 20 mg q.i.d. and was told to return today for follow-up with her regular physician.

Problem List

1. Parkinson's disease × 2 years
2. Seizure disorder (S/P stroke 4 years ago)
3. Hypertension × 15 years, well controlled

Medication History

Levodopa 1 g p.o. q.i.d.
Trihexyphenidyl 2 mg p.o. t.i.d.
Phenytoin 200 mg p.o. qhs
Carbamazepine 200 mg p.o. t.i.d.
Reserpine 0.1 mg p.o. qd
Hydrochlorothiazide 25 mg p.o. qd
Metoclopramide 20 mg p.o. q.i.d

Physical Examination

GEN: Well-groomed, quiet woman, sitting in chair with a facial grimace and restless movements of both legs.

VS: BP 140/80 (supine), 124/68 (standing) HR 90 (supine), 108 (standing) T 37.0 RR 18 Wt 64 kg

HEENT: AV nicking; multiple excoriations on scalp and numerous inflamed areas of dull, yellowish-red lesions and scales with a greasy appearance

COR: Nl S1, S2; no S3, S4

NEURO: (−) nystagmus

EXT: Rhythmic jerking movements of upper extremities

Results of Laboratory Tests

Na 138	HCO$_3$ 28	BUN 11	Phenytoin 11
K 3.9	Cl 104	Cr 1.0	Carbamazepine 5.8

Problem

S:

O:

A:

P:

Problem

S:

O:

A:

P:

Problem

S:

O:

A:

P:

Questions

1. List four drugs that may contribute to the worsening of S.S.'s Parkinson's disease.
2. Do you agree with the current treatment regimen for S.S.'s Parkinson's disease? If not, what drug therapy changes would you suggest? Include dose, route, and schedule.
3. List four side effects currently experienced by S.S. that may be attributed to the levodopa. If you recommend any changes in drug therapy for Question 2, state how you would expect your recommendations to affect each adverse effect (i.e., improve, worsen, or no effect).
4. How should S.S.'s seborrheic dermatitis be treated?

CASE 57

CC: K.R. is a 44-year-old female with a history of generalized tonic-clonic seizures being admitted to the neurology service after having six seizures today. K.R. was observed by her husband to have three seizures this morning that were characterized by loss of consciousness, falling to the ground, a brief state of muscular rigidity, followed by bilateral jerking of the extremities, and urinary incontinence. She did not regain consciousness between convulsions. K.R. was then taken to the ER by ambulance where she has proceeded to have several more generalized tonic-clonic seizures. Again, she has not regained consciousness between seizures and the ER staff suspects she will continue to have seizures unless treated immediately.

Past Medical History

K.R. has had seizures since a motor vehicle accident and evacuation of a left subdural hematoma in 1982. Her last seizure was 2 months ago. Three days ago her phenytoin was discontinued secondary to severe gum hyperplasia and she was given a new prescription for phenobarbital.

Problem List

1. Post-traumatic generalized seizure disorder since 1982
2. Gingival hyperplasia
3. Alcoholism since 1968

Medication History

Phenytoin 300 mg p.o. q hs (discontinued 3 days ago)
Phenobarbital 90 mg p.o. q hs (begun 3 days ago)

Physical Examination

GEN: K.R. is a thin woman looking older than stated age; she is lying unresponsive on gurney.
VS: BP 148/90 HR 100 T 38 RR 20 Wt 55 kg
HEENT: Pallor, poor dentition, new bite wound on tongue

COR: Sinus tachycardia, nl S1, S2; no S3, S4
CHEST: Clear
GU: Deferred
NEURO: Nonresponsive
EXT: Ecchymoses on upper arms and thighs

Results of Laboratory Tests

Na 140   Hgb 9.8   ALT 44 PO_4 2
K 3.6   Hct 30   Alb 3.1   Osm 280
Cl 100   WBC 8.9 k Glu 52   Phenobarbital 4 μg/ml
HCO_3 22 Plts 175 k Ca 7   Phenytoin not detected
BUN 14   MCV 108   Mg 1.1
Cr 1.2   AST 86

Problem _____

S: _____

O: _____

A: _____

P: _____

Problem _____

S: _____

O: _____

A: _____

P: _____

Problem _____

S: _____

O: _____

A: _____

P: _____

CASE 58

CC: R.F. is a 34-year-old male who presents to clinic with the complaint of frequent intense headaches that are only slightly relieved by Cafergot. He has also noticed the recent onset of a tingling sensation of the lower extremities and mild fatigue.

Past Medical History

R.F. has a history of grand mal seizures that were initially treated with phenytoin. When his seizures were not controlled despite optimal blood levels, carbamazepine was added. R.F. complained of confusion and sedation upon starting carbamazepine and the drug was subsequently discontinued. Valproic acid was then added with gradual titration to the current dose. R.F. has had no seizures for the last 2 years. R.F.'s cluster headaches have been occurring almost daily for the past 3 weeks. When the current bout began he was given a prescription for Cafergot by an ER physician. R.F. currently uses 1 Cafergot tablet 2–3 times daily and believes this medication "helps a little".

Problem List

1. Generalized tonic-clonic seizure disorder × 10 years
2. Cluster headaches × 2 years
3. Hypertension × 1 year
4. Primary hypothyroidism × 6 years

Current Medications

Phenytoin 400 mg p.o. qhs
Valproic acid 500 mg p.o. t.i.d.
Cafergot 1 p.o. @ HA onset; may repeat in 30 minutes to a maximum of 3 tabs/HA or 5 tabs/week
Atenolol 50 mg p.o. qd
Thyrolar 2 gr p.o. qd

Social History

R.F. does not smoke; he denies alcohol use.

Physical Examination

GEN: Well-developed, well-nourished male in no apparent distress.
VS: BP 158/98 HR 60 T 37 RR 17 Wt 83 kg
HEENT: WNL
COR: NL S1, S2
CHEST: Clear to auscultation and percussion
ABD: Nontender; no masses
NEURO: (+) Nystagmus on far lateral gaze; otherwise WNL
EXT: Lower extremities cold to touch with decreased distal pulses; NL skin color and texture

Results of Laboratory Tests

Na 139	Cr 0.8	AST 56	PT 11
K 4.1	Hct 45	ALT 70	Glu 100
Cl 104	Hgb 14.4	Alk Phos 110	Chol 240
HCO_3 29	WBC 5k	Alb 4.1	Phenytoin 17
BUN 10	Plts 270k	T Bili 0.1	Valproic acid 65

Thyroid function tests: T_4 13.5, RT_3U 30, TSH 1.0

Problem

S:

O:

A:

P:

Problem

S:

O:

A:

P:

Problem

S:

O:

A:

P:

Problem

S:

O:

A:

P:

Problem

S:

O:

A:

P:

SECTION/**12**

Psychiatric Disorders

CASE 59

CC: B.D. is a 45-year-old male who was brought to the emergency psychiatry unit by the police. He was found sitting and screaming from the top of a Volkswagen parked in a city park. He claimed that he was sent by Mr. Spock to save the city. He stated that the Volkswagen was turning into a double-headed dragon and that he had to sit there until the "crew from the Enterprise beamed down and killed it with their phasers."

Past Medical History

Schizophrenia was diagnosed in B.D. 5 years ago. He has attempted suicide twice. He has seasonal asthma; he visits the ER approximately 3 times per year, where he's been treated with aminophylline and metaproterenol nebulizer. He suffered a single grand mal seizure 10 years ago. He has a history of noncompliance.

Problem List

1. Schizophrenic, acute exacerbation
2. Schizophrenia
3. Seasonal asthma
4. History of a single grand mal seizure
5. Phenothiazine side effects

Social History

B.D. lives with his 75-year-old mother; his father committed suicide 30 years ago. He smokes tobacco (1 pack per day for 15 years) and drinks 2–3 beers per day. He denies intravenous drug abuse.

Allergies

No known drug allergies. Allergic to pollen, dogs, cats, feathers, and dust.

Medication History

Chlorpromazine 300 mg b.i.d. × 2 years (increased to 400 mg b.i.d. 3 weeks ago)
Docusate 250 mg b.i.d.
Theodur 300 mg b.i.d. (last theophylline level, measured 3 weeks ago = 3 μg/ml)
Terbutaline 5 mg p.o. t.i.d.
Phenytoin 300 mg hs (last level, measured 3 weeks ago = 2 μg/ml)

Physical Examination

Unable to perform physical examination.

GEN: This is a dirty disheveled young male who responds to questions in a monotone voice and has a flat affect. He is oriented to person only. He is sunburned and has grayish splotches on his arms and face, which he blames on the dragon. He says that he knew that "the dragon was coming" because his mouth was dry and he got dizzy whenever he tried to stand up. He also complains of constipation and blurred vision because "his power was taken away by the dragon." During the interview, B.D. became more agitated and started shouting and screaming.

Problem 1. Acute Schizophrenia

S: Agitation, hallucinations
O: Patient appears disoriented and disheveled, and speaks in a monotone voice.
A: B.D. needs immediate therapy for the acute schizophrenic episode. High-potency agents are preferred for rapid neuroleptization. Low phenytoin and theophylline levels may be indicative of overall noncompliance, which could have precipitated this psychotic episode.
P: Discontinue chlorpromazine. Begin rapid neuroleptization: haloperidol 5–10 mg i.m. q1h or fluphenazine 5–10 mg i.m. q1h until the patient is calm. Chlorpromazine 50 mg i.m. q1h may also be used but it has more cardiovascular and sedative side effects. Continue antipsychotic therapy after rapid neuroleptization. Convert to the oral route after the patient is stabilized but only while he is hospitalized. The usual maintenance doses for haloperidol and fluphenazine are 5–40 mg p.o./day. Monitor behavior, dystonic reactions, sedation, and blood pressure.

Problem 2. Schizophrenia

S: None.
O: History with multiple hospitalizations.
A: The patient has a history of multiple hospitalizations and probably needs prolonged neuroleptic therapy. The current regimen of chlorpromazine has caused side effects including sedation, constipation, sunburn, pigmentation, dry mouth, and orthostatic hypotension. High-potency neuroleptic agents (such as haloperidol or fluphenazine) have fewer anticholinergic side effects but cause more extrapyramidal reactions.

Prophylaxis for dystonia is controversial. This

patient does not have a history of any extra-pyramidal reactions. Prophylactic therapy may increase anticholinergic side effects, and B.D. most likely will not be compliant with therapy. Begin depot fluphenazine or haloperidol as this patient needs long-term therapy and compliance is a concern. Fluphenazine decanoate and enanthate are equally efficacious, but the decanoate is usually preferred because of its longer duration of action. Haloperidol and fluphenazine appear to be equally effective. Haloperidol decanoate is much more expensive than fluphenazine decanoate but has the advantage of being given once a month. Although phenothiazines may decrease the seizure threshold, this is not a major concern, especially in this patient who has had only one seizure.

P: Once the patient is stabilized on maintenance therapy, begin depot fluphenazine or haloperidol to improve compliance and provide better control. Follow this conversion schedule:

Fluphenazine decanoate—25 mg/ml
   Daily p.o. fluphenazine or its equivalent, round off to the next 0.5 ml (12.5 mg) given every week or every other week, e.g.,
   20 mg/day p.o.→25 mg qw/qow
   50 mg/day p.o.→62.5 mg qw/qow
Haloperidol decanoate—60 mg/ml
   10–15 times the daily dose of oral haloperidol, but no more than a maximum initial dose of 100 mg (2 ml), given monthly or initial doses of 50–100 mg per month with titration upwards if control is not achieved.
   Taper p.o. dose over 1–3 days after the injections begin.

Monitor behavior, sedation, anticholinergic side effects (dry mouth, constipation, blurred vision), orthostatic hypotension (BP, pulse), EPS (dystonia, akathesia, akinesia, pseudo-parkinsonism, and tardive dyskinesia).

Problem 5. Phenothiazine Side Effects

S: Patient complains of dry mouth, dizziness upon standing, blurred vision, and constipation.

O: Patient has a sunburn and grayish splotches on skin.

A: Chlorpromazine has high cardiovascular and anticholinergic side effects. In addition, the dose has been increased recently, which may explain the increasing side effects and perhaps noncompliance. Abnormal pigmentation is usually associated with long-term administration of high-dose, low-potency phenothiazines.

P: Discontinue chlorpromazine. Change to a high-potency agent as discussed in Problem 2. To relieve orthostatic hypotension the patient should be advised to stop drinking alcohol and to stand up slowly. To treat the sunburn the

patient should use a sunscreen that protects against both UVA and UVB. He should use a combination product containing PABA or one of its esters and a benzophenone such as Eclipse Total sunscreen or some of the PreSun products. For constipation, a stool softener or bulk-forming laxatives may be helpful after a trial of nondrug therapy including increasing fiber in the diet, increased fluid intake and exercise. For the dry mouth, sugarless hard candies and rinsing the mouth with water or saliva substitutes may be helpful.

Problem 3. Seasonal Asthma

S: History.

O: Theophylline level = 3 µg/ml

A: The patient needs therapy (multiple ER visits); however, he is noncompliant with daily theophylline therapy. Consider metaproterenol inhaler although it may be difficult to teach this patient how to use an inhaler. Oral β_2-agonists (terbutaline) have increased side effects without increased efficacy.

P: Continue theophylline even though the patient is noncompliant. Discontinue terbutaline. Begin metaproterenol inhaler 2 puffs q.i.d. and prn. Monitor number of asthma attacks, shortness of breath, wheezing, coughing, sputum, HR, BP, and tremor. Patient education: Encourage compliance and teach correct use of the inhaler.

Problem 4. Seizure

S: History of a single seizure 10 years ago.

O: PHT = 3 µg/ml

A: The patient is noncompliant with phenytoin. His only seizure was 10 years ago. It is questionable whether this patient needs therapy especially since PHT level has been subtherapeutic in the absence of seizure activity.

P: Discontinue phenytoin.

CASE 60

History of Present Illness

Billy, a 6-year-old male, has recently been diagnosed with attention deficit disorder (ADD). Billy's problem was first brought to his family's attention by his first-grade teacher. She was concerned that Billy was falling further and further behind academically. Billy's short attention span, memory difficulties, and impaired coordination caused him to become a scholastic underachiever in spite of normal intelligence test results. Behavior problems grew as Billy's inability to sit still, variable emotions, impulsiveness, and interpersonal problems worsened. Discipline was a constant problem in the classroom.

Past Medical History

A skateboard accident last summer produced a seizure disorder, which has been managed through drug therapy. However, since the initiation of pharmacotherapy to manage the ADD, Billy's serum levels of phenytoin have been increasing, though it remains within the therapeutic range. Recently, the patient has been complaining of dizziness and upset stomach.

Problem List

1. ADD
2. Phenytoin toxicity, mild

Medication History

Phenytoin Infatabs 50 mg p.o. chew 2 tablets t.i.d.

Physical Examination

GEN: Male child complaining of nausea and dizziness. Mild ataxia present. Appears restless and irritable.
VS: BP 111/70 HR 100 T 37.6 RR 22
HEENT: Mild nystagmus on far, lateral gaze; no slurred speech
COR: WNL
CHEST: WNL
ABD: Nausea but no pain on deep palpitation.
EXT: Ataxic gait

Results of Laboratory Tests

Na 140	Hct 42	Alb 3.5
K 4.5	Hgb 14	Alk Phos 100
Cl 101	WBC 6k	ESR 10
HCO_3 26	AST 25	Phenytoin 20 mcg/ml
BUN 16	ALT 20	

Urinalysis: Protein (−), Bili (−), Glu (−), pH 5

Problem 1. Attention Deficit Disorder

S: None.
O: Patient shows increased level of motor activity, short attention span, excessive impulsiveness, memory difficulties, impaired coordination and normal IQ test results.
A: Psychological testing and classroom observation by a psychologist showed poor academic performance and behavior problems. A diagnosis of attention deficit disorder was made. Therapy should focus on the reduction of hyperactivity and restlessness while improving motor skills and coordination.
P: Give methylphenidate p.o. 20 mg b.i.d. (given in AM and at noon). Advise parents to place patient in a remedial classroom to improve academic experience. Urge education and/or counseling of teacher regarding the patient's disorder and the pharmacological treatment. Encourage counseling for both the family and the patient. Monitor level of motor activity attention span, impulsiveness, memory, coordination, and educational achievement.

Problem 2. Phenytoin Toxicity

S: Patient complains of feeling dizzy.
O: Patient has mild ataxia, nausea, and a phenytoin serum level of 20 μg/ml.

A: The serum level is approaching the toxic end of the therapeutic range of phenytoin. Methylphenidate inhibits the hepatic metabolism of phenytoin, thus prolonging the half-life of phenytoin, resulting in acute toxicity.
P: Lower the dose of phenytoin: Initially, omit the dose of phenytoin for 1 day. Then begin maintenance therapy at a reduced dose of 100 mg b.i.d. Monitor phenytoin serum levels once a week for the first month and for seizure activity. Monitor ataxia, nausea, nystagmus and other rare adverse reactions to phenytoin.

CASE 61

CC: Cindy is a 17-year-old female admitted this morning to a private psychiatric hospital. She claims she does not have an eating problem.

History of Present Illness

Cindy is the only child of an upper-middle-class family; her father is a corporate attorney and her mother is a real estate agent. Although both parents are very busy with their careers, they are supportive of Cindy and praise her for her high academic performance and interest in ballet. The parents contemplated divorce a few years ago but decided to "stick it out" together for Cindy's benefit. Their dream is for Cindy to join her father's law practice.

About 2 years ago, Cindy lost 5 lb at the request of her ballet instructor in order to improve her performance. She accomplished this and received praise from her parents and instructor. As Cindy approached her 16th birthday, she complained of "feeling fat." Her weight was 100 lb. To lose weight, she placed herself on a restricted diet accompanied by a heavy exercise routine that included running 6 miles/day and doing about 1000 sit-ups. She explains that she also has other methods for weight reduction.

Cindy has few friends, has never dated, and "can't get along" with her parents. She plays with the food on her plate, moves it around, eats slowly, and hides food throughout the house. She is obsessed with calorie counting, chews about 10 packs of sugarless gum per day, and has developed secret rituals. She continually argues with her parents about eating and how she wants to live her life.

These patterns of not eating and bizarre behaviors continued until her frustrated parents become extremely concerned about Cindy's health and appearance.

Past Medical History

None.

Problem List

1. Low body weight
2. Malnutrition/dehydration
3. Menstrual irregularity

4. Hypokalemic nephropathy
5. Parent/child conflicts
6. Medication misuses

Medication History

Ex-Lax p.o. 10 per day to prevent food absorption. Hydrochlorothiazide 25 mg p.o. 2–3 tablets prn weight loss (father's prescription). Syrup of ipecac p.o. 15 ml prn to prevent food absorption.

Review of Systems

Intolerance to cold, dizziness upon standing, frequent headaches, constipation, and straining at stool. Last menstrual period 6 months ago.

Physical Examination

GEN: Cindy is an emaciated female with joints and tendons visible, especially the elbows and hip bones. She has thinning, dry hair and the presence of lanugo (black, fine, downy hair) on the extremities and the face; severe dehydration; extremely dry skin; peripheral edema; rectal bleeding; and a sore throat.

VS: BP 90/60 HR 56 RR 30 T 36 Wt 32 kg Ht 5'5"

Results of Laboratory Tests

K 1.5   Cortisol 15 at 8 PM
BUN 30   Aldosterone 0.025
Ca 7   Increased carotene level

Arterial blood gases: pH 7.6, PCO_2 38, PO_2 85, HCO_3 35, BE +4,
Urinalysis: Sp Gr = 1.010, RBC (+)

Problem 1. Low Body Weight

S: Cindy has an emaciated appearance and hyperactivity; she is dieting, and has a fear of obesity.

O: Patient weighs 32 kg; she refuses to maintain body weight and has a disturbance in body image (denial of emaciation), depressed weight for height, limited fat reserves, and decreased muscle mass.

A: The diagnosis is anorexia nervosa with greater than 15% weight loss. She has no known physical illness to account for weight loss. The problem was precipitated by praise from her parents and ballet instructor at losing weight initially. She is seeking parental approval and love. She is also responding to her parents' pressure for her to excel.

P: Set target weight for weight gain (usually 0.2 kg/day). Provide nutritional rehabilitation. Give cyproheptadine, as appetite stimulant 8 mg p.o. q.i.d. Patient should seek psychotherapy for the disturbance of her body image, depression, and parent-child conflicts and to develop a better self-image, improve self-esteem, overcome her obesity phobia and lessen her obsession with food. Behavior therapy should be initiated to provide positive and negative reinforcement. Positive reinforcement: The patient is allowed privileges or activities (visitors, TV, etc.) if she gains weight. Negative reinforcement: The patient is isolated, given tube feeding, and not allowed privileges if she does not gain weight. Monitor weight gain and the side effects of cyproheptadine including drowsiness and anticholinergic effects.

Problem 2. Malnutrition/Dehydration

S: Patient is dieting, exercising extensively, and misusing a laxative, diuretic, and an emetic.

O: Patient has a 32 kg body weight and abnormal laboratory values.

A: Malnutrition and dehydration are secondary to efforts to keep a low body weight.

P: Rehydrate with appropriate electrolyte solutions. Use the oral route if the patient will cooperate, but intravenous administration may be necessary. Discontinue laxatives and diuretics. Nutritional rehabilitation through a dietician's counseling. Select a suitable dietary regimen. Nutritional education to improve eating habits, food selection, etc. Set up an outpatient eating plan. Patient may possibly require forced feeding (nasogastric tube feeding or i.v) if she does not cooperate. Monitor serum electrolytes.

Problem 3. Menstrual Irregularity

S: Patient has not menstruated in several months.

O: Patient has amenorrhea, elevated aldosterone, and elevated ADH (urine specific gravity <1.020).

A: Cindy has menstrual irregularity secondary to hypothalamic dysfunction and an emotional disorder. The emotional disorder consists of depression and patient's preference for absence of menstrual cycles in order to maintain "little girl" image. The patient fears sexual maturity and is shy and uncomfortable with developing relationships.

P: Begin antidepressant therapy, either amitriptyline or imipramine 50 mg t.i.d. Urge weight gain through improved eating habits. Monitor resolution of the depression and the ability to develop relationships. Monitor return of regular menses.

Problem 4. Hypokalemic Nephropathy

S: None.

O: Patient has hematuria, disturbance in body image, a low potassium level, and metabolic alkalosis.

A: Hypokalemic nephropathy due to severe laxative and diuretic abuse.

P: Patient requires psychotherapy to develop a better self-image and improve self-esteem. Discontinue drugs as above. Provide medication counseling on the proper use of laxatives and the dangers of chronic misuses. Monitor serum electrolytes.

Problem 5. Parent–Child Conflicts

S: Cindy engages in arguments with parents and says she "can't get along."

O: Patient suffers depression and has a lack of identity, and low self-esteem. The child feels guilty over her parent's marital discord.

A: The child views weight loss as means of gaining control and recognition, and is seeking her parent's attention. The conflict problems are not being resolved and there is overprotection.

P: Encourage family, marital, and individual counseling. Monitor resolution of conflicts.

Problem 6. Medication Misuse

S: Patient has constipation, straining with bowel movements, rectal bleeding, and sore throat.

O: Patient has been taking large supplies of Ex-Lax and syrup of ipecac; quantities are missing from father's hydrochlorothiazide prescription. She has abnormal lab values.

A: Patient has been taking inappropriate amounts of listed drugs, usually sporadically, to lose weight and lessen food absorption.

P: Provide medication counseling on the proper use of laxatives and the dangers of emetine toxicity from misuse of syrup of ipecac. Also warn about using another person's medications.

CASE 62

CC: K.C., a 33-year-old male nurse, was admitted to the emergency room (ER). A history taken from his girlfriend, who brought him into the ER reveals he was "speedballing" last night. She also says he "mainlines smack" regularly and "does an eight-ball of snow" when he can afford it.

Problem List

1. Opioid overdose
2. Cocaine overdose
3. Heroin dependence, continuous
4. Cocaine abuse, episodic
5. Thrombophlebitis
6. Rehabilitation

Medication History

"Smack" = heroin i.v. four "bags" per day (bag = 400 mg bulk, 2–15% purity).

"Snow" = cocaine i.v. "eight-ball" prn (eight-ball = ⅛ oz (3.5 g))

"Speedballing" = i.v. combination of cocaine and heroin in the same syringe.

Physical Examination

GEN: K.C. is a comatose male; he is cyanotic, with pinpoint pupils, and respiratory depression. He has a history of one episode of seizure activity just prior to admission.

VS: BP 90/70 HR 50 T 36 RR 10 Wt 80 kg

HEENT: Pupils are symmetrical and pinpoint in size

COR: Sinoatrial bradycardia

CHEST: Depressed respiration

ABD: WNL

GU: WNL

RECTAL: WNL

EXT: Cold, clammy skin, flaccid skeletal muscles, needle puncture marks on both arms.

Results of Laboratory Tests

Urinalysis: Morphine (+), G-MM (+), quinine (+), cocaine (+), ecgonine (+)

Problem 1. Heroin Overdose

S: None. (The patient is comatose.)

O: Coma, pinpoint pupils, respiratory depression, cyanosis, low blood pressure, bradycardia. The urine analysis is positive for morphine, G-MM, quinine, cocaine, and ecgonine.

A: K.C. is suffering from an overdose of heroin as evidenced by the objective signs; urine analysis reveals the metabolites of heroin (morphine and G-MM) plus a common adulterant, quinine, and he has a history of "speedballing". He may also suffer complications (tonic-clonic convulsions) caused by cocaine administration. However, the heroin is the most life threatening at this moment.

P: Immediately administer naloxone i.v. 0.4–2 mg, M.R. × 3 at 2–3 minute intervals to reverse the opioid toxicity. Give cardiopulmonary resuscitation prn. Monitor vital signs, seizures, and signs and symptoms of narcotic withdrawal.

Thirty minutes later K.C. is agitated, fearful and has the following vital signs: BP 115/95, HR 180, T 38.5 °C, RR 24.

Problem 2. Cocaine Overdose

S: History of "speedballing".

O: Patient has increasing anxiety, fever (38.5°), ventricular tachycardia, and hypertension (115/95). His urine test is positive for cocaine and ecgonine; he shows needle puncture marks on both arms.

A: Cocaine toxicity has emerged following the management of the heroin overdose and is manifested by overactivity of the sympathetic nervous system. K.C. is at risk of cocaine-induced convulsions.

P: Immediately administer propranolol i.v. 0.1–1.5 mg/kg; administer in increments of 0.5–0.75 mg every 1–2 minutes to control the cardiovascular abnormalities. Give diazepam i.v. 10 mg × 4 at 5-minute intervals prn cocaine-induced convulsions. Keep the patient in quiet, darkened surroundings to reduce stimuli and enhance recovery. Monitor ECG, cardiac output, seizures, and vital signs.

The next day K.C. is seen on the detoxification unit with complaints of anxiety, nausea, vomiting, diarrhea, body aches, anorexia, weakness, and insomnia. The nurses say that he is very irritable.

VS: BP 150/90 HR 130 T 39.6° RR 28
HEENT: Widely dilated pupils, dry mucous membranes
COR: Sinus tachycardia
CHEST: Clear
ABD: Hyperactive bowel sounds
EXT: Sweating, piloerection, involuntary twitching, hand tremors

Problem 3. Heroin Withdrawal

S: He complains of anxiety, nausea, vomiting, diarrhea, body aches, anorexia, weakness, and insomnia.

O: Patient has mydriasis, elevated blood pressure, piloerection, irritability, involuntary twitching, dry mucous membranes, hyperthermia, tachycardia, hyperactive bowel sounds, positive urine sample for opioid use (heroin metabolites).

A: K.C. is suffering from the classic narcotic withdrawal syndrome due to physical dependence from the daily administration of heroin. It has been 12 hours since his last dose of heroin which is consistent to the beginning of a mild abstinence syndrome. While narcotic withdrawal is not life threatening, it is uncomfortable so K.C. should be treated.

P: Begin methadone detoxification: This detoxification unit substitutes 1 mg of methadone p.o. for every 2 mg of heroin. Then the patient is tapered at a reduction of 5 mg of methadone per day. Symptomatic treatment: hydroxyzine 50–100 mg q4h i.m. or p.o. prn anxiety, tremor or restlessness; diazepam 5–10 mg 4–6 h p.o. prn acute nervousness; aspirin 650 mg q4h p.o. prn body aches and headache. Antacid of choice p.o. prn nausea or gastritis; diphenhydramine 50 mg p.o. prn insomnia. Patient should receive psychotherapy (individual counseling, group therapy, or Narcotics Anonymous) and drug counseling. Monitor signs and symptoms of narcotic withdrawal and of narcotic overdose. Monitor progress in resolving problems that lead to drug abuse.

Later this week, K.C. is seen in the detoxification unit complaining of craving cocaine, weakness, anorexia, and nervousness. He has no interest in any of the activities of the unit and does not want to see or talk to his family or girlfriend. He feels depressed, miserable, and wants to be discharged so he can kill himself. The staff complains that he is very difficult to deal with. He has lost 4 kg.

Problem 4. Episodic Cocaine Abuse

S: Patient complains of "craving cocaine"; he has anorexia, nervousness, weakness, and depression.

O: Dysphoria, irritability, depression, anhedonia, weight loss, sweating. On admission his urine was positive for cocaine and cocaine metabolite (ecgonine).

A: K.C. has used i.v. cocaine by history and had a positive urine screen. There is no physical withdrawal from cocaine and detoxification from cocaine is not necessary. However management of the drug-induced depression may be necessary, since suicidal ideations are present. The depression is due to depletion of neurotransmitters by chronic cocaine use, especially norepinephrine. Therefore a norepinephrine-specific antidepressant such as desipramine is more appropriate. Amantidine is an alternative.

P: Patient should receive psychotherapy (individual counseling, group therapy, or Cocaine Anonymous) and drug counseling. Begin desipramine 50 mg qhs and titrate up to 200 mg/day. Continue for 12 months. Dispense only a 1-week supply. Monitor for resolution of the depression and a decrease in the craving of cocaine. Monitor for side effects of desipramine.

The needle puncture marks have developed into abscesses and his arm is swollen, red, hot and very painful. His WBC is 18.5 with a shift to the left. Temp 38.9°.

Problem 5. Thrombophlebitis

S: Patient complains of pain.

O: Patient has abscesses, cellulitis, swelling on affected limb, high WBC with shift to the left, and fever.

A: Scarring from irritating additives in the heroin such as quinine producing a foreign body reaction and infection are causing these signs and symptoms. The patient probably uses nonsterile injection technique, reuses needles and syringes, and shares needles. K.C. has a soft tissue infection due to repeated injection of adulterated heroin i.v., by contaminated methods. The most likely organisms are Gram positive skin flora including Streptococcus and Staphylococcus.

P: Treat the thrombophlebitis by incision and drainage of abscesses and debridement of necrotic tissue. Begin Antibiotic therapy for the infection: nafcillin i.m. 500 mg q6h or cefazolin 1 g i.v. q8h. Give a non-narcotic analgesic for pain. Monitor WBC, fever, and clearing of the signs and symptoms of infection.

Following methadone detoxification and discharge from the hospital, the patient desires to return to his employment as a registered nurse.

Problem 6. Rehabilitation

S: Patient says he "would like to get [his] nursing license back."

O: Negative urine screen.

A: K.C. would like to return to work, but the state board of nursing will not issue a license to him if he is undergoing methadone maintenance therapy.

P: Give naltrexone p.o. 50 mg q.d. to maintain opioid abstinence, for 12 months. Screen urine twice a week to detect or deter drug use. Counsel for rehabilitation and abstinence/relapse monitoring. Urge patient to join Narcotics Anonymous; membership in a local chapter is required, as well as active involvement and attendance at meetings.

CASE 63

CC: J.D. is a 32-year-old woman who is well known to the ER for drug-seeking behavior. She complains of "severe" abdominal pain and requests parenteral meperidine.

Past Medical History

J.D. has a 16-year-history of Crohn's disease with numerous exacerbations and remissions. Her chief complaint has always been "severe" abdominal pain with very little diarrhea. Her Crohn's disease has been treated with prednisone 40 mg q.d. for about 3 years. Attempts to taper the prednisone have been unsuccessful because of complaints of pain. Colonoscopy and x-ray examinations have shown ileitis but no colonic involvement. J.D.'s diabetes has been fairly easy to control with no history of ketoacidosis. J.D. only occasionally monitors her urine glucose and refuses home blood glucose monitoring.

Problem List

1. Crohn's disease as above × 16 years
2. Insulin-dependent diabetes mellitus × 2.5 years
3. Graves' disease × 2 years
4. Acne
5. Meperidine withdrawal
6. Hypokalemia, dehydration
7. Nausea and vomiting
8. BP 150/95
9. Cushingoid adverse effects

Medication History

Prednisone 40 mg p.o. qd × 3 years
Hydrocortisone enema 100 mg p.r. b.i.d. × 3 years
Sulfasalazine 1 gm p.o. q.i.d. × 3 years
Insulin NPH/regular 15 U/5 U q AM and 5 U/5 U q PM
Propylthiouracil 50 mg b.i.d. × 2 years
Ovral 1 q.d. × 21 days per month

Meperidine 75–100 mg i.m. q3h × 6–8 months, last dose 18 hours ago
Sulfisoxazole 1 g q.i.d. × 3 days for urinary tract infection
Phenazopyridine 100 mg t.i.d. × 3 days for urinary tract infection

Allergies

None known.

Physical Examination

GEN: J.D. is a cushingoid-appearing female complaining of abdominal pain, muscle aches, nausea, vomiting, diarrhea, and who appears very restless and nervous although yawning.

VS: BP 150/95 HR 110 T 37.2 RR 20 Wt 78 kg

HEENT: Sialorrhea, rhinorrhea, lacrimation, normal thyroid, mild proptosis, moderate acne on forehead and cheeks with comedones but no pustules or cysts

COR: Sinus tachycardia

CHEST: WNL

ABD: Voluntary guarding, but no pain on deep palpitation

GU: Deferred

RECT: Guaiac-negative

EXT: Muscle twitchings in lower extremities, several ecchymoses

NEURO: WNL

Results of Laboratory Tests

Na 147	Cr 0.8	ESR 5	FBS 320
K 3.3	Hct 39.9	AST 25	Hgb_{A1c} 13.5
Cl 97	Hgb 13.4	ALT 20	OSM 314
HCO_3 26	WBC 12k	Alk Phos 54	Pregnancy test (−)
BUN 16	Plts 187k	Alb 4.0	

Urinalysis (by dipstick): protein (−), bili (−), glucose (−), pH 5.1
Barium enema: No evidence of active Crohn's disease

Problem 5. Meperidine Withdrawal

S: Patient complains of "severe" abdominal pain, nausea, vomiting, diarrhea and muscle aches.

O: BP 150/95, HR 110, sialorrhea, lacrimation, nervous, restless, yawning, muscle twitching. Last meperidine injection was 18 hours ago. Dose has been 75–100 mg q3h × 6–8 months.

A: Meperidine has a short $t_{1/2}$ with peak withdrawal symptoms occurring in 12 hours. The patient is symptomatic and requires treatment although hers is not a life threatening situation.

P: Give methadone 15 mg p.o. stat, repeat q 2–6 h × 24 hours until stable. Give this dose for 2 days. If dose is greater than 40 mg/day give as a split dose twice a day. Decrease the dose by 20%/day until the patient is off methadone (in 7–10 days). Monitor RR, HR, BP, sialorrhea, lacrimation, nausea, vomiting, diarrhea, abdominal pain, restlessness, nervousness, muscle aches, feelings of flu-like illness, and pupil size. Educate the patient regarding drug abuse and set up counseling.

Problem 2. Insulin-Dependent Diabetes Mellitus

S: Patient complains of nausea and vomiting.

O: FBS 320, Hgb_{A1c} 13.5

A: Her IDDM may be aggravated by her urinary tract infection, prednisone, and oral contraceptive therapy. The acute situation may be aggravated by the stress of meperidine withdrawal. The negative urine glucose may be due to interference by phenazopyridine. J.D. is not well controlled on the current regimen. A better regimen for IDDM should be established when she is stable.

P: Initiate sliding scale insulin until through the meperidine withdrawal and she is stable. Give 5–10 U regular insulin s.c. stat then 1–2 U for every 40 mg that blood glucose is greater than 120 mg. Test blood glucose q3h. If the patient is not eating, do not give insulin if glucose is less than 250 mg. Discontinue phenazopyridine.

Problem 6. Hypokalemia, dehydration

S: Patient complains of nausea, vomiting, and diarrhea.

O: Plasma osmolality 314, fluid deficit 4.3 liters, K 3.3, Na 147, BUN 16

A: Acute dehydration from nausea, vomiting, and diarrhea and glucose diuresis; decreased K aggravated by prednisone.

P: Give NS 1000 ml i.v. over 2 hours, then D5 0.45 NaCl with 40–60 mEq KCl at 175 ml/hour × 24 hours, then reassess. Monitor urine output, serum lytes, BP, and blood glucose.

Problem 1. Crohn's Disease

S: Patient complains of severe abdominal pain, and diarrhea.

O: Patient is guaiac-negative. B.E. shows no evidence of Crohn's disease. There is no abdominal pain on deep palpitation.

A: No evidence of active disease. Steroids are ineffective in maintaining a remission in Crohn's disease. No colonic involvement on a previous examination, therefore, sulfasalazine is ineffective. Sulfasalazine is also ineffective in maintenance of remission in Crohn's disease. Since J.D. has no proctitis, she should not be using steroid enemas. Assume enemas are being 90% absorbed = 50 mg prednisone/day.

P: Discontinue sulfasalazine and hydrocortisone enema. Give prednisone 60 mg qd then taper by 5 mg/week until dose is 7.5–10 mg/day then decrease dose by 0.5–1.0 mg/week or change to hydrocortisone 30 mg/day and decrease dose by 5 mg/week until AM cortisol is > 10. Monitor for flare of Crohn's by pain, diarrhea, guaiac, fever, weight loss, nutrition, albumin, and ESR. Monitor for signs of adrenal insufficiency including electrolytes, BP, HR, blood glucose,

anorexia, nausea, vomiting, flu-like illness with fatigue, and arthralgia. Educate patient regarding signs and symptoms of adrenal insufficiency, reasons for taper, and need for stress coverage up to 1 year after patient is off steroids. Have patient obtain a MediAlert bracelet.

Problem 7. Nausea and Vomiting

S: Patient complaint.

O: Na 147, K 3.3, Cl 97, HCO_3 26

A: Probably due to narcotic withdrawal, needs treatment since dehydrated; may be aggravated by high glucose.

P: Prochlorperazine 10 mg i.m. q6h prn. Monitor nausea and vomiting and extrapyramidal reactions.

Problem 3. Graves Disease

S: Patient has no symptoms of hyperthyroidism

O: Normal thyroid gland, normal TFTs after correcting for binding, normal TGAb, mild proptosis

A: Graves disease has been controlled and adequately treated for 2 years and is probably in remission; eye signs may not reverse. Many of current complaints can be explained by narcotic withdrawal.

P: Wait until after the narcotic withdrawal has resolved to reassess, then may discontinue propylthiouracil (PTU). Monitor T_4; RT_3U; gland size; eye examination; signs and symptoms of hyperthyroidism including HR, palpitations, heat intolerance, tremor, weight loss, muscle weakness, and skin rash; and monitor for signs and symptoms of agranulocytosis secondary to PTU. Patient Education: Review signs and symptoms of hyperthyroidism as reasons to seek medical attention.

Problem 8. BP 150/95

S: No symptoms.

O: BP 150/95

A: May be due to narcotic withdrawal.

P: Take BP three times when stable as an outpatient.

Problem 9. Cushingoid Adverse Effects

S: None

O: Appearance, elevated glucose, elevated WBC, decreased K, ecchymoses, acne

A: Patient needs to taper steroids since they are not effective.

P: Taper as in Problem 1.

Problem 4. Acne

S: None.

O: Moderate acne on forehead and cheeks without pustules or cysts

A: Acne may be aggravated by steroids and birth control pills; it is a cosmetic problem that requires treatment but is not severe. Isotretionin is not indicated.

P: Apply benzoyl peroxide 5% cream to face 30 minutes after washing at bedtime after checking for sensitivity with test dose. Can increase to b.i.d. application and can increase strength to 10% titrating to mild dryness, mild peeling and mild erythema and a decrease in comedones. Patient education: Advise patient that acne will get worse before it gets better and will take approximately 3 months to clear.

CASE 64

CC: D.G. is a 56-year-old man who comes to clinic today with continued complaints of shortness of breath and increased sputum production. He was seen in clinic last week with the same complaints. Today he also complains of a rash that began yesterday. He has been waking up early in the morning and has not been able to go back to sleep, has a decreased appetite, and has had general lack of interest in everything, including his job and his family for the last 6 weeks. Although he has several medical problems, he has been doing well prior to this episode.

Past Medical History

D.G. has chronic bronchitis secondary to smoking, with increasing shortness of breath (SOB) over the last 2 years. Previous pulmonary function tests (PFTs) have shown a prebronchodilator $FEV_1 = 1500$ ml and postbronchodilator $FEV_1 = 2300$ ml. He has had tonic-clonic seizures after a motor vehicle accident in 1985, with one to two seizures every week. D.G. also has atrial fibrillation.

Problem List

1. Chronic bronchitis in an acute exacerbation
2. Seizure disorder secondary to MVA
3. Alcohol abuse
4. Depression
5. Benign prostatic hypertrophy
6. Atrial fibrillation
7. Drug allergy

Medication History

Theodur 600 mg b.i.d. for 2 years
Terbutaline inhaler 4 puffs q.i.d. and prn for 2 years
Cotrimoxazole 160/800 1 tablet p.o. b.i.d. for bronchitis × 10 days
Phenytoin 400 mg hs since 1985
Digoxin 0.25 mg qd
Acetaminophen 1 g q.i.d. for hangovers

Allergies

None known.

Social History

D.G. has a stable and happy marriage; he has two sons in college, both doing well. Ethanol use is heavy, 1–2 six packs of beer every night with frequent blackouts that are interfering with his job. D.G. continues to smoke 1 pack per day; he has 50 pack-year history. D.G. tried marijuana once with his son but did not like it.

Physical Examination

GEN: Obese, middle aged man, in severe distress
VS: BP 120/80 HR 85 reg T 37.6 RR 32 Wt 90 Kg Ht 5'10"
HEENT: Normal
COR: Normal S1 and S2; no S3, S4 or murmurs
CHEST: Numerous rales, rhonchi, and wheezes
ABD: Obese, no organomegaly
GU: WNL
RECT: Benign prostatic hypertrophy, guaiac-negative
EXT: NL DTR's, mild weakness on left side from CVA, maculopapular rash on truck and thighs
NEURO: Oriented × 3, WNL

Results of Laboratory Tests

Na 140	Hct 55	Alb 3	PT 13.9
K 3.5	Hgb 17.5	T Bili 1.6	PTT 38.7
Cl 101	WBC 8.1	Glu 95	Uric acid 7.4
HCO_3 28	Plts 305k	Ca 8.8	Theophylline 12
BUN 37	AST 105	PO_4 2.6	Phenytoin 12
Cr 1.2	ALT 35	Mg 1.8	Digoxin 1.3

WBC differential: Neutrophils 4.8, bands 0, lymphs 3.0, monos 1.0, eos 1.2
ABGs: pH 7.37, PO_2 55, PCO_2 49
Urinalysis: WNL
Chest x-ray: Clear, no signs of pneumonia

Problem 1. Chronic Bronchitis Exacerbation

S: D.G. complains of SOB and increased sputum production.

O: D.G. has a decreased FEV_1, rales, rhonchi, wheezes, an increased respiratory rate, pulse, Hct and Hgb, and arterial blood gases that show an increased PCO_2 and a decreased oxygen. D.G. has a 50 pack-year smoking history.

A: D.G. has a symptomatic exacerbation of his chronic bronchitis that requires treatment. Smoking is the most likely etiology of the chronic bronchitis, while a viral upper respiratory tract infection is probably the cause of the acute exacerbation since D.G. shows no signs of systemic bacterial infection. He has a normal WBC, he is afebrile, and his chest x-ray is clear. The use of antibiotics in this situation is controversial, although recent evidence suggests a benefit. Prebronchodilator and postbronchodilator FEV_1 show reversible airway obstruction. The theophylline level is within the therapeutic range and there is no need to increase the dose.

P: Give methylprednisolone 40–125 mg i.v. stat and continue q6h for 72 hours. Begin nebulized metaproterenol 0.3 ml in 2.5 ml NS q1h until relief or aerosolized metaproterenol 4 puffs stat and 1 puff q 5 minutes until relief or appearance of side effects. Continue oral theophylline. Begin oxygen 2 liters/minute via nasal prongs. Begin ampicillin 500 mg p.o. q.i.d. Monitor SOB, sputum production, FEV_1, AGBs, chest auscultation, theophylline level, nausea, vomiting, pulse, blood glucose, serum potassium, blood pressure, palpitations, tremor, and stool guaiac. Assess D.G.'s ability to use his inhaler correctly and correct any problems. Provide a spacer if necessary. Explain the likely side effects of theophylline, steroids, and ampicillin. D.G. should discontinue smoking; refer him to a smoking cessation clinic.

Problem 2. Seizure Disorder Secondary to Motor Vehicle Accident

S: D.G. has one to two seizures per week.

O: His phenytoin level is reported as 12 μg/ml.

A: D.G.'s seizures are not well controlled. However, when corrected for his decreased albumin, his phenytoin level is approximately 15 μg/ml. Phenobarbital should be avoided since D.G. is already depressed and because it can exacerbate respiratory acidosis. Carbamazepine is effective for tonic-clonic seizures and may be tried in D.G. Carbamazepine induces its own metabolism so the dose will have to be titrated. The phenytoin dose may need to be adjusted if D.G. discontinues drinking or when the carbamazepine is initiated.

P: Continue phenytoin 400 mg qhs. Begin carbamazepine 200 mg b.i.d. and increase the dose over the next two weeks to 900 to 1200 mg/day to achieve a therapeutic level of 8 μg/ml (range 4–12 μg/ml). Monitor seizure frequency, phenytoin and carbamazepine levels, nystagmus, ataxia, slurred speech, liver function tests, rash, serum sodium, symptoms of SIADH, CBC, nausea, and visual disturbances. D.G. should report any fever, chills, stomatitis, or other signs of agranulocytosis. He should practice good oral hygiene.

Problem 3. Alcohol Abuse

S: D.G. admits to frequent blackouts, which are interfering with his job.

O: D.G. drinks one to two 6-packs of beer per day. LFTs reflect alcoholic liver disease: Alb 3.0, AST 105, ALT 35, AST/ALT >2, T. bili 1.6.

A: D.G. has a serious drinking problem that is endangering his job and may endanger his marriage and his relationship with his family. In addition, his alcohol consumption is causing liver disease that could progress to cirrhosis. D.G. is at risk for alcohol withdrawal while he is hospitalized, and he has a history of a seizure disorder. Alcohol withdrawal is likely to occur within 24–72 hours of discontinuing drinking but may occur up to 7 days after

alcohol is discontinued. Acetaminophen in normal doses may be hepatotoxic in an alcoholic patient. Wernicke's encephalopathy may occur in this patient if he receives intravenous glucose. Diazepam may worsen D.G.'s depression. Avoid intramuscular injections because of the elevated PT.

P: Administer thiamine 100 mg i.v. with an ampule of vitamin B complex qd for 3 days. Monitor for anaphylaxis and ophthalmoplegia, ataxia, and mental status changes. Administer diazepam 10 mg p.o. now, then 5 mg q.i.d. × 1 day, then 5 mg b.i.d. × 2 days, then discontinue. Monitor vital signs, tremors, agitation, and hallucinations. The goal is to have a calm but arousable patient. Discontinue the acetaminophen. Monitor LFTs. Administer 1 g $MgSO_4$ i.v. over 4 hours. Monitor Mg and PO_4. Administer phytonadione 10 mg s.c. × 3 days. Monitor PT and any signs of bleeding. Arrange counseling and attendance at Alcoholics Anonymous meetings.

Problem 4. Depression

S: D.G. complains of early morning waking and inability to go back to sleep, a decreased appetite, and a general lack of interest in everything including his job and family for 6 weeks.

O: Alcohol consumption.

A: D.G. has had his current complaints for more than a month. While he does not appear to be suicidal at this point, he needs treatment. An antidepressant with high anticholinergic activity will worsen any symptoms of BPH (e.g., urinary retention). A sedating antidepressant may help him sleep, although he does not complain of difficulty falling asleep. The cardiovascular side effect potential of the antidepressant should be low in this patient due to atrial fibrillation. Desipramine has relatively low anticholinergic and cardiovascular side effects but it is not very sedating. Trazodone has a low rate of anticholinergic and cardiovascular side effects, is highly sedating, and is safer than desipramine in an overdose situation.

P: Begin trazodone 100 mg hs and increase the dose by 50–100 mg every 3–4 nights up to a maximum dose of 400–600 mg/day. Continue therapy for 6 months. Monitor changes in appetite, sleep pattern, interest in life, mood, quality of life, and suicidal thoughts. Physiologic signs and symptoms should improve in 1 week, while mood will take 2–4 weeks to respond. Monitor for orthostatic BP, cardiac arrhythmias, anticholinergic effects, and other side effects. Patient education: advise patient to take trazodone with a light snack. Report prolonged or inappropriate penile erection or palpitations or other signs of cardiac arrythmias. This drug may cause drowsiness, so caution is advised when driving or operating machinery. Also, this drug may enhance the response to alcohol. The dry mouth may be relieved by sugarless candy or gum and the constipation may be prevented by increasing the fiber content in the diet. This drug may cause dizziness. It will take several weeks for this drug to work.

Problem 7. Drug Allergy

S: D.G. complains of a rash that began yesterday, but does not complain of itching.

O: D.G. has maculopapular rash on trunk and thighs, his eos is 1.2.

A: D.G. has developed a rash due to the cotrimoxazole started 9 days ago. The usual drug rash is maculopapular and commonly occurs after 7–10 days of therapy. Avoid antihistamines unless D.G. is itching, because they are sedating and have anticholinergic effects.

P: Discontinue cotrimoxazole. Monitor for resolution of the rash. Aveeno baths for a soothing effect may be needed. Label D.G. allergic to cotrimoxazole.

Problem 5. Benign Prostatic Hypertrophy

S: None

O: Noted on physical examination.

A: Anticholinergic drugs should be avoided since they are likely to cause symptoms.

P: Monitor for symptoms.

Problem 6. Atrial Fibrillation

S: None.

O: Pulse = 85 and regular, digoxin level = 1.3

A: The atrial fibrillation appears symptomatically controlled. Avoid drugs that will elevate the digoxin level. D.G. is not a candidate for anticoagulation at this time.

P: Obtain an ECG. Monitor ECG, pulse, signs and symptoms of hemodynamic decompensation, and for digoxin toxicity.

CASE 65

CC: B.D. is a 45 year old woman brought to the ER by her husband, who stated that she has been very depressed for 3 months. The patient states that she is "stupid" and "worthless". She admits that she is smoking more and is having difficulty staying asleep. She has no appetite and has lost 15 lb over the last few weeks. She also states that she had lost interest in things she used to enjoy. She frequently thinks of killing herself and states that everybody would be happy if she died.

Past Medical History

B.D. has insomnia; hypertension, controlled with HCTZ and diet; and chronic constipation secondary to irritable bowel disease. She had a seizure at age 8.

Problem List

1. Major depression
2. Insomnia
3. Hypertension
4. Irritable bowel syndrome with chronic constipation
5. Seizure at age 8
6. Alcohol abuse

Social History

B.D. drinks 1 pint of scotch every day before bed. She smokes cigarettes: ½ pack per day for 20 years. B.D. has been married for 15 years and has no children. She is employed as a senior computer programmer. Her grandmother died of suicide and her mother has a manic-depressive disorder.

Medication History

Flurazepam 30 mg hs prn
HCTZ 25 mg q.d.
Docusate 250 mg q AM

Physical Examination

VS: BP 130/98 HR 70 T 37.6 Wt 60 kg
GEN: B.D. is a well-nourished female; she is oriented × 3.

Results of Laboratory Tests

Na 137	Cr 1
K 4	Hct 42
Cl 99	Hgb 14
HCO$_3$ 24	WBC 7.3k
BUN 12	Glu 108

B.D. was admitted for observation. She was started on amitriptyline 50 mg t.i.d. A psychiatry consult was obtained and she was discharged 2 days later with

Trimipramine 50 mg tid #100
Methyldopa 500 mg bid #60
HCTZ 50 mg qd #100

One week after discharge, B.D. returns to clinic for follow-up. She complains that the medication has made her mouth dry and caused her to be more constipated. In addition, she has been so sleepy during the day that she can not concentrate.

Problem

S:

O:

A:

P:

Problem

S:

O:

A:

P:

Problem

S:

O:

A:

P:

Problem

S:

O:

A:

P:

Problem

S:

O:

A:

P:

Problem

S:

O:

A:

P:

Questions

1. What symptoms of depression does this patient have?
2. Assess the appropriateness of B.D.'s *discharge medications*: Was the right drug chosen? If so, are the dose, the quantity, and the schedule correct? Support your reason.
3. What changes would you recommend for B.D.'s antidepressant regimen at her *1 week clinic visit*? Be specific. Indicate the drug, starting dose, schedule, and titration of dose. Give your reasons for selecting this drug.
4. Six weeks following discharge, B.D.'s family members bring her to the E.R. They stated that she has been acting strangely for the past few days and is now out of control. She is dressed in a fancy evening gown, wearing heavy make-up and considerable jewelry. She speaks rapidly, mostly about her future trips. She states she is moving very soon because she is going to buy houses in Beverly Hills and Palm Springs, using her lottery money that she will win. Her husband states that during the last few days the patient has been buying excessive amounts of clothes and jewelry, has been very active, sleeps only two to three hours a night, and stays up to design her "houses." The physician found the patient to be extremely talkative, and frequently jumping from one disconnected thought to another. Bipolar affective disorder, manic phase is diagnosed for B.D. List the symptoms of mania demonstrated by B.D.
5. How would you manage B.D.'s acute mania. Be specific as to drug, dose, route, schedule, duration, titration, and/or tapering.
6. List the necessary pre-lithium laboratory tests. Give the rationale for obtaining each test.
7. Discuss the signs and symptoms of lithium intoxication and treatment of patients with lithium toxicity.

CASE 66

CC: R.L., a 79-year-old male, is a retired pharmacist who lives with his daughter's family. Until 4 years ago he enjoyed an active social life, playing cards and golf with friends. At that time he began to experience a slow progressive memory loss for recent events. Now, he frequently forgets food cooking on the stove and is unable to play cards or golf. His physical golfing skills remain intact. Over the past 2 months he has gotten lost twice in his neighborhood. His insomnia has become more difficult to manage and he sometimes appears very restless. He feels "its just part of getting old" and refuses to see a physician. Four days ago, he was seen in the emergency room following a fall resulting in facial bruises, lacerations, muscle spasms in the back, but no broken bones. During the last two days R.L. has been disoriented and awakens during the middle of the night appearing agitated and confused. He demanded breakfast at 2:00 AM and is very hostile and verbally abusive. This morning he could not remember the names of any family members, except his daughter, and accused the children of stealing his money during the night. R.L.'s daughter took him to see a physician stating, "We can no longer cope with Dad's senility."

Problem List

Mental status changes suggestive of Alzheimer's dementia.

Medication History

R.L. was discharged from the emergency room with the following prescriptions:

Diazepam 5 mg tab q.i.d. for muscle spasm
Acetaminophen with codeine 32 mg 1 or 2 tablets q 4–6 hours for severe back pain
Ibuprofen 600 mg q.i.d. with food for 5 days for pain
Triazolam 0.5 mg at bedtime for sleep

R.L. had previously been taking the following:

Diphenhydramine 50 mg (OTC) for sleep
Multivitamin
Lecithin 3 capsules per day

Allergies

None known

Psychiatric Assessment

R.L. is oriented to person but not to time or place. He is alert but falls asleep easily and is very distractable, mumbling about "people stealing flowers", unable to follow simple commands correctly (with motor preservation), giggles inappropriately, picks at sheets, and at examiner's clothes and hair. His speech is normal with normal syntax. The patient is incontinent of urine during the examination. R.L.'s error score on the Short Portable Mental Status Questionnaire (SPMSQ) was 8–10, suggesting severe intellectual impairment. It is recommended that full neuropsychological testing be performed later.

Physical Examination

VS: BP 130/80, 140/84, 136/78 HR 80 T 36.7 RR 20
HEENT: WNL
COR: WNL
CHEST: WNL
ABD: WNL
GU: WNL
RECT: WNL
EXT: WNL
NEURO: Unable to perform

Results of Laboratory Tests

Na 140	Hct 31.2	AST 24	ESR 24
K 3.4	Hgb 12.9	Alk Phos 99	Transferrin 233
Cl 106	WBC 3.8k	T. Bili 0.5	Saturation 20%
HCO$_3$ 27	Plts P	GLU 105	Ferritin 176
BUN 31	MCV 95	Ca 9.7	Serum B12: WNL
Cr 1.3	MCHC 32.1	Mg 2.6	Folate: WNL

TFTs: TT$_4$ 7.6, RT$_3$U 34

Urinalysis: WNL

CT Scan: Negative for subdural hematoma, and normal pressure hydrocephalus Some cortical atrophy.

EEG: Diffuse slowing

Problem

S:

O:

A:

P:

Problem _____

S: _____
_____
_____
_____

O: _____
_____
_____
_____

A: _____
_____
_____
_____
_____
_____

P: _____
_____
_____

Problem _____

S: _____
_____
_____
_____

O: _____
_____
_____

A: _____
_____
_____
_____
_____

P: _____
_____

Questions

1. What early symptoms does R.L. exhibit that are suggestive of a dementia of the Alzheimer's type?
2. What could have caused R.L.'s sudden decline in mental status?
3. Why were so many tests ordered for R.L. when he appears to be physically very healthy?
4. What role could nonprescription products such as lecithin play in patients like R.L.?
5. What drugs might be considered for the treatment of R.L.'s dementia?
6. [A year later, R.L. frequently does not recognize anyone in the household. He has verbal outbursts, he frequently wanders at night, and was once found two miles from the house—so all doors must be locked. Recently he has begun to strike out at individuals when he is stressed.

   What type of drug therapy, if any, is appropriate for R.L.? What special precautions in the selection of an agent, dose and monitoring parameters should be observed?

CASE 67

CC: E.S. is a 64-year-old female brought to the outpatient clinic today by her boyfriend for the first time in 2 months. She complains of shortness of breath. She is also having more difficulty in walking and moving. Activities of daily living such as dressing are now requiring assistance from her boyfriend.

Problem List

1. Rheumatoid arthritis × 10 years
2. Chronic obstructive pulmonary disease secondary to cigarette smoking
3. Seizure disorder secondary to head trauma 5 years ago
4. Paroxysmal atrial tachycardia × 2 months
5. Hypertension × 3 years
6. Depression/anxiety × 6 months
7. History of alcohol abuse

Medication History

Current medications:

Prednisone 20 mg qd × 5 years
Isoetharine inhaler 2 puffs q6h × 2 years
Phenytoin 3×100 mg qhs × 5 years
Methyldopa 500 mg q.i.d. × 3 years
HCTZ 50 mg qd × 3 years
Propranolol 40 mg q.i.d. × 2 months
Haloperidol 1 mg b.i.d. prn for nerves × 2 years
Tylenol #3 two tablets q6h prn headache × 3 years
Metoclopramide 10 mg q.i.d. prn for nausea × 2 years
Milk of magnesia 30 ml qhs prn constipation × 5 years

E.S. is compliant with all her medications because her boyfriend administers the drugs *except* she does not use the inhaler because of her hand tremor. Her boyfriend increased her dose of phenytoin to 4 capsules hs 1 month ago because E.S. had a seizure.

Allergies

None known.

Social History

Tobacco: 100 pack-year smoker; smokes about 2 packs/day.

Ethanol: History of alcohol abuse in the past. E.S. began an alcoholic treatment program 5 weeks ago and has not had alcohol since.

Physical Examination

GEN: Mildly confused female in mild respiratory distress.

VS: BP 110/65 HR 66 T 37 RR 28 Wt 60 kg Ht 5′4″

HEENT: Mask-like facies; sialorrhea; seborrheic appearing skin on the forehead and scalp. (+) nystagmus with lateral gaze. Posterior subcapsular cataracts seen in both eyes.

COR: NSR, without S3, S4

CHEST: Decreased breath sounds; expiratory wheezes heard throughout lungs.

ABD: WNL

GU: WNL

RECT: WNL

EXT: Mild clubbing of fingernails; 3+ cogwheel rigidity; coarse hand tremor; bilateral MCP joint degeneration, with no destruction to the PCP joints. (−) hot and tenderness.

NEURO: Oriented×2; moderately lethargic; decreased DTRs. Unstable gait with moderate difficulty in initiating walking.

Results of Laboratory Tests

Na 140	Hct 39	LDH 120
K 3.9	Hgb 13	Alb 2.4
Cl 98	WBC 7.8k	T Bili 1.2
HCO$_3$ 28	MCV 104	FBG 138
BUN 28	MCHC 38	PT 13.8
Cr 1.5	AST 84	Phenytoin level 19

WBC differential: 80% P, 11% L, 1.2% mono, 5% eos

Urinalysis: Sp Gr 1.003, pH=6, 1% glucose, trace protein

ABGs: PO$_2$ 65, PCO$_2$ 55, pH 7.38

Sputum culture: Negative

PFTs: Prebronchodilator FEV$_1$=800 ml; postbronchodilator FEV$_1$=1500 ml, FEV$_1$/FVC=0.61

Chest x-ray shows bilateral hyperinflated lungs with barrel chest configuration and flattened diaphragms. Osteoporotic thoracic spine. No evidence of pneumonia.

Problem

S: _____

O: _____

A: _____

P: _____

Problem

S:

O:

A:

P:

Problem

S:

O:

A:

P:

Problem

S:

O:

A:

P:

Problem

S:

O:

A:

P:

Problem

S:

O:

A:

P:

Problem

S:

O:

A:

P:

Problem

S:

O:

A:

P:

Questions

1. Recommend a drug therapy for E.S.'s Parkinson's disease. Choose drug(s), dose(s), schedule, duration, and titration if necessary. Give reasons why this is the drug, or drugs, of choice for E.S.

2. Assess E.S.'s current treatment for her chronic obstructive pulmonary disease. Make any changes in her therapy that you feel would be appropriate. Be specific, give drug, dose, route, schedule, and duration. Give reasons why you are making each change in therapy.

3. E.S. is showing signs and symptoms of phenytoin toxicity. Identify four signs and symptoms seen in E.S. on physical examination. Why does E.S. have phenytoin toxicity? Make appropriate changes in her phenytoin therapy.

4. E.S. has evidence of adverse reactions to prednisone and her rheumatoid arthritis is inactive at this time. For these reasons, her prednisone will be discontinued and other appropriate therapy instituted.

a. Identify the signs and symptoms of steroid toxicity in E.S.

b. Design a tapering regimen for ES that will get her totally off systemic steroids. List monitoring parameters that you would follow during the taper.

c. Institute appropriate therapy for her rheumatoid arthritis.

CASE 68

CC: T.J. is a 45-year-old male admitted to the ER with extreme agitation, disorientation and status post a generalized, tonic-clonic seizure.

Past Medical History

T.J. is well known to the general medicine clinic (GMC). He has a long history of alcohol abuse characterized by frequent binges, with many alcohol-related problems. T.J. has been a heavy drinker since his late teens and has failed many attempts to quit drinking through Alcoholics Anonymous (AA) and other related programs. In addition, he has a significant history of noncompliance with clinic appointments and his medications. T.J. was last seen at the GMC 2 weeks prior to admission with complaints of "heartburn" and was prescribed cimetidine. He also complained of increasing pain in his left shoulder. A synovial fluid sample proved negative for uric acid crystals, and he was given a prescription for acetaminophen to take as often as needed. T.J. also suffers from moderately controlled exertional angina, from a generalized seizure disorder secondary to head trauma after one of his numerous "blackout" episodes, and from chronic bronchitis secondary to cigarette smoking. Although T.J. has hyperuricemia, he has never had an attack of gout.

Past Surgical History

Status post pancreatitis

Problem List

1. Delirium tremens
2. Posttraumatic epilepsy
3. Gastroesophageal reflux
4. Hyperuricemia
5. Angina
6. Chronic bronchitis
7. Alcohol abuse
8. Tinea onychomycosis

Medication History

Phenytoin 400 mg p.o. q.d.
Cimetidine 300 mg p.o. q.i.d.; also uses Maalox 2 tblsp prn
Allopurinol 300 mg p.o. q.d.
NTG 0.4 mg s.l. prn
Theodur 200 mg t.i.d.
Terbutaline 5 mg p.o. q.i.d.
Tetracycline 500 mg p.o. q6h prn sputum changes

Allergies

None known.

Social History

T.J. is currently unemployed; he is a former factory worker. He has a history of chronic alcoholism, drinks between 1–2 pints of whiskey/day, along with a few beers. He smokes tobacco, 2 ppd for 30 years. He occasionally uses marijuana.

Physical Examination

GEN: Tremulous, combative male, nauseated and sweating profusely

VS: BP 150/90 lying, 140/82 sitting T 40 RR 20 Wt 85 kg Ht 5'9"

HEENT: PERRLA, icteric sclera, bite wound on tongue

COR: NL S1, S2; no S3, S4; no M

CHEST: Coarse rhonchi throughout, few rales, (−) wheezes

ABD: (+) fluid wave, mild RUQ pain with guarding, liver palpable to 6 cm below costal margin

GU: WNL

RECT: Guaiac negative

EXT: Skin jaundiced, spider angiomata on chest, toenails on right foot thickened, white and brittle consistent with tinea unguium

NEURO: Oriented × 1, CN II-XII grossly intact; exam difficult to perform as the patient is uncooperative; decreased deep tendon reflexes

EXT: Without edema, some muscle wasting, very dry skin

Results of Laboratory Tests

Tests were done by autoanalyzer:

Na 134	Hct 36	AST 500	D Bili 2.1	PTT P
K 3.2	Hgb 12.2	ALT 350	Glu 65	Uric Acid 10
Cl 102	WBC 10.5k	Alk Phos 180	Ca 7.8	
HCO₃ 26	Plts 160k	To Prot 5.5	PO₄ 2.0	
BUN 22	MCV 110	Alb 2.6	Mg 1.2	
Cr 1.2	MCHC P	T Bili 3.1	PT 19.8	

WBC differential: 45%P, 45%L, 3%M, 4%B, 3%E
ABGs: PO_2 68, PCO_2 25, pH 7.42
Urinalysis: Bili (+), glu (−), protein (−), tox screen pending
ECG: Atrial fibrillation with ventricular rate of 120
Chest x-Ray: Clear, no evidence of pneumonia
Pulmonary function test: Prebronchodilator, FEV_1/FVC 1200/2000; postbronchodilator, 1600/2400.

Problem

S: _____

O: _____

A: _____

P: _____

Problem

S: _____

O: _____

A: _____

P: _____

Problem

S: _____

O: _____

A: _____

P: _____

Problem

S: _____

O: _____

A: _____

P: _____

Problem

S:

O:

A:

P:

Problem

S:

O:

A:

P:

Problem

S:

O:

A:

P:

Problem

S:

O:

A:

P:

Problem

S:_____

_____

_____

_____

O:_____

_____

_____

_____

A:_____

_____

_____

_____

P:_____

_____

_____

Questions

1. In the ER, T.J. experienced another generalized seizure. Suggest an i.v. loading dose and suitable p.o. maintenance dose to keep T.J.'s phenytoin at an average level of 12 mg/liter.

2. T.J. is diagnosed as having the DTs (delirium tremens). How would you proceed in managing this condition? State drugs, doses, routes, frequency, maximum doses, criteria for adjusting doses, and rationale for use. As part of your rationale for using, state comparable drugs that you would avoid and why.

3. Identify six alcohol-related problems seen in T.J. For each problem describe the indicated drug treatment (including drug, dose, route, frequency, duration, and how you would adjust therapy) and other drugs to be avoided in this patient because of his alcohol-related problems. If no treatment is indicated, discuss why.

4. After several days, T.J.'s intern thinks it would be a good idea to begin disulfuram therapy, once T.J. has been stabilized. Do you agree or disagree with this? State your reason(s).

5. What, if any, phenytoin drug interactions would you discuss with the medical team? Explain the mechanism of the interaction and discuss the therapeutic implications or alterations required.

6. T.J. complains of difficulty walking due to his toenails being infected. The physician decides to treat T.J.'s onychomycosis with ketoconazole 400 mg p.o. q.d. Do you agree with this? If so, state your reasoning. If not, suggest an alternative agent (include dose, route, frequency, and duration of therapy). Also include monitoring parameters for the therapy suggested.

7. How would you recommend that T.J.'s hyperuricemia be treated? Be specific. Also state any patient education for the therapy that you select that would be appropriate for T.J.

8. T.J. is being treated for chronic bronchitis with Theodur 200 mg t.i.d., terbutaline 5 mg p.o. q.i.d. and tetracycline prn. Predict a theophylline level that will result from this dosing regimen. Make any appropriate adjustments in his theophylline regimen.

9. Are the other two drugs for his chronic bronchitis appropriate? Discuss your reasons and give alternatives.

10. Make appropriate drug therapy recommendations for treating his chronic bronchitis. State your reasons for treating and reasons for selecting each therapy. Include all specifics of the drug therapy, i.e., dose, route, and frequency.

CASE 69

CC: R.R. is a 60-year-old woman looking older than her stated age who is brought to the ER today, March 18, after 2 days of nausea, vomiting, and shortness of breath. She also complains of no bowel movements for 5 days and states that she would kill herself if she had a gun.

Past Medical History

The following was obtained from an old chart and a clinic visit note from March 11:

1. Rheumatoid arthritis for 13 years.

2. Essential hypertension for many years. BP on March 11, 120/70.

3. Chronic bronchitis due to cigarette smoking. PFTs March 11 showed prebronchodilator $FEV_1 = 1200$ ml and postbronchodilator $FEV_1 = 1600$ ml. Theophylline level = 12 $\mu g/ml$ on March 11.

4. Peptic ulcer disease: March 11 endoscopy showed healing of all ulcers, so cimetidine 400 mg b.i.d. and Mylanta 30 ml 1 and 3 hours p.c. and h.s. were discontinued.

5. Depression diagnosed 2 years ago and was treated with nortriptyline for 1 year with good response.

6. Chronic insomnia for many years.

7. Chronic constipation for many years with a

history of laxative abuse; worse during the last 3 months.

8. Psoriasis for 2 years.

Problem List

1. Exacerbation of PUD
2. Exacerbation of COPD/chronic bronchitis.
3. Depression with suicidal ideation
4. Severe rheumatoid arthritis with deformities, uncontrolled
5. Medication abuse/misuse
6. Alcoholism
7. Insomnia
8. Constipation
9. Psoriasis

Medication History

Piroxicam 20 mg qd since March 11
Percodan 12–16 tabs per day for 3 months
HCTZ 50 mg b.i.d. × 8 years
Nadolol 120 mg qd × 8 years
Clonidine 0.3 mg b.i.d. × 8 years
Theodur 300 mg b.i.d. × 4 years
Metaproterenol 20 mg t.i.d. × 4 years
Terbutaline inhaler 2 puffs PRN × 4 years
SSKI 10 drops q.i.d. × 4 years
Flurazepam 30 mg hs prn (she often increases dose × 3 years)
Diphenhydramine 50 mg hs, may repeat × 1 for 3 months
Docusate 100 mg qd × many years
Phenolphthalein, herbs and enemas prn
TAC cream 0.25% × 2 years

Allergies

R.R. has had one episode of rash in reaction to gold injections and is allergic to penicillin.

Social History

R.R. was forced to retire 2 years ago because of immobility from arthritis. She is divorced and lives alone. She has a history of ethanol abuse for many years; binge drinking in last 6 months. Her last drink was 12 hours ago. She has a 75 pack-year smoking history and she still smokes. She denies any recreational drug use and drinks 8 to 10 cups of coffee per day.

Review of Systems

Decreased appetite, loss of interest in everything, feels worthless.

Physical Examination

GEN: Hostile, confused, middle-aged woman in acute distress.
VS: BP 140/90 HR 80 (reg) T 38.0 RR 32 Wt 48 kg Ht 5'0"
HEENT: Thyroid normal
COR: Normal
CHEST: Coarse rales and rhonchi throughout, numerous expiratory wheezes, pulsus paradoxus 12 mm HG
ABD: Tender in midepigastric region, vomitus guaiac (−), stool guaiac (+)
GU: Deferred
EXT: Severe arthritis with deformities in hands, ankles, and knees. Decreased range of motion in both knees and hips. Large plaques of psoriasis on elbows and knees.
NEURO: NL DTRs, Ataxia, unable to cooperate with remainder of exam. Mental status oriented × 2.

Results of Laboratory Tests

Na 137	Hct 31.4	AST 203	Ca 8.0	Uric Acid 8
K 3.9	Hgb 10.1	ALT 95	PO_4 2.6	ESR 108
Cl 98	WBC 8.9k	Alk Phos 138	Mg 1.2	
HCO_3 24	Plts 105k	Alb 2.5	Theophylline 6	
BUN 11	MCV 101	T Bili 2.6	PT 13.9	
Cr 1.0	MCHC 30	Glu 70	PTT 38.6	

Urinalysis: Sp Gr 1.025, pH 6, ketones (−), protein (−)

Thyroid function tests: T_4 8, RT_3U 24, TSH < 10

ABGS: pH 7.44, PCO_2 37, PO_2 62, 85% sat

ECG: Sinus rhythm with occasional PVCs

Chest x-ray: Clear, no pneumonia; severe osteoporosis of the spine

Problem _____

S: _____
_____
_____
_____

O: _____
_____
_____
_____

A: _____
_____
_____
_____
_____
_____

P: _____
_____
_____

Problem

S:

O:

A:

P:

Problem

S:

O:

A:

P:

Problem

S:

O:

A:

P:

Problem

S:

O:

A:

P:

Problem

S:

O:

A:

P:

Problem

S:

O:

A:

P:

Problem

S:

O:

A:

P:

Problem

S:

O:

A:

P:

Questions

1. Endoscopy in the emergency room confirms the presence of a gastric ulcer.
   a. Recommend how this ulcer should be treated. Give drug, dose, route, schedule, duration, and your reasons for selecting this drug over other available alternatives.
   b. List two drugs included in her previous therapy that may have contributed to this exacerbation of R.R.'s ulcer disease.
2. Recommend a treatment plan for R.R. for her exacerbation of COPD/chronic bronchitis.
   a. Calculate an i.v. loading dose of aminophylline for R.R. that would achieve a serum theophylline level of 15 μg/ml.
   b. Calculate an *oral* maintenance dose that will maintain R.R. at a Cpss avg level of 15 μg/ml.
   c. Recommend drug treatment other than theophylline that is required for R.R.'s COPD/chronic bronchitis in the emergency room and during her 7-day hospitalization. For each recommendation give dose, route, schedule, duration and reasons for your selection.
   d. Evaluate her previous outpatient therapy for her COPD/chronic bronchitis by identifying three errors that appeared in her outpatient regimen and for each explain why her outpatient regiment was not optimal.
3. R.R. has several problems with drug/substance misuse/abuse.
   a. Recommend how R.R. should be treated in the emergency room for the problems caused by her alcohol abuse. Give drug(s), dose(s), route(s), schedule(s), duration, and reasons for your choice(s).
   b. Recommend how R.R. should be treated during her hospitalization to prevent alcohol withdrawal symptoms. Give drug, dose, route, schedule, duration and reasons for your choice. List three monitoring parameters that you would follow to determine the efficacy of your treatment.
4. Does R.R.'s depression require treatment with drugs or not? Why or why not? Explain your reasons. If drug treatment is required, recommend a treatment plan giving drug, dose, route, schedule, duration, and reasons for your selection. What special precautions would you tell R.R. about this medication?
5. Recommend drug treatment for R.R.'s rheumatoid arthritis. Give drug(s), dose(s), route(s), schedule(s), dosage titration if applicable, and reasons for your selection. List four monitoring parameters for efficacy and four monitoring parameters for side effects that are specific for the therapy that you chose.
6a. List the three most likely drugs that may be contributing to R.R.'s current complaint of constipation and list the mechanism of causing constipation.
   b. Recommend a treatment plan for the immediate relief of her complaint and establish a long-term treatment regimen for her constipation. In each case, be specific and give drug, dose, schedule, route, and duration. Discuss your reasons for selecting this drug in this patient. What four items of patient education would you provide about non–drug therapy for constipation?
7. R.R.'s psoriasis is not currently controlled and in talking to her, you discover that the plaques are a source of embarrassment to her and they cause her considerable distress. Why is her current therapy not working although she has been compliant with the treatment? What therapy would you recommend? Be specific and give drug, dose, vehicle, duration and patient education for the appropriate use of this therapy.
8. Now that R.R. is ready to be discharged, her physician wants to approach the problem of insomnia. R.R. has had a chronic problem with insomnia for many years. She was treated in the past with pentobarbital that was discontinued because of abuse. R.R. has taken flurazepam 30 mg hs for 3 years and often takes more than the prescribed dose. Three months ago in order to decrease her use of flurazepam, her physician also prescribed diphenhydramine 50 mg hs, may repeat × 1.
8a. Identify three possible causes of R.R.'s complaint of insomnia.
   b. Recommend how R.R. should be tapered off the flurazepam that she has been using to treat her insomnia. Give drug, dose, route, schedule, duration, and reasons for your choices.

CASE 70

CC: J.M.S. is a 50-year-old male who was admitted to the hospital on February 25 with a chief complaint of melena of several days duration. Emergency endoscopy demonstrated a 4-cm duodenal ulcer with active bleeding. Esophageal varices were also noted but were not actively bleeding.

Past Medical History/Problem List

1. Chronic obstructive pulmonary disease (COPD): 90-pack-year history of smoking.)
2. Seizure disorder secondary to head trauma: J.M.S. has had multiple falls and has been in numerous fights. His last seizure was 2 weeks ago. He averages about one seizure per month.
3. Insulin-dependent diabetes, which was first diagnosed 2 years ago: He has never suffered from diabetic ketoacidosis (DKA) and only occasion-

ally becomes hypoglycemic in relation to his alcohol abuse.

4. Chronic alcohol abuse: J.M.S. has drunk 1–2 fifths per day for about 25 years. At the beginning of the month, when he has money, he drinks whiskey. At the end of the month, he drinks cheap wine.
5. Hepatic encephalopathy: J.M.S. has disturbed mentation and forgetfulness.
6. Ascites: He has been stable for several months.
7. History of intravenous heroin abuse.
8. Mild degenerative joint disease (DJD).
9. Skin rash: Due to tinea corporis on a small area of the trunk and in the left axillae. It is very inflamed and pruritic with severe excoriations.

Medication History

Medication prior to admission:

Theodur 100 mg b.i.d.
Metaproterenol 2 puffs q.i.d.
Terbutaline 5 mg p.o. q.i.d.
Prednisone 20 mg qd × 2 years
Phenytoin 200 mg b.i.d.
NPH 20 U qd
Lactulose 30 cc b.i.d.
Spironolactone 25 mg t.i.d.
Methadone 25 mg qd in a maintenance program
ASA 650 mg q.i.d.

Allergies

None known.

Social History

J.M.S. lives in a board and care home. The staff administers his medications daily. He smokes cigarettes, 2 packs per day. He has a history of ethanol abuse.

Physical Examination

GEN: Disheveled-looking man who appears chronically ill and jaundiced. No venous access. Oriented to person and place but not date. Cannot remember physician's name. Looks much older than stated age.
VS: BP 100/60 HR 120 T 36.6 RR 24 Wt 84 kg Ht 6'0"
HEENT: Scleral icterus
COR: Normal S1 and S2; no murmurs, rubs, or gallops
CHEST: Distant breath sounds, coarse rhonchi throughout, few expiratory wheezes
ABD: Ascites, hepatomegaly, active bowel sounds
GU: WNL

RECT: Guaiac-positive
EXT: Normal deep tendon reflexes, symmetrically decreased sensation to vibration and pin prick over both lower extremities. Paraesthesias in both lower limbs. Asterixis.
NEURO: Ataxia and ophthalmoplegia

Results of Laboratory Tests

Na 128	Hct 24.9	ALT 40	Ca 8.9	PT 16.6
K 5.6	Hgb 8.6	LDH 130	PO_4 1.5	PTT 39
Cl 95	WBC 12.0k	Alk Phos 34	Mg 1.0	
HCO_3 25	Plts 68.6k	Alb 2.3		
BUN 45	MCV 74	T. Bili 5.6		
Cr 1.8	AST 38	Glu 185		

LFTs: Prebronchodilator $FEV_1/FVC = 1375/2350$; Postbronchodilator $FEV_1/FVC = 1750/2500$
ABGs on room air: pH 7.42, PO_2 62, PCO_2 34
Urinalysis: Bili (+)

Problem

S:

O:

A:

P:

Problem

S:_____
_____
_____

O:_____
_____
_____

A:_____
_____
_____
_____

P:_____
_____
_____

Problem

S:_____
_____
_____

O:_____
_____
_____

A:_____
_____
_____
_____

P:_____
_____
_____

Problem

S:_____
_____
_____

O:_____
_____
_____

A:_____
_____
_____

P:_____
_____
_____

Problem

S:_____
_____
_____

O:_____
_____
_____

A:_____
_____
_____

P:_____
_____
_____

Problem

S:

O:

A:

P:

Problem

S:

O:

A:

P:

Problem

S:

O:

A:

P:

Problem

S:

O:

A:

P:

Questions

1. Identify the six contributing factors in the development of his bleeding duodenal ulcer.
2. Assess the treatment of his PUD as prescribed on February 25. Are all the drugs necessary? Is each drug the drug of choice for this patient? Are the doses correct? Are there any drug interactions? Recommend treatment for his PUD. Be patient specific; give drug, doses, schedule and reasons.
3. Assess the past and present treatment for his COPD. Are all drugs necessary? Is each drug the drug of choice in this patient? Are the doses correct? Are the specific drug product formulations (dosage forms) appropriate for this patient? Why or why not?
4. [On February 27 the intern states that she is afraid that J.M.S. will have a seizure and requests that you calculate a phenytoin loading dose to bring his level up to a therapeutic level.] What is your recommendation regarding this request? How would you support your recommendations?
5. [On February 27, the stat blood glucose is noted to be 485. Insulin has not been administered since admission.] Give your recommendation for managing his diabetes while he is in the hospital and is acutely ill. Be patient specific; give drug, dose, schedule, and monitoring parameters. Include frequency for monitoring parameters.
6. Recommend treatment for his tinea corporis. Be specific as to drug, product formulation (i.e., cream, lotion, ointment) and schedule.

CASE 71

CC: J.R. is a 68-year-old retired fire fighter who returns to university clinic for his regular check-up. He denies any problems including pain, dizziness, headache or symptoms of hypoglycemia or hyperglycemia. However, you notice that he is not as talkative and cheerful as before. When talking to his wife, you find out that his only son was killed in a motor vehicle accident 8 weeks ago. Since then J.R. has been very depressed, constipated and has a poor appetite and has been having trouble sleeping as he wakes up early in the morning and can not fall back to sleep. He has been getting worse over the past few days because his son's divorced wife is going to take their grandchildren (who are staying with them now) and they will never see the children again. J.R.'s wife is very worried because J.R. talks about death a lot, he has mentioned suicide, and has been drinking a lot more lately. You also find out that he saw a psychiatrist who gave him two prescriptions for his depression. His wife states that she will have the prescriptions filled as soon as they receive their Social Security payment.

Past Medical History

J.R. has had hypertension (HTN) for 10 years; he also has coronary artery disease (CAD), myocardial infarction (MI) × 2, degenerative joint disease (DJD), and type II diabetes mellitus for 5 years.

Problem List

1. Major depression
2. Hypertension
3. Coronary artery disease
4. Myocardial infarction × 2
5. Degenerative joint disease (DJD)
6. Type II diabetes mellitus

Family History

J.R.'s father died of MI at age 60. His mother committed suicide 3 months after the death of her husband.

Social History

J.R. smokes cigarettes, 2 packs per day for 30 years. He drinks alcohol occasionally but has been drinking one-fifth of brandy lately.

Allergy

J.R. has experienced SOB and hives in reaction to aspirin.

Medication History

Dyazide 1 cap p.o. q AM
Clonidine 0.2 mg p.o. b.i.d. × 1 year
Propranolol 60 mg p.o. q.i.d. × 2 years
Glyburide 5 mg p.o. q AM × 3 years
Bisacodyl 10 mg p.o. q hs
Maalox prn
Nitroglycerin 0.4 mg s.l. 1 tablet for CP MR q 5 minutes × 3 then go to ER
Acetaminophen 650 mg 1–2 tablets p.o. q4h prn pain
Multivitamin 1 tablet p.o. qd
Vitamin C 500 mg 1 tablet p.o. qd

The following are newly prescribed medications:

Amitriptyline 25 mg t.i.d. and hs, may increase to 2 tablets hs prn #100
Valium 10 mg p.o. hs prn sleep #100

Physical Examination

VS: BP 110/86 P 65 T 37.6 R 25 Wt 65 kg

Results of Laboratory Tests

Tests taken 3 months ago:

Na 135	BUN 15
K 5.6	Cr 1.4
Cl 110	FBS 98
HCO$_3$ 25	Hgb$_{a1c}$ 9%

PT 19 (baseline = 10; has been stable at 17–20)

Today's results:

Na 136	BUN 18
K 4.4	Cr 1.9
Cl 111	FBS 108
HCO$_3$ 25	PT 35

Problem

S:

O:

A:

P:

Problem

S:

O:

A:

P:

Problem

S:

O:

A:

P:

Problem

S:

O:

A:

P:

Problem

S:

O:

A:

P:

Problem

S:

O:

A:

P:

CASE 72

CC: M.M. is a 72-year-old female who comes to the clinic today for follow-up of multiple medical problems. M.M. is a chronic schizophrenic who lives in a board and care home. The staff administers her medications, which ensures compliance. She can be seen at the bus station on most days carrying many of her belongings in a shopping bag. She complains of new onset of midepigastric pain that is gnawing in nature and relieved by food.

Past Medical History

M.M. has chronic asthma, which first occurred when she was 55 years old. It has been difficult to control at times but has not required steroids or intubation for ventilation. M.M. has difficulty using her inhalers because of tremors and lack of coordination. She also has degenerative joint disease, particularly of the knees and ankles. She has peptic ulcer disease, which has recurred four times but has not required transfusions or surgery. Current treatment includes a bland diet. She suffers from chronic schizophrenia, which is relatively well controlled. M.M. has fewer hallucinations but still has delusions, poor judgement, and inappropriate social skills. M.M. has grand mal seizures. Her last seizure, two days ago, was similar in nature to her previous seizures. She averages three to four seizures per week. M.M. also has chronic constipation.

Problem List

1. Chronic schizophrenia
2. Asthma
3. Degenerative joint disease
4. Peptic ulcer disease
5. Grand mal seizures
6. Constipation
7. Parkinsonism? Drug-induced

Medication History

Theophylline 200 mg b.i.d.
Albuterol 2 puffs q.i.d.
Terbutaline 5 mg q.i.d.
Beclomethasone 2 puffs q.i.d.
Piroxicam 20 mg b.i.d.
Maalox 5 ml prn
Perphenazine 16 mg q.i.d. with a drug holiday every Sunday
Phenytoin 300 mg q hs
Docusate 100 mg qd prn

Allergies

None known.

Social History

M.M. smokes one-half pack of cigarettes per day and drinks several drinks per day.

Review of Systems

Patient complains of dry mouth, dizziness

Physical Examination

GEN: Shuffling gait, stooped posture, slow, monotonous speech
VS: BP (supine) 140/80, BP (sitting) 135/82
HEENT: Mask-like facies
COR: No murmurs, rubs, or gallops
CHEST: Few expiratory wheezes
ABD: Soft, nontender, no masses
GU: WNL
RECT: Guaiac (+)
EXT: tremors in both hands and legs

ECG: Nonspecific T wave changes

Results of Laboratory Tests

Na 143	Cr 2.9	MCV 82	Alb 3.3	Mg 2.3
K 3.9	Hct 31.6	AST 22	T Bili 0.8	PT 11.2
Cl 108	Hgb 10.3	ALT 21	Glu 100	PTT 28.7
HCO_3 23	WBC 8k	LDH 130	Ca 8.9	Theo 8
BUN 49	Plts 180k	Alk Phos 70	PO_4 2.4	Phenytoin 7

PFTs: FEV_1/FVC 500/1000 ml (prebronchodilator), 800/1800 ml (postbronchodilator)
Urinalysis: WNL

Problem

S:

O:

A:

P:

Problem

S:

O:

A:

P:

Problem

S:

O:

A:

P:

Problem

S:—————————————————

——————————————————————

O:—————————————————

——————————————————————

A:—————————————————

——————————————————————

——————————————————————

P:—————————————————

——————————————————————

Problem

S:—————————————————

——————————————————————

O:—————————————————

——————————————————————

A:—————————————————

——————————————————————

——————————————————————

P:—————————————————

——————————————————————

Problem

S:—————————————————

——————————————————————

O:—————————————————

——————————————————————

A:—————————————————

——————————————————————

——————————————————————

P:—————————————————

——————————————————————

Problem

S:—————————————————

——————————————————————

O:—————————————————

——————————————————————

A:—————————————————

——————————————————————

——————————————————————

P:—————————————————

——————————————————————

SECTION/13

Infectious Diseases

CASE 73

CC: A.L. is an 18-month-old male who is brought into the pediatric clinic. His mother states that the baby developed an upper respiratory infection (URI) 5 days ago with nasal congestion, a nonproductive cough, sneezing, and fever. Last night he became more irritable, refused dinner, and began tugging on his left earlobe.

Past Medical History

A.L. was diagnosed with Fallot's tetralogy (a congenital heart defect) at birth and is status post placement of a right ventrical outflow tract patch × 2. Ten weeks ago he underwent a percutaneous pulmonary artery balloon angioplasty. This procedure was complicated by fever and a diagnosis of acute endocarditis with blood cultures positive for *Staphylococcus aureus* × 3. The organism was sensitive to nafcillin and A.L. was to receive a total of 8 weeks of home antibiotic therapy. After 5 weeks on nafcillin, A.L. became neutropenic. The neutropenia was felt to be secondary to prolonged high-dose nafcillin, and his therapy was changed to vancomycin for the remaining 3 weeks. A.L.'s medical history also includes otitis media at 7, 9, and 12 months (treated with ampicillin, amoxicillin, and cefaclor) and pneumonia at 12 months (treated with cefotaxime).

Problem List

1. Acute otitis media
2. Upper respiratory infection
3. Chronic otitis media
4. Congenital heart disease, status post endocarditis
5. Anemia
6. Immunizations

Medication History

Poly-Vi-Sol 1 cc p.o. q.d.
Fer-in-Sol gtts 0.6 cc p.o. q.d. (10 mg Fe^{++} q.d.)
Digoxin 50 μg p.o. b.i.d.
Furosemide 10 mg p.o. t.i.d.
Nafcillin 500 mg i.v. q 6 × 5 weeks
Vancomycin 100 mg i.v. q 6 × 3 weeks (last dose 2 weeks ago)

Immunization History

DPT, TOPV at 2, 4, and 6 months

Social History

A.L. is an only child; his mother is 8 months pregnant.

Allergies

Morphine (excitation, nausea, vomiting)

Physical Examination

VS: BP 80/60 HR 120 T 38.8 Wt 11 kg
HEENT: Rhinorrhea with congestion; PERRL, sclerae pearly white; erythematous left ear with bulging tympanic membranes and loss of landmarks
CHEST: Mild chest wall deformity, well healed scar. Rales, rhonchi, occasional cough
COR: NSR, grade III/VI mid systolic murmur, grade II/VI EDM, (consistent with history of congenital heart defect)
ABD: Bowel sounds +, liver 2 cm below the right costal margin
CNS: Irritable
SKIN: Pale, dry

Results of Laboratory Tests

Na 147	Hct 27.5	AST 22	Digoxin 1.6
K 3.8	Hgb 9.4	ALT 20	
Cl 108	WBC 7.3k	Alk Phos 37	
HCO₃ 18	Plts 304k	Alb 3.7	
BUN 10	MCV 68		
Cr 0.4	MCH 20		

Problem 1. Acute Otitis Media

S: Patient has irritability, anorexia and is tugging on ear.

O: Patient has erythematous, bulging tympanic membranes with loss of landmarks and increased WBC; he is febrile (38.8°C)

A: A.L. has a history of URI for 5 days. Complications of URI include otitis media (OM). Usual organisms in an 18-month-old-child include H. flu, streptococcal pneumonia, and Branhamella catarrhalis. A.L. is symptomatic and must be treated to prevent further complications of OM (hearing loss, meningitis). He has had three additional episodes of OM during the last year, which have been treated with ampicillin, amoxicillin, and cefaclor. His medication history includes 5 weeks of nafcillin therapy and 3 weeks of vancomycin therapy.

P: Treat with antibiotics:
Begin therapy with amoxicillin/clavulanic acid; or as a second choice, erythromycin/sulfame-

159

thoxazole, cotrimoxazole TMP/SMX). Monitor for improvement of signs and symptoms of OM; diarrhea, rash secondary to antibiotic therapy; neutropenia (history of neutropenia with nafcillin). Patient education: Advise A.L.'s parents with respect to completing the full 10-day course of antibiotics; shaking the suspension well prior to administration; keeping the suspension refrigerated; giving the drug to A.L. 1 hour before or 3 hours after meals.

Problem 2. Upper Respiratory Infection

S: A.L. has nasal congestion and a nonproductive cough; he has been sneezing for 5 days.

O: A.L. has rhinorrhea, congestion, rales, rhonchi, cough, and is febrile to 38.8°C.

A: A.L. has been symptomatic for 5 days. The etiologic agent is most likely viral. The baby developed a secondary bacterial infection presenting as OM. Colds are self-limiting; treat symptomatically.

P: Give acetaminophen (APAP) for aches, pain, and fever (10–15 mg/kg/dose). Begin appropriate antibiotic treatment for secondary otitis media. Avoid OTC products containing pseudoephedrine, ephedrine, phenylpropanolamine because of the potential cardiovascular side effects. Avoid nose drops containing decongestants as A.L. may develop tolerance or rebound congestion. Antihistamines can be helpful as drying agents, but only in the initial stages of a cold. They also have undesirable side effects for this patient (i.e., anticholinergic effects). Dextromethorphan may be useful as an antitussive agent at 1 mg/kg/day in divided doses. Monitor signs and symptoms of URI. Patient education: Advise mother with respect to OTC products available for the treatment of colds.

Problem 3. Chronic Otitis Media

S: A.L. is currently diagnosed with otitis media.

O: A.L.'s OM was diagnosed at 7, 9, and 12 months of age.

A: A.L. has chronic otitis media, with four episodes occurring within the last year. A.L. is a candidate for prophylaxis.

P: Treat the current episode of OM as outlined above. Treat prophylactically with ampicillin or amoxicillin 50 mg/kg p.o. q day × 4–6 weeks. TMP/SMX 8 mg/kg p.o. q day × 4–6 weeks can be used as prophylaxis but TMP/SMX may cause neutropenia in pediatric patients. Monitor for diarrhea, rash, candidal overgrowth, and neutropenia. Patient education: Advise mother concerning administration, compliance, and side effects of the prophylactic antibiotic therapy.

Problem 4. Congenital Heart Disease

S: A.L. has a history of Fallot's tetralogy and is stable after receiving right ventrical outflow patching twice.

O: A.L. has a grade III/VI midsystolic murmur and a grade II/VI EDM.

A: CHD has been surgically repaired twice. A.L. is currently stable, receiving digoxin 50 μg b.i.d. (9 μg/kg/day; digoxin level 1.6) and furosemide 10 mg t.i.d. (2.7 mg/kg/day). A.L. is stable after an episode of acute endocarditis (*Staphylococcus aureus*).

P: Monitor the patient for signs and symptoms of worsening heart disease (changes in murmur, HR, BP, and fatigue). Monitor for side effects of digoxin and furosemide (digoxin levels may not be useful in pediatric patients for monitoring response to therapy, but are useful in dosage adjustments and monitoring toxicities). Monitor for signs and symptoms of endocarditis (changes in murmur, fever, petechiae, anorexia, cough, sweats). Patient education: Counsel mother with respect to prophylaxis for dental or surgical procedures.

Problem 5. Anemia

S: None.

O: A.L. has pale, dry skin; pearly white sclerae; and decreased Hgb, Hct, MCH, and MCV.

A: He has iron deficiency anemia secondary to chronic disease or poor nutritional intake. Decreased Hgb and Hct may also be secondary to blood loss from surgeries or frequent blood draws.

P: Check TIBC. Increase Fer in Sol gtts to 0.6 ml p.o. t.i.d. (Fe^{++} 3 mg/kg/day—therapeutic) and continue for 3 months. Monitor for signs and symptoms of bleeding. Check reticulocytes in 1 month. Recheck Hgb, Hct, MCV, MCH, TIBC in 3 months. Minimize blood draws. Patient education: Counsel mother with respect to compliance, side effects, and administration of iron therapy.

Problem 6. Immunizations

S: Not applicable.

O: A.L. was immunized with DPT, TOPV at 2, 4, and 6 months of age.

A: His immunizations are not up to date.

P: When current febrile illness resolves, administer a TB skin test. At the same time or 1 month later administer MMR. One month later administer DPT, TOPV. At age 4–6 years administer DPT, TOPV. At age 14 years and q 10 years administer Td. Consider administration of *Haemophilus influenzae*, type B vaccine. Ensure that his pregnant mother has adequate titers to rubella and polio. Patient education: Advise mother with respect to compliance with immunization schedule, contraindications to immunizations, side effects of immunizations; and record keeping.

CASE 74

CC: A.B. is a 63-year-old obese female who presents to the general medicine clinic with a 3-day history of urinary frequency and dysuria.

Past Medical History

A.B. has a long history of Type II diabetes mellitus, which has been poorly controlled on chlorpropamide, with complications of diabetic retinopathy, neuropathy, and nephropathy. A.B. also has a history of hypertension. A.B. was most recently treated 1 month prior to this visit with a 10-day course of cotrimoxazole for an *Escherichia coli* urinary tract infection (UTI). Six weeks prior to the *E. coli* UTI, she was treated for another UTI with a single 3-g dose of amoxicillin. This was her third UTI in 6 months.

Problem List

1. Recurrent urinary tract infections
2. Type II diabetes mellitus
3. Hypertension

Medication History

Chlorpropamide 250 mg p.o. q.d. for many years
Dyazide 1 p.o. q.d.
Propranolol 40 mg q.i.d.

Physical Examination

GEN:	Obese female in no apparent distress.
VS:	BP 150/85 HR 65 Temp 37 RR 13 Wt 85kg
HEENT:	Grade I AV nicking/narrowing
NECK:	No JVD
LUNGS:	Clear
COR:	NL S1, S2, no S3; II/VI SEM
ABD:	Soft, nontender; no flank pain
GU:	No discharge; no vaginal itching
EXT:	Decreased pulses in both feet, tingling feet and toes
NEURO:	Alert and oriented × 3

Results of Laboratory Tests

Na 140	Cr 1.8
K 4.0	Hct 36
Cl 100	Hgb 12
HCO_3 26	WBC 7k (without left shift)
BUN 27	Random glucose 280

Urinalysis: 2% glucose, with Testape
2% glucose with Clinitest
>20 bacteria per HPF, 10–20 WBC per HPF
Urine culture: >10^5 cfu/ml *E. coli* (pan-sensitive)

Problem 1. Recurrent Urinary Tract Infection

S: Patient complains of frequency and dysuria.
O: Patient has an urinalysis with >20 bacteria/

HPF and 10–20 WBC/HPF no flank pain; history of two UTIs in the past 2 months.

A: Elderly women with diabetes mellitus have an increased risk for recurrent UTIs. Most likely this is a lower UTI since the patient has no fever or flank pain and does not appear acutely ill. Parenteral antibiotics are not necessary in this case.

P: Ampicillin 500 mg p.o. q.i.d. or Cotrimoxazole DS 1 tablet p.o. b.i.d. × 14 days. Both these antibiotics are good choices in this patient since they achieve high urinary concentrations despite renal insufficiency. Some cephalosporins may interfere with urine glucose tests such as Clinitest. Monitor temperature, signs and symptoms of UTI, urine culture and sensitivities; urinalysis, side effects of ampicillin (rash, GI upset, diarrhea) or cotrimoxazole (rash, GI upset). Patient education: Counsel A.B. regarding compliance with the medication for the entire course of therapy and side effects of ampicillin or cotrimoxazole.

Problem 4. Prophylaxis of Recurrent Urinary Tract Infections

S: Patient has history of three UTIs within 6 months.

O: None.

A: This patient is a candidate for UTI prophylaxis since she has a history of frequent UTIs. Because this patient has reduced renal function and diabetic peripheral neuropathy, nitrofurantoin would not be the best choice for prophylaxis.

P: Give cotrimoxazole SS ½ tablet p.o. qhs or TMP 100 mg p.o. qhs for 6 months; then reevaluate. Monitor recurrence of the UTI and side effects of the antibiotic. Patient education: Counsel A.B. about compliance and the side effects of the drug.

Problem 2. Type II Diabetes Mellitus with Complications

S: None.

O: A.B. has a random glucose of 280 mg/dl, glucosuria; tingling feet and toes; and SCr 1.8.

A: She has uncontrolled DM on chlorpropamide. UTI may be contributing to the hyperglycemia. Chlorpropamide is not the best choice of oral hypoglycemics in an elderly patient with renal insufficiency because its active metabolites may accumulate in renal dysfunction.

P: Discontinue chlorpropamide. Begin glipizide 2.5 mg or tolazamide 250 mg qd. Maximize the oral hypoglycemic dose for control. The maximum dose for glipizide is 40 mg given as 20 mg b.i.d. and for tolazamide 1 gm. Check fluid status and keep well hydrated. Monitor fasting blood glucose, urine S/A q.i.d., signs and symptoms of hypoglycemia or hyperglycemia, progression of nephropathy and neuropathy. Educate patient regarding diet and weight control; why her medication is being changed; to recognize the signs and symptoms of hypoglycemia and hyperglycemia, treatment of hypoglycemia; and proper foot care.

Problem 3. Hypertension

S: None.

O: BP 150/85.

A: Hypertension controlled on current medications. Propranolol may be relatively containdicated in a diabetic patient. May want to consider a selective beta blocker.

P: Continue propranolol. Monitor BP, HR, and side effects of propranolol. Educate patient regarding diet (low salt), weight control, side effects of propranolol, and not to abruptly stop taking medications.

CASE 75

CC: M.G. is a 69-year-old male admitted for right foot ulcer and cellulitis whose admission chest x-ray revealed RUL area of cavitation and hilar adenopathy.

Past Medical History

M.G. is a recent immigrant who has a long history of rheumatoid arthritis (steroid dependent), coronary artery disease (CAD) and has had a coronary artery bypass graft (CABG). He also has peripheral vascular disease (PVD) and a seizure disorder (last seizure 8 months ago). He has no history of fever, cough, night sweats, or hemoptysis. He also denies previous history of TB or TB exposure. M.G., however, relates a recent weight loss of 10 lb over the past several months.

Problem List

1. Right foot ulcer
2. Rheumatoid arthritis
3. CAD, status post CABG
4. Peripheral vascular disease
5. Seizure disorder

Medication History

Prednisone 10 mg p.o. qd × 2 months (recently increased from 5 mg qd)
Cotrimoxazole DS 1 tab p.o. b.i.d. × 3 days
Ranitidine 150 mg p.o. b.i.d.
Naprosyn 500 mg p.o. b.i.d.
ASA 650 mg p.o. b.i.d.
Phenytoin 300 mg p.o. qhs

Physical Examination

GEN: Well-developed well-nourished pleasant man without complaints.
VS: BP 150/85 HR 80 T 37.3 RR 15 Wt 75kg
HEENT: Normocephalic, no pharyngeal hyperemia
NECK: Supple, no JVD/nodes noted
LUNGS: No wheezes, rhonchi, rales
THORAX: No point tenderness or CVA tenderness
ABD: Soft, nontender; BS present
EXT: Ulnar deviation with mild joint deformation; good ROM; well-healing ulcer on plantar surface of right toe
NEURO: Alert and oriented × 3

Results of Laboratory Tests

Na 138	Cr 1.2	AST 9	T Bili 0.6
K 4.3	Hgb 13.3	ALT 10	D Bili 0.1
Cl 101	Hct 39	Alb 3.0	RF 1:80
HCO$_3$ 27	WBC 12 k	Alk Phos 84	
BUN 24	Plts 342 k	LDH 150	

Skin tests: PPD (−), *Candida* skin test (−); mumps skin test (−)

Chest x-ray: RUL and LLL infiltrate with RUL area of cavitation; hilar adenopathy

Urinalysis: No hematuria; no WBC

Ulcer culture: *Staphylococcus aureus*, *Escherichia coli*

Sputum: AFB(+)

Problem 6. Active Tuberculosis

S: M.G. has a history of recent weight loss.

O: Chest X-ray with infiltrate, area of cavitation and hilar adenopathy. Sputum positive for acid-fast bacilli. Negative PPD along with rest of anergy panel.

A: The patient is asymptomatic however the x-ray and sputum are positive and consistent with active tuberculosis. The negative PPD is not surprising given the history of a recent increase in his prednisone dose. Triple drug therapy is required until the culture and sensitivities are completed to cover for possible resistant strains of *Mycobacterim tuburculosis* since the patient is a recent immigrant from a country of known resistance. TB drugs may interact with both the steroids and phenytoin. Observe for phenytoin toxicity and arthritis flare.

P: Give isoniazid 300 mg p.o. q.d.; rifampin 600 mg p.o. q.d.; ethambutol 15 mg/kg p.o. q.d. Give triple drug therapy for 2 months until sensitivities are known. If the strain is sensitive to INH and rifampin, may discontinue ethambutol at that time. If a resistant strain is isolated, must continue triple drug therapy. Treat for 9 months. Check his close contacts and if indicated give INH 300 mg q.d. for 12 months. Monitor baseline ophthalmologic examination and LFTs. Continue to monitor LFTs, signs and symptoms of hepatitis (abdominal pain, jaundice, flu-like symptoms), eye examinations, chest x-ray, and sputum culture after the course of antibiotics. Educate patient regarding compliance with medication during the long course of antibiotics, signs and symptoms of hepatitis, discoloration of body fluids with rifampin, and the need to report any changes in vision. Inform the patient regarding prophylaxis for close household contacts.

Problem 2. Rheumatoid Arthritis

S: No complaints of joint tenderness.

O: Ulnar deviation with mild joint deformity with good ROM.

A: Good pain control with good ROM. Try to taper steroids back down to lowest effective dose since this patient has active TB. A remitting agent such as gold may benefit this patient.

P: Continue Naprosyn and ASA. Taper steroids 1.0 mg/week until daily dose of 5 mg is reached if possible. Monitor for flare of RA (increased joint tenderness/pain, decreased ROM), signs and symptoms of adrenal insufficiency (electrolytes, BP, HR, blood glucose, flu-like symptoms, nausea and vomiting). Patient education: Counsel regarding signs and symptoms of adrenal insufficiency and reasons for the steroid taper.

Problem 5. Seizure Disorder

S: Last seizure 8 months ago.

O: None.

A: Phenytoin is currently providing good seizure control. INH and rifampin may interact with phenytoin by altering phenytoin metabolism.

P: Continue current regimen of phenytoin. Monitor phenytoin serum level before initiating TB medications and periodically during the antibiotic course, frequency of seizures, and side effects of phenytoin. Educate patient regarding reporting any changes in the frequency of seizures and side effects of phenytoin (drowsiness, ataxia).

Problem 1. Right-Foot Ulcer

S: None.

O: Physical examination revealed a well-healing ulcer on plantar surface of right toe.

A: He has received appropriate antibiotic treatment of infection with good response.

P: Continue cotrimoxazole for a total of a 2-week course of antibiotics and give adequate local wound care such as dressing changes. Monitor side effects of cotrimoxazole (rash, GI upset) and wound for proper healing. Educate patient regarding completion of antibiotics and side effects of cotrimoxazole.

Problem 3. Coronary Artery Disease

S: History of CABG.

O: No complaints of chest pain.

A: M.G. is asymptomatic.

P: Monitor for any changes in current status.

Problem 4. Peripheral Vascular Disease

S: None.

O: M.G. has right foot ulcer; M.G. has no complaints of claudication.

A: M.G. is at risk for getting nonhealing ulcers of his extremities because of poor circulation.

P: Educate patient regarding foot care and awareness of increased risk for wounds of his extremities and to seek immediate medical attention if ulcers occur.

CASE 76

CC: L.F. is a 25-year-old male with a 2-week history of cough and increased sputum production after jogging who presents to the outpatient medical clinic with new chest pain when he coughs, shortness of breath, and blood-tinged sputum.

Past Medical History

L.F. has had asthma since childhood, with attacks induced by exercise. He also has sickle cell anemia.

Problem List

1. Pneumococcal pneumonia with bacteremia
2. Asthma
3. Sickle cell anemia
4. Pain secondary to sickle cell crisis; narcotic use
5. Renal insufficiency

Social History

L.F. works as a carpenter, but is on disability because of frequent sickle cell crisis. He smokes cigarettes, 1 pack/day for 8 years. He does not drink alcohol.

Allergies

Sulfa (nausea)

Medication History

Theodur 300 mg p.o. b.i.d.
Beclomethasone inhaler 2 puffs t.i.d.
Oxycodone and aspirin tablets 2 p.o. q6h prn pain

Physical Examination

GEN: DOE and pleuritic chest pain
VS: BP 120/75 HR 75 T 39.5 RR 35 Wt 90 kg Ht 6'4"
HEENT: Slight scleral icterus
CHEST: Bilateral wheezes, dullness RUL
ABD: splenomegaly
GU: WNL
RECT: WNL
NEURO: Tinnitus
SKIN: Multiple bruises noted

Results of Laboratory Tests

Na 142	Cr 1.5	ALT 15	Theophylline
K 3.7	Hct 30.2		level 3
Cl 102	Hgb 10.1		
HCO$_3$ 19	WBC 30k		
BUN 25	Plts P		

WBC differential: 75% P, 10% B, 5% L, 10% E

Arterial blood gases (on room air): PO_2 70, PCO_2 30, pH 7.35

Sputum Gram stain: 25–50 WBC/HPF, 0–5 epithelial cells/HPF; many Gram-positive cocci in pairs

Blood cultures: one of two positive *Streptococci pneumoniae*

Chest x-ray: Right upper lobe consolidation is consistent with bacterial pneumonia

Problem 1. Pneumococcal Pneumonia with Bacteremia

S: The patient has noted sputum production and cough, DOE, and pleuritic chest pain.

O: RUL dullness, T = 39.5, chest x-ray findings, increased WBC count with left shift, poor ABGs, sputum Gram stain consistent with pneumococci, and positive blood culture.

A: This is disseminated pneumococcal pneumonia in a patient who was at increased risk because of sickle cell anemia. Parenteral antibiotics are indicated because of the severity of this infection and its associated mortality. Avoid sulfa drugs since he is allergic.

P: Begin aqueous penicillin G 500,000 U q4–6h i.v. or procaine penicillin 600,000 U q12h i.m. for 7–10 days. Monitor ABGs, chest x-ray, WBC count with differential, cough, and sputum production. Note any color change in sputum. The chest x-ray will not resolve as quickly as other subject/objective parameters, and may actually worsen after the patient is hydrated. Consider pneumococcal vaccine after this acute infection.

Problem 2. Asthma

S: Patient complains of DOE and has a history of asthma.

O: Patient has bilateral wheezes and poor ABGs.

A: The patient has an acute exacerbation of asthma that is consistent with his history of recently jogging and the association of asthma with respiratory tract infections. Also, noncompliance may be a factor since his theophylline level is only 3 μg/ml. Intravenous aminophylline may or may not be helpful in the acute situation.

P: Begin oxygen administration via mask or nasal cannula and hydration to improve the clearing of dried mucus plugs. Treat with epinephrine or terbutaline 0.01 mg/kg (0.5 mg maximum) subcutaneously. May repeat × 2 q15–20 minutes if response is inadequate or use an inhaled β_2 agonist (i.e., metaproterenol, terbutaline, albuterol) 4 puffs stat and 2 puffs q5min until relief. Short-course steroid therapy may be indicated since this patient has been on a steroid inhaler. Begin methylprednisolone 40 mg i.v. q6h × 24–72 hours. Calculate a loading dose of theophylline (taking into account TBW and C_{pobs}

$V_d = 0.45$ liter/kg × 90 kg = 40.5 liter.

Choose 10–20 μg/ml as C_{pss} (peak)

$LD = Vd \times (C_{pdes} - C_{pobs})/ S \times F$

$LD = 40.5$ liter × 12 μg/ml/ 0.85 × 1

$LD = 572$ mg = 600 mg

Calculate a maintenance dose (taking into account the C_{pobs} and IBW = TBW). Calculation of Cl should utilize the factor for smoking.

$Cl = 0.04$ L/kg/hr × 90 kg × 1.6 = 5.8 liter/hr

rate out = rate in (at steady state)

$Cl \times C_{pss}$ (avg) = F × S × MD/ interval

$Cl \times C_{pss}$ (avg)/ F × S = MD/ interval

5.8 liter/hour × 12 μg/ml/ 1 × 0.85 = 82 mg/hour

Monitor wheezing, ABGs, FEV_1. Monitor theophylline levels after steady state. Monitor for signs and symptoms of theophylline toxicity (e.g., CNS and cardiac).

Problem 3. Sickle Cell Anemia

S: None.

O: L.F. has Hct 30.2, Hgb 10.1, PO_2 70, pH 7.35. He also has history of numerous painful crises.

A: L.F. is at risk for another painful crisis due to acidosis and infection. Treatment as outlined above should avoid a crisis. There is no drug treatment that prevents a painful crisis.

P: Give oxygen, antibiotics, and hydration as above. Monitor ABGs, pain, and Hct/Hgb. For pain, see below.

Problem 4. Pain Secondary to Sickle Cell Crisis and Narcotic Use

S: L.F. is unemployed because of the frequency of crisis.

O: L.F. is using oxycodone/aspirin to the extent that the aspirin component has caused tinnitus.

A: He is uncontrolled with frequent crisis; however, patient is not currently in pain.

P: Discontinue oxycodone/aspirin because of overuse, which has led to salicylate toxicity. Monitor vital signs for indications of narcotic withdrawal.

Problem 5. Renal Insufficiency

S: None.

O: Increased BUN, increased serum creatinine.

A: Mild, asymptomatic renal insufficiency is possibly associated with excessive aspirin use, sickle cell disease, or dehydration (from pneumonia and asthma).

P: Obtain blood for salicylate plasma concentration. Rehydrate patient with i.v. NS. Diuretic therapy is not indicated at this time. Check urinalysis for specific gravity, and a 24-hour urine collection for creatinine clearance. Also monitor input and output. Monitor BUN and creatinine after hydration.

CASE 77

CC: M.H. is a 42-year-old male, who comes to the emergency room with a 2-day history of cramping and abdominal pain.

Past Medical History

M.H. has had constipation alternating with diarrhea for 3 months. He has stress-related headaches and dental abscesses. M.H. is a long-time alcoholic who has had numerous hospital admissions related to his alcoholic liver disease and ascites.

Problem List

1. Spontaneous bacterial peritonitis and bacteremia
2. Hepatic encephalopathy from alcoholic liver disease
3. Clindamycin-induced *Clostridium difficile* colitis
4. Anemia
5. Acute alcoholic hepatitis with ascites
6. Dental abscesses
7. Chronic stress-related headaches

Social History

M.H. does not smoke. He drinks 3 six-packs of beer/day (for 15 years).

Allergies

Penicillin (mild rash)

Current Medications

Titralac prn stomach upset
Ibuprofen 600 mg p.o. q4–6h prn headaches
Clindamycin 150 mg p.o. t.i.d.

Physical Examination

    GEN: Male oriented × 2 in severe respiratory distress
     VS: BP 140/78 HR 100 reg RR 50 shallow T 40 Wt 75 kg (dry weight 60 kg) Ht 5′3″
  HEENT: Scleral icterus, poor dentition, foul breath
    COR: NL heart sounds
  CHEST: Clear to auscultation and percussion.
    ABD: Rebound tenderness, diffuse pain RUQ, hepatomegaly, decreased bowel sounds, + fluid wave
   RECT: No masses, guaiac (+)
  NEURO: Lethargic
   SKIN: Jaundice, spider angiomas

Results of Laboratory Tests

Na 148	Hct 28	ALT 600	Ca 8.9	PT 14
K 3.8	Hgb 9.2	LDH P	PO$_4$ 2.5	PTT 40
Cl 102	WBC 25k	Alk Phos P	Mg 1.9	ETOH .2
HCO$_3$ 18	Plts p 180k	Alb 2.6		
BUN 40	MCV 100	T Bili 6.8		
Cr 1.0	AST 1205	Glu 80		

WBC differential: Left shift
Peripheral blood smear: Microcytic and macrocytic cells
Blood cultures: Two of two positive for a Gramnegative rod
Peritoneal fluid Gram stain: Many WBC; few Gramnegative bacilli
Stool: Ova and parasite × 3, negative; *Clostridium difficile* toxin, positive.

Problem 1. Spontaneous Bacterial Peritonitis and Bacteremia

S: M.H. complains of cramping abdominal pain.
O: M.H. has rebound tenderness, RUQ pain, decreased bowel sounds, increased WBC count with left shift, T=40°, increased pulse and respirations, positive blood cultures, and a positive Gram stain of peritoneal fluid.
A: M.H. is a male alcoholic in severe distress with SBP and bacteremia. Parenteral antibiotics are required for this serious infection. Antimicrobials should cover for both aerobic (enterics) and anaerobic gram negative bacilli (e.g., *B. fragilis* vs. *B. melanogenicus*), since culture results are still pending. Penicillin allergy excludes "antipseudomonal" penicillins (e.g., mezlocillin, piperacillin). May use cephalosporin since allergy was not severe in nature. An aminoglycoside is not necessary and would be used with caution in this patient with prerenal azotemia.
P: Discontinue oral clindamycin. Begin ceftizoxime 2 g q8h i.v. Avoid cefotetan since patient has bleeding tendencies. Monitor vital signs, WBC count, and differential, peritoneal fluid and blood cultures. Obtain peritoneal fluid for chemistries. Monitor rebound abdominal tenderness and bowel sounds.

Problem 2. Hepatic Encephalopathy from Alcoholic Liver Disease

S: None.
O: M.H. is oriented × 2 and lethargic.
A: M.H. is in moderate distress with impending encephalopathic coma. Predisposing factors are his constipation; GI bleeding as evidenced by guaiac-positive stool; ETOH-related CNS depression; dehydration as evidenced by BUN to serum creatinine ratio and increased pulse; and acute infection.
P: Give thiamine 100 mg i.v. to rule out the possibility or contribution of Wernicke's syndrome to this patient's changing mental status. Relieve stool impaction if indicated. Carefully rehydrate with i.v. fluids. Discontinue GI irritants including alcohol and ibuprofen along with gastric lavage if bleeding is acute. Discontinue calcium carbonate, which may be contributing to his constipation. Reduce dietary

protein to 0–20 g/day. Begin lactulose p.o. 30–45 ml q.i.d. or until 3–4 stools/day or retention enema—300 ml of 50% qs with water to 1 liter. Monitor for asterixis and changing mental status. Obtain CSF to rule out bacterial meningitis and to monitor CSF glutamine concentration. May check stool pH if lactulose does not appear to be effective (approximately 5.5). Neomycin sulfate is not contraindicated in this patient with colitis and azotemia, and could be instituted carefully in addition to the lactulose. Neomycin sulfate p.o. 0.5–1 g q6h for 5–7 days or retention enema 2–4 g/200 ml NS and methylcellulose up to 8–12 g for acute treatment, however, neomycin is probably not required. Avoid any medications that may cause CNS depression.

Problem 3. Clindamycin-Induced *Clostridium difficile* Colitis

S: M.H. has cramping abdominal pain, diarrhea, and constipation.

O: *C. difficile* toxin positive stool, guaiac-positive stool.

A: This is clindamycin-induced colitis, which may have caused microintestinal perforation that resulted in SBP.

P: Discontinue clindamycin per above order. Give vancomycin p.o. 125–250 mg p.o. q.i.d. × 5–7 days. Oral metronidazole is contraindicated at this time in this patient because of the potential for a disulfiram-reaction, since the ethanol level is 0.2 mg/dl but the alcohol level should decline quickly. Rehydrate as per encephalopathy. Avoid clindamycin therapy in the future.

Problem 4. Anemia

S: M.H. is lethargic.

O: M.H. has decreased HCT, a smear with microcytic and macrocytic cells, and increased MCV.

A: This is probably a mixed anemia from colitis/gastritis–related blood loss (Fe deficiency), anemia of chronic disease, and probable folate and B_{12} dietary deficiencies.

P: Obtain blood specimen for serum folate, iron, TIBC, ferritin, and B_{12} levels. Give folate 1 mg p.o. q.d. Give B_{12} 100 μg i.v. q.d. × 5 doses, then twice monthly for approximately 10 weeks. Give B_{12} only after obtaining the specimen for a level as the administration of folate will improve the anemia, but not the CNS signs of B_{12} deficiency. Wait for serum Fe level and resolution of the colitis before instituting oral Fe sulfate 325 mg p.o. t.i.d. Monitor Hct, Hgb, corrected recticulocyte count, and smear.

Problem 5. Acute Alcoholic Hepatitis with Ascites

S: M.H. complains of cramping abdominal pain.

O: Scleral icterus, diffuse RUQ pain, hepatome-

galy, + fluid wave, jaundice, spider angiomas, increased liver enzymes, AST>ALT, decreased albumin, increased PT, increased T. bilirubin, ETOH=0.2%, fluid weight gain of 15 kg over dry weight.

A: M.H. is in severe respiratory distress that may be excerbated by 15 kg of ascitic fluid. Paracentesis may be indicated to relieve the respiratory distress.

P: Encourage bedrest. Discontinue alcohol use. Monitor vital signs, watch for DTs. Vitamin K 10 mg p.o./s.c. × 3. Avoid intramuscular injections. Mobilize ascites with slow diureses, especially since the patient has pre-renal azotemia. Spironolactone 100 mg p.o. q.d.; the maximal effect will be observed in 3–5 days. May increase the dose by 100 mg/day, up to a maximum of 400 mg/day. Monitor urine Na:K excretion. Ratio should reverse to greater than 1. Monitor serum electrolytes, BUN and Cr during diureses. Monitor abdominal girth and weight loss. Daily weight loss should not exceed 1 kg/day.

Problem 6. Dental Abscesses

S: History.

O: M.H. has foul-smelling breath and poor dentition.

A: The patient is an alcoholic male with poor dentition resulting in oral abscess formation.

P: Parenteral antibiotics for SBP should also be effective for oral abscesses. Further evaluation necessary in view of this patient's foul-smelling breath (may indicate active anaerobic infection).

Problem 7. Chronic Stress-Related Headaches

S: History.

O: None.

A: No current complaint of headache.

P: In future, avoid NSAIs and aspirin because of their GI tract toxicity (gastritis) and antiplatelet effects.

CASE 78

CC: J.W. is a 52-year-old male with a 15-year-history of type I diabetes mellitus, diabetic neuropathy and hypertension. He presents to the emergency room with a swollen right foot with a puncture wound of the sole, which is draining a green, foul smelling pus.

History of Present Illness

J.W. reports that he stepped on a nail approximately 2 weeks ago. He states that because he had received a tetanus booster approximately 6 months ago, he was not worried about an infection. His foot had become progressively more swollen, but it was not painful, and therefore he did not become alarmed until he noticed the drainage.

Past Medical History

J.W. has Type I diabetes mellitus requiring insulin for the past 15 years. J.W. reports compliance with the insulin and he monitors his own blood sugars once or twice daily. He reports that he has not had a checkup for the past 6 months. He reports no visual changes, headaches, or signs and symptoms of hypo, or hyperglycemia.

Problem List

1. Presumed osteomyelitis, right foot
2. Type I diabetes mellitus
3. Hypertension
4. Diabetic neuropathy
5. Diabetic retinopathy
6. Slight renal impairment

Social History

J.W. lives alone. He smokes 1 ppd, but does not drink alcohol. His father died of myocardial infarction (MI) at age 50. His mother is 78; has type II diabetes for 20 years. J.W. has one brother, age 49, with HTN for 5 years.

Medication History

Insulin NPH/Reg 20 U/10 U q AM and 10 U/10 U q PM
Mylanta II 30 ml prn indigestion,
Diltiazem 30 mg p.o. q8h×1 year
Prazosin 2 mg p.o. b.i.d. ×5 years

Allergies

PCN→mild rash

Physical Examination

GEN: Mildly overweight male complaining of swelling and drainage from the right foot, no other complaints.
VS: BP 150/96 HR 86 (reg) T 38.0 RR 14 Wt 85 kg Ht 6'0"
HEENT: Retinopathy
COR: Regular heart rate and rhythm, no murmurs
CHEST: WNL
ABD: WNL
EXT: Decreased sensation, decreased deep tendon reflexes (DTR); purulent drainage from the right foot.

X-ray: Plain film of foot: consistent with bony destruction.

Results of Laboratory Tests

Na 138	BUN 22	WBC 17k
K 4.0	Cr 1.4	Plts 300k
Cl 102	Hct 45	FBS 290
HCO$_3$ 24	Hgb 15	

Urinalysis: heme (+), protein (+), glucose 1/4%.
Cultures: Trans swab: wound, foot (anaerobic and aerobic): *Pseudomonas aeruginosa*, sensitivities pending
Urine culture and sensitivities: negative
Blood cultures × 2: negative
Home blood glucoses: 6 AM, 290; 10 AM, 190; 8 PM, 160.

Problem 1. Osteomyelitis of Right Foot: *Pseudomonas aeruginosa*

S: Patient has green, foul smelling pus draining from the swollen right foot.
O: Culture: (+) for *Pseudomonas aeruginosa*, T 38, WBC 17,000
A: J.W. needs either amputation or 6 weeks of i.v. antibiotics to prevent progression of the bony involvement.
P: Because of his slight penicillin allergy, avoid antipseudomonal penicillins. Begin a cephalosporin and an aminoglycoside. The drugs of choice would be ceftazidime (best third generation cephalosporin against *Pseudomonas*) and tobramycin (best aminoglycoside against *Pseudomonas*). Give ceftazidime 2 g i.v. q8h×6 weeks; give tobramycin 110 mg i.v. q8h×6 weeks to achieve a peak level of 6.3 and a trough of 1.5. Initiate nondrug therapy: drainage of the wound, surgical debridement, and immobilization of J.W.'s foot. Monitor aminoglycoside levels, Cr, BUN, bactericidal titers, *Pseudomonas* sensitivities to antimicrobial agents, hypersensitivity reaction to the cephalosporin, i.v. infiltration, phlebitis, WBCs, temperature, signs and symptoms of sepsis. Educate patient about possible home antibiotic therapy; instruct patient on proper wound care and foot care for diabetics.

Problem 2. Type I Diabetes Mellitus

S: None.
O: FBS 290, retinopathy, neuropathy, urine 1/4% glucose.
A: J.W. needs tighter control than he is achieving with his current insulin regimen. J.W. is presently taking NPH/Reg 20 U/10 U in AM, 10 U/10 U in PM. He needs better control in the AM: the NPH evening dose may be too low or he may be having the Somogyi effect. J.W. is fairly well covered with AM regular, however the AM regular may be increased slightly for tighter control. J.W. is well controlled with afternoon regular insulin.
P: Check 2 AM BS for hypoglycemia. If BS is >140, then increase PM NPH to 14. For tighter control of morning BS increase AM regular to 12 U. Advise patient to stop smoking. Monitor FBS and BS throughout the day, and signs and symptoms of hypoglycemia or hyperglycemia. The goal is negative urine sugar, negative urine ketones, FBS <160, normal glycosolated Hgb. Patient education: Review and emphasize the necessary items of home blood glucose monitoring, insulin administration, signs and symptoms of hypoglycemia or hyperglycemia, foot care, and diet.

Problem 3. Hypertension

S: None.
O: BP 150/96, retinopathy, renal impairment

A: J.W. has poorly controlled hypertension on his current drug regimen. He is currently taking two drugs and neither are at maximal doses. However, both are appropriate medications for a patient with diabetes.

P: Either increase the prazosin to 4 mg p.o. b.i.d., giving the first dose at bedtime, or increase the diltiazem to 60 mg q6h. Patient should decrease his weight, stop smoking, and begin a low-salt diet. Monitor BP (140/90), weight loss; decreased sodium intake; and for side effects of medications: Prazosin—postural hypotension, dizziness, lightheadedness, headache, drowsiness, lack of energy, weakness, palpitations, nausea, and syncope. Diltiazem—anorexia, nausea, other GI effects, headache, arrhythmias, rash, Cr, and LFT changes. Educate patient about regular BP monitoring, compliance with medications, decreased salt intake, and decreased weight; urge him to discontinue smoking.

Problem 4. Diabetic Neuropathy

S: Patient complains of peripheral numbness and loss of the sensation of pain in foot

O: Patient has decreased deep tendon reflexes.

A: There is no effective treatment for this problem. Treat the underlying disease, diabetes, with tighter control of his blood sugar.

P: Discontinue smoking. If the neuropathy worsens, consider low-dose amitriptyline 10 mg p.o. b.i.d. Refer to a podiatrist for foot care. Monitor for worsening signs and symptoms. Educate patient about proper foot care, (i.e., cleaning feet daily, no tight shoes, do not go barefoot, etc.) proper BS control, and the need for a podiatrist.

Problem 5. Diabetic Retinopathy

S: None.

O: Ocular changes consistent with retinopathy.

A: To prevent progression of the ocular damage, maintain tighter control of the diabetes. Retinopathy is irreversible. There is no specific drug therapy for the problem.

P: Refer patient to an ophthalmologist. Advise patient to discontinue smoking and decrease BP. Maintain tighter control of blood glucose. Educate patient about proper eye care by the ophthalmologist.

Problem 6. Slight Renal Compromise

S: None.

O: Cr, BUN, U/A.

A: J.W. needs tighter control of his diabetes and hypertension to prevent worsening of his renal impairment. Avoid nephrotoxic drugs if possible.

P: Keep a close watch on J.W.'s renal function by monitoring Cr, BUN, drug levels, drug doses, and urinalysis. Patient Education: Teach patient to recognize signs of worsening renal failure.

CASE 79

CC: M.C. is a 26-year-old homosexual male who comes to the emergency room complaining of a tender, red, swollen left knee, fever, dizziness, an unsteady gait, and nonspecific aches and pains for the last 3 days. He also reports a 15-lb weight loss since his return from Mexico 3 months ago and he occasionally suffers abdominal cramping.

History of Present Illness

M.C. noticed swelling in his left knee 3 days ago, which has progressively worsened and become more hot and red. He states that it has become progressively more difficult to walk over the past 24 hours. He denies hitting or being hit in the knee.

Past Medical History

M.C. has had grand mal seizures for 20 years. (M.C. reports approximately one seizure every 2–3 months when he is noncompliant with his phenytoin and phenobarbital.) He has a history of gonorrhea (1 and 4 years ago; both times treated with penicillin); a history of herpes simplex type II (genitalis) for 8 years with occasional flares, now dormant; and a history of schizophrenia, first diagnosed in 1984.

Problem List

1. Probable gonococcal septic arthritis
2. Probable gonorrhea (gonococcal urethritis)
3. Taenia saginata (beef tapeworm)
4. Seizures, Phenytoin toxicity
5. Schizophrenia, Haloperidol side effects

Medication History

Phenytoin 400 mg p.o. qhs × 5 years
Phenobarbital × 20 years (current dosage 120 mg p.o. qhs)
Haloperidol 10 mg p.o. qd (recently reduced from 20 mg/day)

Social History

M.C. lives with a 55-year-old male and works as a stock person in a local grocery. M.C. admits to occasional binges of alcohol. He also smokes approximately one marijuana "joint" per day.

Physical Examination

GEN: Nervous-appearing male in moderate distress complaining of knee pain and stiffness.

VS: BP 120/74 HR 90 T 38.5 RR 20 Wt 60 kg (previous Wt 66 kg, 4 months ago)

HEENT: Nystagmus on lateral gaze, "lip smacking"

COR: WNL

CHEST: WNL
    ABD: Hyperactive bowel sounds, no pain on deep palpation
     GU: Scant, white urethral discharge
RECTAL: Normal prostate, no evidence HS type II
    EXT: Rhythmic tremor
NEURO: Alert and oriented × 3, slight gait ataxia

Results of Laboratory Tests

Na 140	Cr 1.0	Alb 2.5
K 4.5	Hct 48	Phenytoin 16
Cl 99	Hgb 16	Phenobarbital 25
HCO$_3$ 24	WBC 13k	
BUN 14	Plts 250k	

Urinalysis: WNL
Joint fluid, knee: turbid, many PMNs, GM (−) diplococci on Gram stain.
Urethral swab: Gram (−) diplococci, chlamydia (−).
Stool for ova and parasite: Taenia saginata
HIV antibody-negative

Problem 1. Probable Gonococcal Septic Arthritis

S: M.C. has a hot, red, swollen, and tender left knee. He has progressive difficulty walking with stiffness and fever.

O: Joint fluid Gram-negative diplococci, many PMNs, T = 38.5, WBC 13k

A: He needs immediate treatment for his gonococcal septic arthritis to prevent destruction of the joint. He has probable seeded the joint from a disseminated gonococcal urethritis.

P: Because of M.C.'s history of gonococcal infections, there is a need to check for penicillinase-producing *Neisseria* gonorrhea (PPNG). If M.C. is in a PPNG endemic area, give ceftriaxone 1 g q24h × 7–10 days. Otherwise, begin high-dose penicillin 20 MU/day divided every 2–4 hours for 7–10 days. When β-lactamase results return, switch M.C. to the appropriate agent. Apply ice packs to the knee to decrease swelling. Keep the joint immobile. Acetaminophen or aspirin may be used for both the fever and inflammation (ASA only). Monitor signs and symptoms of septic arthritis, culture results, temperature, WBC, and for ceftriaxone or penicillin side effects: phlebitis, rash, drug fever, nausea, diarrhea, and possible seizures (from high-dose penicillin, as M.C. does have a seizure history). Patient education: Advise as per Problem 2.

Problem 2. Probable Gonorrhea (Gonococcal Urethritis)

S: Urethral discharge, fever.

O: WBC count: 13k, urethral Gram's stain, Gram-negative diplococci, T = 38.5.

A: M.C. needs treatment for his gonococcal urethritis. There is a need to watch for PPNG because of his history of exposure.

P: The treatment for gonococcal septic arthritis will more than adequately cover urethritis. His partner should also be treated. Monitor signs and symptoms of gonococcal urethritis and ceftriaxone or penicillin side effects. Patient Education: Educate M.C. on use of condoms and safe sex. Educate M.C. about sexually transmitted diseases including AIDS.

Problem 3. Taenia Saginata (Beef Tapeworm)

S: Patient complains of abdominal cramping and weight loss of 15 lb over the last 4 months.

O: Fecal ova and parasite: (+) for Taenia saginata

A: M.C. probably ate uncooked beef while in Mexico. He needs to be treated to kill the tapeworm.

P: Give niclosamide 2 g as a single dose (preferred treatment). Monitor for abdominal cramping and nausea. Look for fragments of the worm in the stool for up to 6–12 weeks after the dose. A mild laxative in the evening after the dose may help.

Problem 4. Seizures, Phenytoin Toxicity

S: Dizziness, ataxia, nystagmus

O: Phenytoin level: 16 mg/liter→27.1 mg/liter (when corrected for low albumin)

A: Phenytoin toxicity possibly as a result of decreased albumin, which is secondary to weight loss and protein loss from the tapeworm infection. However, his seizures have been well controlled.

P: Hold the phenytoin × 24 hours, then check a phenytoin level. When the phenytoin level is within the therapeutic range, restart phenytoin at a lower dose (e.g. 300–350 mg p.o. qd). Monitor phenytoin level, albumin levels (albumin should rise over the next few months and phenytoin level may decrease, at which time the dose should be readjusted), compliance, and reversal of signs and symptoms. Patient Education: Educate M.C. as to the signs and symptoms of phenytoin toxicity and the need for compliance.

Problem 5. Schizophrenia, Haloperidol Side Effects

S: None.

O: M.C. is observed to have tremor of his hands and "lip smacking" consistent with tardive dyskinesia (TD). He is on long-term haloperidol.

A: M.C. had developed TD. This is very common in patients taking butyrophenones for periods of >1 year. His schizophrenia appears to be well controlled.

P: No treatment is available except possibly increasing the dose slightly. Urge patient to discontinue marijuana use and alcohol. Monitor for any improvement in signs and symptoms. Patient Education: Educate M.C. as to the signs and symptoms of haloperidol TD. M.C. should be told that this is potentially irreversible.

CASE 80

CC: S.C., a 40-year-old female, is an intravenous heroin user with a 3-day history of weakness, fatigue, anorexia, and DOE. She had felt fine since she got out of the hospital 6 months ago for the treatment of Group A streptococcal endocarditis.

Past Medical History

S.C. has had chronic headaches for 5 years. She has had peptic ulcer disease for 3 years.

Problem List

1. Bacterial endocarditis
2. Urinary tract infection (UTI), rule out pyelonephritis
3. Peptic ulcer disease
4. Chronic headaches
5. Heroin abuse, possible withdrawal

Social History

Tobacco, none; alcohol, none.

Allergies

None known.

Medication History

Empirin with codeine p.o. q2–3h prn headache
Milk of Magnesia 1 teaspoonful q4h for constipation
Cimetidine 800 mg p.o. qhs

Physical Examination

GEN: Female in moderate distress (she has lost 10 lb over the last 2 weeks)
VS: BP 120/74 HR 80 RR 40 Wt 50 kg Ht 5′5″ afebrile
HEENT: WNL
CHEST: Decreased breath sounds bilaterally
COR: III/VI SEM
ABD: Nontender, palpable spleen
RECT: Guaiac negative
SKIN: WNL, except "track marks"

Results of Laboratory Tests

Na 140	Cr 2.5	AST 26	T Bili 1.2	PT 12.1
K 4.0	Hct 39	ALT 23	Glu 65	PTT 38
Cl 104	Hgb 13	LDH 95	Ca 8.5	ESR 80
HCO₃ 31	WBC 15.8k	Alk Phos 110	PO₄ 3.6	
BUN 25	Plts 90 k	Alb 3.2	Mg 2.9	

Rheumatoid factor: positive; HIV antibody–negative
Arterial blood gases: (on 2 liters O_2 via nasal prongs) PO_2 95, PCO_2 44, pH 7.35
Blood cultures: (3/3+) Gram-positive cocci in clusters
Urinalysis: Gram-negative rods 50–100/HPF, RBC and WBC 5–10/HPF, glucose and bili negative
Chest x-ray: Findings consistent with pulmonary embolism.

Problem _____

S: _____
_____
_____

O: _____
_____
_____
_____

A: _____
_____
_____
_____
_____
_____

P: _____
_____

Problem _____

S: _____
_____
_____

O: _____
_____
_____
_____

A: _____
_____
_____
_____
_____

P: _____
_____

Problem

S:

O:

A:

P:

Problem

S:

O:

A:

P:

Problem

S:

O:

A:

P:

Problem

S:

O:

A:

P:

Questions

1. What is the most likely pathogen causing this patient's endocarditis?
2. What empiric antimicrobial therapy is indicated?
3. What are the possible etiologies for this patient's renal insufficiency?
4. In view of this patient's renal disease, make recommendations on her drug therapy prior to admission. Give all rationale.

CASE 81

CC: L.D. is a 38-year-old male admitted for elective colectomy with ileostomy as treatment for his ulcerative colitis

Past Medical History

L.D. was diagnosed as having ulcerative colitis approximately 10 years ago. At that time he elected medical therapy. However, in the past several years the attacks have occurred more frequently; they consist of bloody diarrhea and cramping, and L.D. notes a 15-lb weight loss.

Problem List

1. Ulcerative colitis for 10 years
2. Anemia for 4 months
3. Arthritis, painful joints for 8 months

Current Medications

Sulfasalazine 500 mg p.o. q6h × 8 years
Prednisone 40 mg p.o. qd × 4 months
$FeSO_4$ 325 mg p.o. qd × 4 months
Ibuprofen 600 mg p.o. q6h prn

Allergies

None known.

Physical Examination

GEN: Thin, tired looking male in no apparent distress, although somewhat anxious due to anticipated surgery.
VS: BP 120/80 HR 89 T 99 RR 15 Wt 66 kg
HEENT: WNL
COR: WNL
CHEST: WNL
ABD: Diffusely tender with voluntary guarding, active bowel sounds
GU: WNL
RECT: Proctitis, guaiac (+)
EXT: Tender, swollen fingers and knee.
NEURO: WNL

Results of Laboratory Tests

Na 141	Cr 0.8	Glu 111	PT 10.5
K 4.1	Hct 35		PTT 36.7
Cl 102	Hgb 11		ESR 5
HCO_3 24	WBC 10k		
BUN 16	Plts 180k		

Urinalysis: WNL

Problem _____

S: _____

O: _____

A: _____

P: _____

Problem _____

S: _____

O: _____

A: _____

P: _____

Problem

S:—————————————————————

—————————————————————

—————————————————————

—————————————————————

O:—————————————————————

—————————————————————

—————————————————————

—————————————————————

A:—————————————————————

—————————————————————

—————————————————————

—————————————————————

—————————————————————

P:—————————————————————

—————————————————————

—————————————————————

Problem

S:—————————————————————

—————————————————————

—————————————————————

—————————————————————

O:—————————————————————

—————————————————————

—————————————————————

—————————————————————

A:—————————————————————

—————————————————————

—————————————————————

—————————————————————

—————————————————————

P:—————————————————————

—————————————————————

—————————————————————

Questions

1. Under what surgical classification will L.D.'s colectomy fall?
2. What are the likely organisms that prophylaxis should be directed against?
3. Recommend a suitable bowel preparation for L.D.
4. Should an intravenous antibiotic be added to the oral antibiotics. If so which one, give drug, dose, schedule, and duration.
5. Discuss postsurgical complications that could occur in L.D. because of his prednisone therapy.

CASE 82

CC: H.G. is a 40-year-old homosexual male with acquired immunodeficiency syndrome (AIDS) who is admitted for new-onset headaches, altered mental status, chills, and a temperature of 40C. H.G. was found having a tonic-clonic seizure and foaming at the mouth by his roommate, who brought him to the hospital. His roommate has also noted H.G. to be more confused for about 3 weeks prior to hospital admission.

Past Medical History and Medication History

History of *Pneumocystis carinii* pneumonia (PCP) treated 3 months ago with cotrimoxazole.

History of gonorrhea (GC) treated 3 months ago with benzathine penicillin 4.8 MU i.m. × 1 shot

(+) PPD untreated; last PPD (−) 1 year ago.

History of pseudomembraneous colitis with clindamycin.

History of prosthetic valve replacement 3 years ago, on warfarin 2 mg daily.

Underwent partial gastrectomy for UGI bleed 5 years ago.

Problem List

1. AIDS
2. ? CNS infection (toxo??)
3. ? Pneumonia
4. Seizures
5. S/P PCP pneumonia
6. S/P GC, possible reinfection
7. History of pseudomembraneous colitis
8. Prosthetic valve replacement
9. S/P GI bleed with partial gastrectomy
10. Possible TB

Allergies

None known.

Social History

H.G. lives with his healthy partner. He has smoked two packs of cigarettes for 20 years. History of alcoholism with "blackouts" after heavy binges. He denies IVDA.

Physical Examination

GEN: Obtunded, stuporous male

VS: BP 90/60 HR 100 T 40 RR 15 Wt 43 kg Ht 5'9"

HEENT: Rigid neck

COR: NL S1 S2, (−)S3 (+) 3/6 SEM

CHEST: Course bibasilar diffuse rhonchi and wheezes

ABD: WNL

GU: (+) Urethral discharge

RECT: WNL

EXT: WNL

NEURO: Oriented ×0; withdraws all extremities to painful stimuli.

Results of Laboratory Tests

Na 133	Cr 3.4	MCV 80	Glu 200	PT 18
K 3.6	Hct 30	AST 25		PTT 35
Cl 110	Hgb 13	ALT 33		
HCO$_3$ 13	WBC 8.5k	Alb 3.8		
BUN 34	Plts 80k	T.Bili 1.0		

ABG: pH 7.5, PCO$_2$ 35, PO$_2$ 70

WBC 8.5 with 84P, 13B, 3L (H.G.'s baseline WBC is about 4.5)

LP: 10–20 WBCs, 20 RBCs, protein 180, glucose 50; Gram stain: Gram (−) diplococci

BC×3 pending

Sputum Gram stain: numerous PMNs, mixed oral flora, (−) epithelial cells, AFB pending

Chest x-ray: New RML infiltrate, inconsistent with PCP

Head CT scan: Ring-enhancing lesions in frontal and parietal lobes

Problem _____

S: _____

O: _____

A: _____

P: _____

Problem _____

S: _____

O: _____

A: _____

P: _____

Problem _____

S: _____

O: _____

A: _____

P: _____

Problem _____

S: _____

O: _____

A: _____

P: _____

Problem _____

S: _____

O: _____

A: _____

P: _____

Problem _____

S: _____

O: _____

A: _____

P: _____

Problem _____

S: _____

O: _____

A: _____

P: _____

Problem

S:

O:

A:

P:

Problem

S:

O:

A:

P:

Problem

S:

O:

A:

P:

Problem

S:

O:

A:

P:

Questions

1a. Recurrent pneumocystis carinii pneumonia (PCP) pneumonia is not suspected. What is the most likely etiology of his pneumonia and explain why.

b. Based on H.G.'s clinical presentation, recommend an empiric treatment regimen (drug, dose, route, interval) for his pneumonia and state your rationale for the antibiotic(s) selected.

2. What is the most likely cause of his meningitis? Recommend an appropriate treatment plan and regimen (drug, dose, route, duration) to eradicate his meningitis.

3. Current Gram stain of his urethral discharge shows Gram-negative intracellular diplococci. Recommend a complete management plan and treatment regimen (drug, dose, route, interval, duration, and rationale) for his current urethral discharge. Explain why you agree or disagree with the treatment that H.G. received 3 months ago for his GC.

4a. Discuss the risks versus benefits of INH prophylaxis in H.G. and defend your decision to treat or not to treat.

b. If his sputum returns positive for AFB, recommend a complete treatment regimen (drug, dose, route, duration, and rationale) for his TB. Explain any other considerations necessary to accommodate the addition of this regimen.

CASE 83

CC: K.M. is a 29-year-old female who came to the emergency room complaining of abdominal pain that started early this morning.

Past Medical History

K.M. was in her usual state of health until this morning, when she awoke with crampy abdominal pain. She also noted a 3/4% urine glucose upon testing and therefore administered an additional 5 U regular insulin with her morning injection. At work, she remembered feeling nauseous and was unable to eat lunch. As the day progressed, the pain increased, she had two episodes of vomiting, and therefore decided to come to the hospital.

Allergies

None known.

Problem List

1. Abdominal pain as above for approximately 16 hours
2. Type I diabetes mellitus for 16 years
3. Asthma for 10 years

Medication History

Insulin reg/NPH 10/20 q AM and 5/5 q PM
Ortho-Novum 1/50 one p.o. q.d.

Theodur 400 mg p.o. b.i.d.
Albuterol inhaler 2 puffs q 4–6 h prn
ASA 650 mg p.o. prn headache (about two doses per day)

Physical Examination

GEN: Young woman in moderate distress, complaining of abdominal pain.
VS: BP 140/83 HR 124 T 38.5° RR 18 WT 58kg
HEENT: WNL
COR: Sinus tachycardia
CHEST: Few scattered expiratory wheezes
ABD: RLQ tenderness, rebound tenderness RLQ
GU: Deferred
RECTAL: Guaiac positive
EXT: WNL
NEURO: WNL

Results of Laboratory Tests

Na 148	Cr 0.9	Glu 240	PT 10.4
K 3.8	Hct 32		PTT 34.2
Cl 98	Hgb 10		
HCO_3 26	WBC 16k		
BUN 17	Plts 200k		

Urinalysis: ½% glucose

Problem

S:

O:

A:

P:

Problem _____

S: _____

O: _____

A: _____

P: _____

Problem _____

S: _____

O: _____

A: _____

P: _____

Questions

1. During the operation, it is found that the appendix has perforated and the surgery is now considered contaminated or "dirty". List the probable organisms and the appropriate antibiotic therapy.
2. List monitoring parameters for the antibiotic therapy.
3. Due to her serious infection, K.M. is transferred to the surgical ICU and will be npo for at least several days. Recommend appropriate i.v. therapy for her theophylline.

CASE 84

CC: G.B. is a 35-year-old male admitted with increased abdominal pain, nausea, vomiting, and diarrhea for 3 days; increasing abdominal girth for 2 weeks; and fever, chills, and dysuria for 8 days.

Past Medical History

G.B. has a history of recurrent UTI, approximately six times a year and has had an UGI bleed.

Problem List

1. Alcoholism
2. Ascites
3. Fever, possible spontaneous bacterial peritonitis
4. Possible UTI

Medication History

Ranitidine 150 mg p.o. qhs

Allergies

None known.

Social History

(+) Alcoholism
(+) Smoking 3 ppd
(+) IVDA denies

Physical Examination

GEN: Ill-appearing nonobese male in moderate distress
VS: BP 90/60 HR 120 T 40 RR 30 and shallow Wt 80 kg (elevated 10 kg over baseline which was within 20% of his IBW)
HEENT: WNL
COR: Normal S1, S2, (−)S3, (−)S4, (+)3/6 SEM
CHEST: Clear without wheezes or rales
ABD: Tender RUQ, (+) shifting dullness, decreased BS
GU: Normal prostate, (+) CVAT
RECT: Guaiac (−)
EXT: (−) Pedal edema
NEURO: Oriented ×3

Results of Laboratory Tests

Na 130	Cr 1.5	AST 50	T Bili 1.0	PT 12
K 3.0	Hct 13	ALT 45	Glu 110	PTT 28
Cl 103	Hgb 39	LDH P	Ca 9.3	HIV (−)
HCO_3 26	WBC 17.5k	Alk Phos 80	PO_4 2.5	
BUN 16	Plts 50k	Alb 3.6	Mg 1.6	

WBC Differential: 60P, 25B, 10L, 5M

Urinalysis: Urine Gram stain: (+) PMNs, fat Gram-negative rods; Urine culture: Pending

Stool examination: (−) WBCs, no organisms seen; stool culture pending

Abdominal tap: 1000 WBC, 90% polys, peritoneal fluid culture pending

Blood cultures × 3: pending

Chest x-ray: WNL

ECG: WNL

Problem

S:

O:

A:

P:

Problem

S:

O:

A:

P:

Problem

S:

O:

A:

P:

Problem

S:

O:

A:

P:

Problem

S:

O:

A:

P:

Questions

1. Tobramycin and ceftazidime are prescribed pending results of the abdominal tap and urine cultures. Recommend a tobramycin dosing regimen to achieve a therapeutic C_p max and a nontoxic trough.

2. List the three most likely causative organisms for G.B.'s fever that must be covered pending cultures and explain why.

3. Ceftazidime and tobramycin were prescribed pending results of the abdominal tap and urine cultures.
   a. If you agree with the antibiotics selected, explain why and recommend a dosing regimen for the ceftazidime.
   b. If you disagree with the antibiotics selected, explain why and recommend a new antibiotic(s) regimen, including an appropriate dosing regimen and rationale for all antibiotic(s) selected.

4. Later that evening, G.B. complains of increased abdominal pain, sweating and diarrhea and reluctantly admits to using intravenous heroin three times a day for 6 months prior to admission. Morphine is given to cover his withdrawal symptoms.

   Explain how and why this new information affects or does not affect your previous recommended antibiotic regimen (from Question 3). Explain any antibiotic changes (additions or deletions) to your previous regimen based on this new information. Give a complete dosing regimen for any antibiotic(s) added.

5. G.B. is improving on day 3 of the recommended antibiotic regimen. That night he develops nausea, vomiting, diarrhea and abdominal cramping 6–8 hours after ingesting creamed turkey a la king from the hospital cafeteria. The intern wants to prescribe cotrimoxazole for his diarrhea and cramps. Explain whether you agree or disagree with this treatment. If you agree, give a dosing regimen and duration of treatment. If you disagree, recommend an appropriate treatment regimen and duration.

   Examination: T 37; stool Gram stain: (−) WBCs, (−) organisms (−) RBCs

6. The urine culture and sensitivities from admission show 10^6 colonies of *E. coli* sensitive to everything. Defend or refute the following statement: G.B. should have been a candidate for single-dose therapy upon admission to the hospital. Give evidence to support your conclusions. If you agree, recommend a drug, dose, route, and dosing interval.

CASE 85

CC: F.H. is a 65-year-old male that was admitted to the hospital 1 week ago for elective hip revision surgery.

The patient has been recovering from surgery without complications until today when he was noted to have a spiking fever to 40°C along with increased production of yellow-green sputum.

Past Medical History

F.H. has had chronic obstructive pulmonary disease (COPD) for 8 years with a chronic, productive cough. He has had type II diabetes mellitus for 7 years and had hip repair 2 years ago after traumatic injury.

Problem List

1. Pneumonia
2. COPD
3. Type II diabetes mellitus
4. Hip surgery

Social History

F.H. worked as a coal miner for 30 years. He smoked cigarettes, 2 packs/day for 40 years but quit 6 years ago. He drinks beer occasionally.

Allergies

NKDA; allergic to pollen and dust

Current Medications

Prednisone 7.5 mg p.o. qd
Metaproterenol inhaler prn
Tolbutamide 500 mg p.o. b.i.d.

Physical Examination

GEN: Male with shortness of breath (SOB)
VS: BP 120/85 HR 85 T 39.5 RR 35 Wt 80 kg Ht 5' 6"
HEENT: Retinopathy
COR: WNL
CHEST: Bilateral wheezes and rhonchi
ABD: WNL
GU: WNL
RECT: WNL
EXT: No signs of thrombophlebitis, thinning of skin noted
NEURO: Neuropathy upper extremities

Results of Laboratory Tests

Na 145	Hct 56	LDH 110	PO_4 3.1
K 3.5	Hgb 17.6	Alk Phos 58	Mg 2.2
Cl 101	WBC 15.3k	Alb 3.9	PT 11.2

HCO_3 19	Plts 208k	T.Bili 0.9	PTT 36.7
BUN 10	AST 24	Glu 320	
Cr 1.9	ALT 18	Ca 9.3	

WBC differential: 85% polys, 10% bands, 5% lymphs

Arterial blood gases (on room air): PO_2 60, PCO_2 47, pH 7.2

Sputum Gram stain: 50–100 WBC/HPF; 0–5 epithelial cells/HPF; many Gram-negative coccobacilli

Culture: *Hemophilus influenzae* (β-lactamase +)

Urinalysis: WNL, except 2% glucose

Chest x-ray: Slight cardiomegaly, diffuse bilateral infiltrates consistent with bacterial pneumonia

Problem _____

S:_____

O:_____

A:_____

P:_____

Problem

S:

O:

A:

P:

Problem

S:

O:

A:

P:

Problem

S:

O:

A:

P:

Problem

S:

O:

A:

P:

CASE 86

CC: C.W. is a 29-year-old female prostitute, who comes to clinic for follow-up of a number of complaints including vaginal green discharge (foul-smelling), abdominal cramping, watery diarrhea (> 6 bowel movements/day x 2 days) and a temperature of 39°.

Past Medical and Social History

C.W. has been a prostitute for approximately 10 years. She occasionally works as a prostitute now. She is single with two children living in a condemned apartment with no running water. She reports having gonorrhea three times, chlamydia twice and syphilis once; all were previously treated.

Her mother died of miliary TB in 1984. She has six brothers and sisters, alive and well. Father unknown.

Medications

None.

Problem List

1. Gonorrhea
2. Chlamydia urethritis
3. Trichomonas vaginalis
4. Recent TB convertor
5. Giardiasis
6. Mild hypokalemia
7. Malnutrition
8. Hypovolemia/Pre–renal azotemia

Physical Examination

GEN: Thin, cachectic, ill-appearing female looking older than her stated age.
VS: BP 110/70 (supine) 90/60 (sitting) HR 90 (supine) 100 (sitting) T 39 RR 20 Wt 40 kg Ht 5'2"
ROS: (−) cough, (−) Night sweats, (+) Wt loss
HEENT: Normal
COR: WNL
CHEST: No Cough, (−) chest X-ray
ABD: Diffusely tender w/o rebound, hyperactive bowel sounds, suprapubic tenderness, no hepatosplenomegaly
GU: Greenish vaginal discharge
NEURO: WNL

Results of Laboratory Tests

Na 135	HCO$_3$ 30	Hct 39
K 3.3	BUN 22	Hgb 13
Cl 100	Cr 1.1	WBC 17

Cultures from 2 days ago:
Trans swab cervix: gonococcus, *Chlamydia*
Slide of vaginal trans swab (wet mount): motile trichomonads
Bacterial culture: gonococci, chlamydia (+) Methylene blue (−)
Stool for ova and parasites x 3: (+) for Giardia
PPD: 10 mm induration; negative 1 year ago
HIV: Pending

Problem

S:

O:

A:

P:

Problem

S:

O:

A:

P:

Problem

S:

O:

A:

P:

Problem

S:

O:

A:

P:

Problem

S:

O:

A:

P:

Problem

S:

O:

A:

P:

Problem

S:

O:

A:

P:

Problem

S:

O:

A:

P:

CASE 87

CC: L.C. is a 30-year-old female prostitute who is admitted to general hospital with complaints of shortness of breath, fever, chills, abdominal-pelvic pain, myalgias, and arthralgias. She also notes nausea and weight gain the last month which she attributes to her birth control pills.

Past Medical History

L.C. has had asthma for 15 years. She had a tooth extraction 3 months ago for tooth impaction. L.C. has seizures secondary to head trauma from a motor vehicle accident. She has a history of rheumatic heart disease and chronic asymptomatic bacteruria, untreated at present.

OB/GYN History

G_2P_0 (two miscarriages).
Missed last menstrual period.

Problem List

1. Endocarditis
2. Pelvic inflammatory disease (PID)
3. Pregnancy (desires to carry pregnancy)
4. Asymptomatic bacteruria
5. Asthma
6. Seizures
7. Rheumatic heart disease

Medication History

Theodur 400 mg b.i.d.
Tri-norinyl-28 (Ethinyl estradiol 35/norethindrone 0.5/1.0/0.5) 1 tablet hs x 3 months
Phenytoin 300 mg q.d. x 1 year

Allergies

None known.

Social History

L.C. is unmarried. She smokes, 2 ppd for 10 years. She drinks approximately four rum and cokes per night. She denies using recreational drugs and IVDA.

Family History

L.C.'s mother is alive and has Type II diabetes mellitus and hypertension. His father had hypertension and died at age 50 of a myocardial infarction.

Physical Examination

GEN: Well developed well nourished female in acute distress
VS: BP 130/80 T 40.5 R 30 Wt 65 kg (60 kg 2 months ago)
HEENT: (+) Roth spots
COR: NL S1, S2, −S3, grade III/VI SEM
CHEST: (−) wheezes, (+) rhonchi, (+) rales, (+) echophony
ABD: (+) Rebound tenderness
GU: (−) CVAT (−) dysuria
RECT: WNL
EXT: + Petechiae, splinter hemorrhages
NEURO: WNL

PELVIC: Enlarged uterus, consistent with 10 weeks of pregnancy + cervical motion adexenal tenderness

Results of Laboratory Tests

Na 140	Cr 1.0	Theophylline 15
K 4.5	Hct 35	DPH level 15
Cl 100	Hgb 12	Serum preg test (+)
HCO$_3$ 26	WBC 20.3k	
BUN 10	FBS 155	

WBC differential: 80P, 10B, 7L, 3M

Gram stain vaginal discharge: + PMNs, Gram-negative diplococci

Blood cultures x 3: Gram (+) cocci in chains

Urinalysis: Sp Gr 1.015, pH 7, 10–20 RBC, 20–50 WBC, 1% glucose, 4 (+) Bacteria, Gram stain: GNR, C&S: 10^6 *Proteus mirablis*, Ⓢ-Amp, gent, cefaz, TCN, TMP/SMX, nitrofurantoin

Chest x-ray: WNL

Problem

S:

O:

A:

P:

Problem

S:

O:

A:

P:

Problem

S:

O:

A:

P:

Problem

S:

O:

A:

P:

Problem

S:

O:

A:

P:

Problem

S:

O:

A:

P:

Problem

S:

O:

A:

P:

CASE 88

CC: M.B. is a 44-year-old male who has returned 1 week ago from a 2-month trip around the world. He is brought by his roommate to the ER with altered mental status, seizures and a temperature of 40°. He complains of night sweats, cough, fatigue, shortness of breath (SOB), headache, and malaise, which has progressed over the last 2 months. He also developed watery diarrhea and abdominal pain 2 weeks prior to returning despite his prophylaxis with doxycycline 100 mg qd for 4 weeks. He discontinued his doxycycline 1 week ago.

Past Medical History

M.B. has asthma; seizures, complex partial x 10 years; and untreated (+) PPD for 8 months (last PPD 1 year earlier was negative). He is a chronic hepatitis-B carrier and is status post cadaver renal transplant.

Problem List

1. Dehydration due to *C. difficile* colitis
2. Meningitis, probable cryptococcal
3. Pulmonary tuberculosis
4. Glaucoma
5. Asthma
6. Seizures
7. S/P cadaver renal transplant
8. Chronic hepatitis-B carrier
9. Hypokalemia

Medication History

Metaproterenol inhaler prn
Phenytoin 350 mg qd
Prednisone 40 mg daily for 6 months
Cyclosporine 300 mg po qd

Allergies

Sulfas (Stevens-Johnson syndrome)

Social History

ETOH, two drinks per day
Smokes 1 ppd for 20 years

Physical Examination

GEN: Agitated, anxious, thin male in acute distress
VS: BP 100/50 HR 110 T 40 RR 30 Wt 50 kg
HEENT: Nuchal rigidity present, dry mucous membranes; bilateral loss of peripheral vision, IOP 40 mm with open angles, papilledema
COR: WNL
CHEST: (−) Wheezes, (+) coarse rhonchi
ABD: RLQ tenderness and cramping
GU: WNL
RECT: WNL
EXT: Palpable fistula (L) arm
NEURO: Oriented × 2, cranial nerves II–XII intact

Results of Laboratory Tests

Na 154	Cr 1.8	AST 25	Phenytoin level 15
K 2.6	Hct 34	ALT 23	Cyclosporine level P
Cl 110	Hgb 12	Alb 4.0	
HCO_3 14	WBC 24k	Glu 150	
BUN 30	Plts 159k	Hb_sAg (+)	

Arterial Blood Gases: PO_2 50, PCO_2 38, pH 7.5
WBC Differential: 30% P, 6% M, 4% E, 60% L
Urinalysis: WNL
Stool examination: *C. difficile* toxin (+); (−) leukocytes;
Stool C&S: (−) *Shigella, Salmonella,* or *Camplyobacter*
Sputum AFB (+); PPD now (−)
CSF LP: protein 180; gluc 15 mg/100 ml; 10–20 WBC, Gram stain, no organisms seen; (+) cryptococcal antigen; india ink stain cryptococcus seen.
Chest x-ray: Right cavitary lesion, consistent with TB.
Head CT: No masses, no evidence of hydrocephalus.

Problem

S:_____

O:_____

A:_____

P:_____

Problem

S:

O:

A:

P:

Problem

S:

O:

A:

P:

Problem

S:

O:

A:

P:

Problem

S:

O:

A:

P:

Problem

S:

O:

A:

P:

Problem

S:

O:

A:

P:

Problem

S:

O:

A:

P:

Problem

S:

O:

A:

P:

CASE 89

CC: J.B. is a 29-year-old male who was admitted to University Hospital 10 days ago with newly diagnosed acute nonlymphocytic leukemia (ANLL) to begin induction chemotherapy. This morning he had a fever spike to 39°, developed rigors, and a cough.

Past Medical History

Strep infection at age 12 followed by chronic glomerulonephritis

Appendicitis at age 17

Hickman catheter placed upon admission to hospital

Problem List

1. ANLL
2. Fever, rigors and cough in a neutropenic patient, possible pneumonia
3. Thrombocytopenia
4. Chronic glomerulonephritis
5. Anemia

Current Medications

Induction chemotherapy
Allopurinol 300 mg p.o. qd

Allergies

Penicillin (rash only)

Family History

No history of cancer.

Social History

J.B. currently lives alone. He smokes 1 pack per day of cigarettes and denies using alcohol.

Physical Examination

GEN: Septic-looking male in moderate distress
VS: BP 129/77 HR 95 T 38.6 RR 27 Wt 70 kg Ht 5'6"
HEENT: WNL except for pale sclera
COR: NL S1, S2
CHEST: Hickman catheter exit site erythematous and tender
Decreased breath sounds in LLL
ABD: Benign
GU: NL
RECT: Deferred in neutropenic patient
EXT: WNL except for petechiae
NEURO: Oriented × 3

Results of Laboratory Tests

Na 135	Hct 29	AST 35	Glu 80
K 3.9	Hgb 9.8	ALT P	Ca 8.9
Cl 101	WBC 900	LDH 110	PO$_4$ 3.8
HCO$_3$ 28	Plts 69k	Alk Phos P	Mg 1.8
BUN 30	MCV P	Alb P	PT 11.3
Cr 1.5	MCHC P	T Bili 1.1	PTT 36

WBC differential: 30% polys
Urinalysis: Pending
Blood and urine cultures: pending
Chest x-ray: LLL infiltrate

Problem

S:

O:

A:

P:

Problem

S:

O:

A:

P:

Problem

S:————————————————

O:————————————————

A:————————————————

P:————————————————

Problem

S:————————————————

O:————————————————

A:————————————————

P:————————————————

Problem

S:————————————————

O:————————————————

A:————————————————

P:————————————————

SECTION/14

Neoplastic Diseases

CASE 90

CC: T.O. is a 35-year-old female diagnosed with acute nonlymphocytic leukemia (ANLL) 2 weeks ago. She was admitted to the hospital and induction chemotherapy was started with cytarabine and daunorubicin. She tolerated treatment well until this morning, when she complained of productive cough, sore mouth, and fatigue.

Past Medical History

T.O. was healthy until the diagnosis of ANLL.

Problem List

1. ANLL
2. Immunocompromised host with signs and symptoms of pneumonia
3. Anemia
4. Thrombocytopenia
5. Oral candidiasis

Medication History

Prochlorperazine 10 mg p.o. q6h prn nausea.

Allergies

None.

Physical Examination

GEN: Patient appears very fatigued and feverish.
VS: BP 135/85 HR 95 T 38.7 RR 20 Wt 68 kg Ht 5'5"
HEENT: Mouth, tender; white plaques on tongue and soft palate; gums, hemorrhagic.
COR: WNL
CHEST: Bibasilar rales
ABD: Hepatosplenomegaly, tender
GU: Deferred
RECT: Guaiac positive
EXT: Hematoma left lower extremity; petechiae over forearms
NEURO: WNL

Results of Laboratory Tests

Na 140	Hct 25	AST 25
K 3.5	Hgb 9.5	ALT 20
Cl 100	WBC 800	LDH 100
HCO$_3$ 30	Plts 45 k	Alk Phos 70
BUN 14	MCV 98	T.Bili 1.3
Cr 1.0	MCH 32	

WBC Differential: polys 5%, lymphs 45%, unclassifiable 50%

KOH preparation of mouth swab: (+) for hyphae
Day 15 bone marrow: Hypoplastic, no blasts

Problem 1: ANLL Status Post Chemotherapy

S: None.
O: Patient's bone marrow shows lowered blood counts.
A: Patient's ANLL is in remission based on bone marrow.
P: No further chemotherapy at this time.

Problem 2. Rule Out Pneumonia

S: T.O. has productive cough.
O: T.O. has T 38.7 °C and bibasilar rales.
A: In the immunocompromised host, the most likely pathogens to cause pneumonia or septicemia are P. aeruginosa, E. coli, K. pneumoniae, as well as staphyloccocal sp. Therefore, empiric treatment must cover these organisms until cultures come back and therapy can be tailored to the specific pathogen.
P: Perform blood culture and sensitivity x 3, sputum culture and sensitivity x 3, and chest x-ray. Start mezlocillin 3 g i.v. every 4 hours; tobramycin 135 mg loading dose then 100 mg i.v. every 8 hours; nafcillin 2 g i.v. every 4 hours; and acetaminophen 325 mg prn T > 38.5C every 4 hours. Monitor temperature, cough, WBC, flu-like symptoms, chest x-ray and examination, and culture and sensitivities, Cr, and tobramycin levels.

Problem 3. Anemia

S: T.O. complains of fatigue.
O: Hct 25, Hgb 9.5, MCV 98, MCH 32
A: Anemia is normocytic, normochromic and secondary to chemotherapy.
P: Give 2 units of packed red blood cells. Monitor Hct, Hgb, urine output, renal function, and fatigue.

Problem 4. Thrombocytopenia

S: T.O. has bleeding gums.
O: Platelet count = 45 K, guaiac-positive stools, petechiae over forearms, hematoma over LLE.
A: Thrombocytopenia secondary to Problem 1. Avoid antiplatelet drugs and intramuscular injections.

P: Give 10 U platelets because of bleeding. Monitor signs of bleeding and platelet count.

Problem 5. Oral Candidiasis

S: T.O. complains of sore mouth.

O: Erythematous mucosa with white plaques. KOH preparation is positive for hyphae.

A: The patient has oral candidiasis.

P: Give clotrimazole 10 mg p.o. (dissolve in mouth) 5 times per day.

CASE 91

CC: L.L. is a 36-year-old male who presents to clinic with a 3-week history of nonspecific symptoms including fever, anorexia, fatigue, and weight loss.

Past Medical History

Past medical history is unremarkable.

Problem List

1. Stage IV diffuse histiocytic lymphoma (DHL).
2. Risk of acute tumor lysis syndrome (TLS)
3. Risk of nausea/vomiting secondary to emetogenic chemotherapy

Medication History

None.

Allergies

None known.

Physical Examination

VS: BP 130/70 HR 72 T 38 Wt 62 kg (down from 69 kg 3 months ago)

HEENT: Slightly enlarged (2 cm) hard fixed left cervical node

COR: WNL

CHEST: Clear to ascultation and percussion

ABD: Hepatosplenomegaly

GU: WNL

RECT: WNL

EXT: Left axilla matted lymph nodes

NEURO: WNL

Results of Laboratory Tests

Na 136	Hct 33.7	AST 70	Glu 80
K 4.1	Hgb 11.8	ALT 80	Ca 9.7
Cl 101	WBC 6.7k	LDH 346	PO_4 3.9
HCO_3 25	Plts 176k	Alk Phos 209	Mg 2.0
BUN 16	MCV 85	Alb 3.9	PT 11.9
Cr 0.9	MCHC 32	T Bili 1.1	PTT 38.6

Urinalysis: WNL

Abdominal CT scan: enlarged para-aortic lymph nodes, enlarged liver with masses, enlarged spleen

Axillary lymph node biopsy: consistent with diffuse histiocytic lymphoma

Liver biopsy: consistent with diffuse histiocytic lymphoma

Bone marrow biopsy: diffuse histiocytic lymphoma

Chest x-ray: WNL

Problem 1. Stage IV Diffuse Histiocytic Lymphoma

S: L.L. complains of nonspecific symptoms such as anorexia, fatigue, and fever.

O: Patient has positive lymph node, bone marrow, and liver biopsies, nopathy, hepatosplenomegaly, fever, weight loss, elevated LFTs.

A: L.L. needs immediate treatment since DHL is an aggressive malignant lymphoma. Additional tests needed prior to institution of chemotherapy include an uric acid level. Induction chemotherapy with CHOP will cause massive neoplastic cell lysis that can result in electrolyte abnormalities, urate nephropathy, and renal insufficiency. The risk of acute tumor lysis syndrome should be considered in this patient and he should be treated prophylactically (see Problem 2). CHOP chemotherapy may cause significant nausea and vomiting (see Problem 3).

P: After adequate hydration and assessment of renal function start chemotherapy.

Cyclophosphamide	750 mg/M^2 i.v. day 1
Doxorubicin	50mg/M^2 i.v. day 1
Vincristine	1.4 mg/M^2 i.v. day 1
Prednisone	100 mg/M^2 p.o. days 1–5

Repeat chemotherapy every 21 days, pending blood counts. Monitor CBC, platelets, electrolytes, BUN, creatinine, serum uric acid, calcium, serum phosphate, urine output, nausea, vomiting, and liver function tests. Monitor for and educate patient about the following side effects: (a) Cyclophosphamide may cause nausea/vomiting, anorexia, and bone marrow depression. (This is often dose limiting. The WBC nadir occurs in 8–14 days, recovery occurs 18–25 days. The depression of RBC and platelets is not as severe as WBC.) It can also cause hair loss (not permanent), and hemorrhagic cystitis (usually preventable with proper hydration of a minimum 3 liters/day). (b) Doxorubicin may cause nausea/vomiting, anorexia, and bone marrow depression. (This is often dose limiting. The WBC nadir occurs in 10–14 days; recovery occurs 18–25 days; RBC and platelets are not as severely depressed as WBC.) It can also cause cardiotoxicity or cardiomyopathy (the total lifetime dose is 550 mg/M^2), skin and local tissue damage if it is extravasated, marked alopecia, and stomatitis. (c) Vincristine may cause neurotoxicity. (A common side effect that is often dose limiting. Manifestations include decreased deep tendon reflexes, numbness, weakness, myalgias, cramping, constipation, and paralytic ileus. All are reversible upon discontinuation of the drug.) It can also cause bone marrow depression (mild if it occurs at all), alopecia, and skin and local tissue damage, if extravasated. *(d)* Prednisone may cause GI irritation (take with meals or antacid), fluid retention, electrolyte changes (increased Na, decreased K), increased appetite, increased blood glucose, and adrenal suppression (unlikely with 5-day therapy).

Problem 2. Risk of Tumor Lysis Syndrome

S: None, or changes in mental status if TLS occurs

O: If it occurs, the following changes are observed: increased serum uric acid, BUN, creatinine, potassium, and phosphate; decreased calcium and urine output.

A: L.L has a large tumor burden from DHL. Chemotherapy will result in rapid neoplastic cell destruction. Adequate renal function and hydration are needed for elimination of cell byproducts.

P: Start allopurinol 600 mg for 1 day, then 300 mg p.o. qd.

Problem 3. Chemotherapy-Induced Nausea and Vomiting

S: Nausea probably will occur as L.L. is to receive emetogentic agents.

O: Vomiting and retching if they occur.

A: L.L. should receive prophylactic antiemetics prior to CHOP. Severe vomiting could result in electrolyte derangements, decrease intake and further decrease in nutritional status, and could psychologically harm the patient.

P: Start metoclopramide 0.5–1.0 mg/kg i.v., diphenhydramine 25–50 mg i.v., and dexamethasone 10 mg i.v. x 1. Give the above combination ½ hour prior to starting chemotherapy, repeat the metoclopramide and diphenhydramine in 3–4 hours, and then every 4–6 hours as needed. Monitor extrapyramidal symptoms, sedation, nausea/vomiting, and blood pressure.

CASE 92

CC: G.S. is a 49-year-old female with breast cancer who presents with complaints of increasing fatigue and pain, which is most pronounced in her left shoulder and right upper quadrant. In addition, she complains of vaginal itching and a malodorous vaginal discharge.

Past Medical History

Four years prior to admission, the patient had a left radical mastectomy for ductal infiltrating carcinoma of the breast. The tumor was found to be positive for both estrogen and progesterone receptors. Five of 14 lymph nodes were positive. G.S. was not given adjuvant treatment. Four years PTA the disease was found to have metastasized to the right humerus. Radiation treatment and tamoxifen 10 mg twice daily were started.

Problem List

1. Hypercalcemia
2. Recurrent carcinoma of the breast with progressive liver and bone metastases
3. Trichomonas vaginalis

Medication History

Hydrochlorothiazide 50 mg daily
Tamoxifen 10 mg twice daily
Acetaminophen 500 mg 2 every 6 hours prn pain

Allergies

None known.

Social History

Moderate alcohol; no cigarettes.

Physical Examination

GEN: Mildly distressed female appearing to be of stated age.
VS: BP 120/78 HR 78 T 37.0 Wt 68 kg
HEENT: WNL
COR: Normal sinus rhythm and S1 and S2, no murmurs.
CHEST: Well-healed scar from left mastectomy; lymphedema of the left arm which has been present since mastectomy.
ABD: Soft without masses, tenderness, or ascites; palpable liver, 2 cm below right coastal margin
RECT: Guaiac negative
EXT: WNL
NEURO: WNL
PELVIC: KOH negative; NaCl slide positive for mobile trichomonads
SKEL/MUSC: Tenderness noted in right upper humerus and at S3-4.

Results of Laboratory Tests

Na 140	Hct 33.3	AST 73	Glu 100
K 3.9	Hgb 10.8	ALT 101	Ca 13.4
Cl 106	WBC 5.2k	LDH 302	PO_4 2.7
HCO_3 19	Plts 320k	Alk Phos 190	
BUN 18	MCV 90	Alb 4.0	
Cr 1.3	MCH 29	T Bili 1.6	

Bone scan: Hot spots consistent with bone metastases in the right humerus, rib, and S3-4.

Abdominal CT scan: Normal except for lesions consistent with liver metastases

Problem 1. Hypercalcemia

S: G.S. has bone pain and fatigue.

O: Ca = 13.4

A: G.S. has hypercalcemia secondary to bone metastases and HCTZ use.

P: Discontinue HCTZ. Start normal saline i.v. 300 ml/hour. Once urine output has reached 100 ml/hour, start furosemide 20–80 mg/i.v. Titrate to urine output of 200 ml/hour. Monitor Ca, Mg, Na, and K levels, fatigue, bone pain, mental status, and urine output. Monitor for signs and symptoms of fluid overload.

Problem 2. Progressive Metastases to Bone and Liver

S: G.S. is experiencing bone pain in her right shoulder and right upper quadrant.

O: Pain elicited upon skeletal/muscle examination, palpable liver, elevated LFTs, (+) bone scan, (+) CT scan, elevated Ca^{++}.

A: G.S. has metastases to her right humerus, liver, rib, and S3-4. She should have received adjuvant chemotherapy after her surgery because she had (+) lymph nodes.

P: Discontinue tamoxifen. Start chemotherapy for systemic disease: Cyclophosphamide 100 mg/M^2 p.o. d 1–14; Methotrexate 40–60 mg/M^2 i.v. d 1 and 8; 5-fluorouracil 600 mg/M^2 d 1 and 8; repeat the cycle every 28 days. Start radiation treatment (3,000 rads over 4 weeks) for right humerus. Start naprosyn 250 mg p.o. b.i.d. with food for bone pain due to bone metastases. Monitor CBC, platelets, LFTs, Cr, CT scan, bone scan, liver size, and patient's symptoms. Monitor for side effects of chemotherapy (nausea, vomiting, stomatitis, hemorrhagic cystitis, and diarrhea). Patient Education: Advise G.S. about hydration (drink 3–5 liters of fluid/day) and to report any nausea, mucositis, blood in urine or stool, or diarrhea.

Problem 3. Trichomonas Vaginalis

S: Patient has vaginal itching and malodorous discharge

O: NaCl slide

A: Trichamonas vaginalis

P: Metronidazide 250 mg p.o. t.i.d. x 7 days or 2 g p.o. x 1. Treat all male partners.
Patient education: Advise G.S. about compliance with medication and to complete full course of therapy. Avoid alcohol while taking metronidazole.

CASE 93

CC: W.B. is a 74-year-old male who was brought to the emergency room with a 2-week history of increasing fatigue, lethargy, anorexia, and mental confusion. In addition, he has experienced a 4-month history of increasing urinary retention and lower back and hip pain.

Past Medical History

Status post cholecystectomy 20 years ago

Problem List

1. Dehydration/hypercalcemia
2. Adenocarcinoma of the prostate stage D_2
3. Pain secondary to bone metastases

Medication History

Maalox prn GI upset
MOM prn constipation
Acetaminophen 2 tablets q.i.d.

Allergies

Reaction to horse serum

Physical Examination

VS: BP supine 130/80, HR 84; standing BP 100/60, HR 104 T 37.2 Wt 72 Kg
HEENT: Dry mucous membranes
COR: WNL
CHEST: Clear to ascultation and percussion
ABD: Healed surgical scar
GU: WNL
RECT: Enlarged, nodular prostate, guaiac negative
EXT: Pain in hip with external rotation
NEURO: WNL

Results of Laboratory Tests

Na 144	Hct 48.7	AST 30	Glu 85	PT 12.2
K 4.4	Hgb 14.5	ALT 27	Ca 12.7	PTT 31
Cl 107	WBC 6.7k	LDH 89	PO_4 2.2	
HCO_3 24	Plts 225k	Alk Phos 102	Mg 3.1	
BUN 40	MCV 90	Alb 2.5	Chol 205	
Cr 1.2	MCHC 32	T.Bili 0.9	Tri 60	

Urinalysis: WNL

CT scan of the abdomen/pelvis: Enlarged retroperitoneal lymph nodes, enlarged irregular prostate

Fine-needle aspirate of the prostate: Poorly differentiated adenocarcinoma

Radionuclide bone scan: Lytic lesions involving the pelvis, vertebrae, and ribs

Chest x-ray: WNL

Problem 1. Dehydration/Hypercalcemia

S: Patient is experiencing lethargy, fatigue, anorexia, and mental confusion.

O: Patient has Ca 12.7 mg/dl (corrects to approximately 13.9 mg/dl), orthostatic hypotension with increased pulse, dry mucous membranes, and poor skin turgor.

A: W.B. has hypercalcemia secondary to bone metastases and dehydration secondary to hypercalcemia and decreased intake due to anorexia and mental confusion. W.B. needs immediate treatment to restore his vascular volume. Once adequate hydration is achieved, additional therapy aimed at lowering serum calcium should be instituted.

P: Acute treatment: Start an intravenous infusion of normal saline to get a urine output of >100 ml/hour. Once the patient is adequately hydrated, (urine output >100 ml/hour, without orthostasis, normal skin turgor) start furosemide 1 mg/kg. Titrate the furosemide dose (usually 20–60 mg every 4–8 hours) and i.v. fluid infusion rate to achieve urine output of 300–500 ml/hour. Monitor electrolytes (Na, K, Cl, CO_2, Mg^{++}, Ca^{++}), vital signs (BP, pulse), hydration status (skin turgor, mucous membranes), mental status, and urine output (I/O). If forced diuresis is inadequate in lowering serum calcium, then mithramycin 25 μg/kg/day (1.8 mg/day) i.v. over 3–6 hours should be administered.

Problem 2. Adenocarcinoma of the Prostate

S: Patient complains of urinary retention, fatigue, and lethargy.

O: The needle aspirate is positive for adenocarcinoma. The rectal examination and CT scan are positive for an enlarged and nodular prostate.

A: W.B. has adenocarcinoma of the prostate, stage D_2 (distant mets). Additional laboratory tests that are needed include serum prostatic acid phosphatase and alkaline phosphatase. W.B. needs treatment since he is symptomatic but treatment of stage D_2 prostate cancer is only palliative. Hormonal therapy is the treatment of choice and may be accomplished by a variety of methods. Choices A, B, and C are equally efficacious and the choice should be based on the side effect profile and patient preference.

Choice A: Bilateral Orchiectomy (Surgical)

Advantage: No problem with compliance

Disadvantage: Requires surgery, low patient acceptability

Side effects: Nausea, vomiting, breast tenderness, impotence, and psychological effects

Monitor laboratory tests (serum testosterone, alkaline phosphatase, prostatic acid phosphatase) and clinical symptoms (pain, urinary symptoms, prostate size), and radiologic studies (CT scan, bone scans).

Choice B: Diethylstilbesterol (DES) 3 mg/day orally. Continue DES as long as the symptoms are adequately controlled.

Advantage: Noninvasive, inexpensive

Disadvantage: Contraindicated in patients with a history of thromboembolic disease

Side effects: fluid retention, gynecomastia, impotence, decreased libido, risk of thromboembolic disease, nausea, and vomiting

Monitor laboratory tests (liver function tests, testosterone, prostatic acid phosphatase), clinical symptoms (pain, urinary symptoms, prostate size), and radiologic studies (CT scan, bone scan)

Choice C: Leuprolide 1 mg s.c. daily. Continue as long as symptoms are adequately controlled.

Advantage: Noninvasive, lack of estrogen-related side effects

Disadvantage: Expensive, requires daily subcutaneous injections

Side effects: Transient disease flare (preventable with coadministration of DES) hot flashes, impotence, decreased libido

Monitor laboratory tests (alkaline phosphatase, testosterone, prostatic acid phosphatase), clinical symptoms (pain, urinary symptoms, prostate size), and radiologic studies (CT scan, bone scan)

Patient education: Counsel W.B. about possible disease flare, the proper injection technique, and the need to rotate injection site and to store unused vials in refrigerator.

In this patient, DES, leuprolide, or surgery would offer equally efficacious therapy. W.B. has no contraindication to DES, and this is the cheapest; nor are surgery or daily injections required.

P: Start DES 3 mg p.o. qd.

Problem 3. Pain Secondary to Bone Metastases

S: Lower back and hip pain.

O: Bone scan positive for metastatic disease in pelvic, vertebral, and rib bones.

A: The pain is secondary to bone metastases. The pain should improve with response to hormonal therapy, but this may take a few weeks. Nonsteroidal anti-inflammatory agents are effective for the treatment of bone pain. There are many to choose from and all are equally efficacious.

P: Begin ibuprofen 600 mg p.o. q.i.d. with food. Monitor pain and GI irritation. Patient education: Advise W.B. to take ibuprofen with meals or antacids.

CASE 94

CC: D.T. is a 46-year-old male who recently immigrated to the United States. He presented to clinic last week complaining of right upper quadrant pain, early satiety, fevers to 38.5°C, and generalized weakness. These symptoms have gradually worsened over the last few weeks. D.T. states he has been relatively well the last 5 years or so. He denies exposure to radiation, industrial solvents, or waste.

Past Medical History

S/P pneumonia 6 years ago

S/P right ankle fracture and surgery 8 years ago

Hepatitis B 10 years ago, chronic active hepatitis B

Appendectomy 15 years ago

Problem List

1. Hepatoma, not surgically resectable
2. Chronic active hepatitis B

Current Medications

Cimetidine 300 mg prn for epigastric pain

Acetaminophen with codeine 30 mg 1 to 2 tablets q 4–6 h prn pain

Allergies:

None known.

Social History

Used intravenous drugs 10–12 years ago, none recently. He has smoked one pack per day of cigarettes for 20 years; drinks alcohol occasionally.

Physical Examination

VS: BP 130/76 HR 72 T 38 Wt 63 kg (down from 70 kg 3 months ago) Ht 5'10" BSA 1.77 m²

HEENT: Sclera slightly icteric

COR: WNL

CHEST: Decreased breath sounds right lung base

ABD: Enlarged, tender liver, without ascites

GU: WNL

RECT: Guaiac negative

EXT: 2 (+) pedal edema

NEURO: WNL

Results of Laboratory Tests

Na 141	Hct 41.0	AST 230	Glu 97	PT 11
K 3.7	Hgb 13.9	ALT 109	Ca 8.3	PTT 29
Cl 99	WBC 6.7k	LDH 222	PO$_4$ 3.8	HBsAg (+)
HCO$_3$ 24	Plts 124k	Alk Phos 430	Mg 1.9	
BUN 18	MCV 95	Alb 2.1	Chol 210	
Cr 1.1	MCHC 32	T.Bili 3.2	TG 78	

α-Fetoprotein 3220 ng/ml; CEA: WNL

Urinalysis: WNL

Abdominal CT scan: multiple low-density lesions involving both the right and left hepatic lobes.

Liver biopsy: (CT-guided, fine-needle aspirate) consistent with hepatocellular carcinoma, no evidence of cirrhosis.

Bone scan: WNL

Chest x-ray: Elevated right hemidiaphragm secondary to enlarged liver; no evidence of active disease.

Problem _____

S: _____

O: _____

A: _____

P: _____

Problem _____

S: _____

O: _____

A: _____

P: _____

Problem _____

S: _____

O: _____

A: _____

P: _____

Questions

1. State two risk factors that predispose D.T. to hepatoma.
2. What subjective and objective evidence does D.T. have that is consistent with hepatoma?
3. Since D.T.'s hepatoma is unresectable it is decided to start chemotherapy with doxorubicin. The following order is written:
   Doxorubicin 120 mg i.v. p.b. every 4 weeks.
   Evaluate this order for appropriateness of dose, route, and frequency of administration in this patient.
4. What patient education should D.T. be given regarding doxorubicin therapy?

CASE 95

CC: M.N. is a 73-year-old female who presents to the ER complaining of severe right upper quadrant pain.

Past Medical History

M.N. had an appendectomy at age 29, but otherwise has been well all of her life.

Problem List

M.N. has primary gallbladder cancer with peritoneal metastases.

Medication History

None.

Allergies

None known.

Physical Examination

GEN:	Ill-appearing woman in severe pain.
VS:	BP 126/78 HR 75 T 37 RR 26 Wt 65 kg Ht 5'4"
HEENT:	Normal
COR:	WNL
CHEST:	Clear
ABD:	Tender
GU:	WNL
RECT:	WNL
EXT:	WNL
NEURO:	WNL

Results of Laboratory Tests

Na 131	Hct 42	AST 56	Glu 110	PT 10.8
K 4.6	Hgb 14	ALT 37	Ca 8.4	PTT 35
Cl 100	WBC 4.8k	LDH 145	PO_4 3.2	
HCO_3 26	Plts 230k	Alk Phos 55	Mg 1.8	
BUN 17	MCV 98	Alb 3.1	Chol 171	
Cr 0.9	MCHC 31	T.Bili 0.7	Trigyclerides 90	

Urinalysis: WNL
Chest x-ray: WNL
Abdominal CT scan; mass in gallbladder consistent with primary gallbladder cancer.

M.N. is taken to surgery for cholecystecomy. The gallbladder is successfully removed, but M.N. is found to have peritoneal metastases. Following 2 weeks of convalescence, she is begun on the following chemotherapy:

Adriamycin 50 mg/M^2 i.v. q 4 weeks
Mitomycin 10 mg/M^2 i.v. q 8 weeks
5-Fluorouracil 1 g/M^2 i.v. q 4 weeks

Problem

S:

O:

A:

P:

Problem

S: _____

O: _____

A: _____

P: _____

Questions

1. Should M.N. have received prophylactic antibiotics for her cholecystecomy? Explain. If so, give drug(s), dosage regimen, and duration of therapy.

2. M.N. returns to clinic 12 days after receiving her first doses of chemotherapy (all three agents) and her WBC is now 2.7 and her platelet count is now 120,000. Which two agents are most likely responsible for this myelosuppression? Explain why you believe these two agents are responsible.

3. M.N. returns to the clinic 7 days after her third complete 8-week cycle of chemotherapy. She complains of hair loss, and a very sore mouth which is preventing her from eating. On examination, her mouth is found to be erythematous with white patches which are consistent with stomatitis and oral candidiasis.

   a. Which agent is most likely responsible for M.N.'s alopecia?

   b. Which two agents are most likely responsible for M.N.'s stomatitis?

   c. How should her oral candidiasis be treated?

CASE 96

CC: R.R. is a 50-year-old obese female who was diagnosed with acute lymphocytic leukemia (ALL) 3 weeks ago. She is currently receiving day 15 of her induction chemotherapy. She complains of fever, sweats, sore mouth, nausea, and vomiting which begins ½ hour prior to each dose of chemotherapy.

Past Medical History

R.R. has had hypertension since age 45. She had appendicitis at age 22 and hepatitis A 5 years ago. R.R. has had CHF for 5 years. A Hickman catheter was placed on day 1 of admission.

Problem List

1. ALL
2. Fever with neutropenia
3. Thrombocytopenia
4. Stomatitis/candidiasis
5. Nausea/vomiting
6. Hypertension
7. Asthma
8. CHF

Medication History

HCTZ 50 mg p.o. qd
Digoxin 0.25 mg p.o. qd
Cotrimoxazole 2 tabs p.o. b.i.d.
Prochlorperazine 10 mg i.v. q6h prn nausea
Daunorubicin 95 mg i.v. days 1–3
Vincristine 2 mg i.v. days 1,8,15,22
Prednisone 110 mg p.o. days 1–28 given t.i.d.
Asparaginase 11,000 U i.v. days 17–28

Allergies

None known.

Social History

R.R. drinks one to two beers a day. She smokes one pack per day of cigarettes.

Physical Examination

GEN: Ill-appearing female in severe distress
VS: BP 110/60 HR 93 T 39.7 RR 28 Wt 85 kg Ht 5'6"
HEENT: Erythematous mouth with white plaques that are KOH-positive for pseudohyphae. Nose bleeds (approximately one per day for last 3 days). No JVD.
COR: (−) S3
CHEST: No rales
ABD: Petechiae; Hickman catheter exit site erythematous
GU: WNL
RECT: Stool guaiac (+)
EXT: WNL (no edema)
NEURO: WNL

Results of Laboratory Tests

Na 137	Hct 21	AST 37	Glu 104	PT 12.6
K 3.9	Hgb 8.1	ALT 39	Ca 8.5	PTT 41
Cl 102	WBC 550	LDH 101	PO$_4$ 2.5	
HCO$_3$ 22	Plts 30K	Alk Phos 70	Mg 1.3	
BUN 16	MCV 98	Alb 3.3	Chol 149	
Cr 0.9	MCHC 30	T. Bili 0.6	TG 71	

WBC differential: 30% P
Day 7 bone marrow: 28% leukemic cells
Urinalysis: WNL

Problem

S:

O:

A:

P:

Problem

S:

O:

A:

P:

Problem

S:

O:

A:

P:

Problem

S:

O:

A:

P:

Problem

S:

O:

A:

P:

Problem

S:

O:

A:

P:

Problem

S:

O:

A:

P:

Problem

S:

O:

A:

P:

Questions

1. Calculate a tobramycin dosing regimen for R.R. The tobramycin is to be infused over ½ hour.
2. The intern begins R.R. on the dose of tobramycin that you recommended, ticarcillin 3 g i.v. q4h, and vancomycin 600 mg i.v. q12h. Four days later, a vancomycin peak level is drawn 1 hour after a 1-hour infusion and a trough level is drawn just before the next dose. The peak level is 31 and the trough is 16. Based upon these levels, revise the vancomycin dosing regimen to obtain a trough level of 10 and a nontoxic peak level.
3. Explain why you agree or disagree with the intern's empiric selection of antibiotics for R.R. If you disagree, recommend alternative antibiotics and justify your selection.
4. After 7 days of appropriate antibiotic therapy, R.R. remains febrile. The resident wishes to add amphotericin B to the antibiotic regimen. Recommend an appropriate dose, complete administration guidelines, and list three laboratory tests that should be followed to monitor for potential toxicities.
5. Recommend an additional antiemetic that may help control R.R.'s nausea and vomiting. Be specific: list drug, dose, route, duration, and justify your answer.
6. While receiving the induction chemotherapy, R.R. develops hyperglycemia, alopecia, and paresthesias. For each toxicity list the chemotherapeutic agent that is most likely responsible.

CASE 97

CC: A.H. is a 60-year-old male admitted with altered mental status. Over the last week, A.H. experienced nausea, anorexia, increased pain, and slurred speech.

Past Medical History

A.H. had small cell carcinoma of the lung diagnosed 6 months ago, with newly diagnosed bone and liver metastases. He also has hypertension, a history of urinary retention secondary to prostatic hypertrophy, and a history of pneumonia and chronic obstructive pulmonary disease (COPD).

Problem List

1. Dehydration/electrolyte abnormalities
2. Small cell lung cancer with bone and splenic mets
3. Pain
4. Rule out infection
5. Hypertension
6. History of urinary retention secondary to prostatic hypertrophy
7. History of pneumonia/COPD
8. Constipation

Current Medications

HCTZ 50 mg qd
Metaproterenol inhaler 1–2 puffs prn q4h
Multivitamins 1 tablet qd
Morphine SO_4 10 mg p.o., 1 tablet q4h prn pain
Ibuprofen 600 mg q.i.d. p.o. prn pain

Allergies

None known.

Social History

A.H. has smoked two packs per day of cigarettes for 30 years. He drinks alcohol occasionally.

Review of Systems

A.H. complains of left-arm pain, nausea, anorexia and constipation (last bowel movement 5 days ago). He has had little urine output for the last 3 days.

Physical Examination

GEN: Cachectic-looking, thin male in moderate distress
VS: BP 100/60 HR 105 R 34 T 40 Wt 50 kg
HEENT: (+) Stiff neck, PERRLA
COR: NL S1 S2 (−) S3 (−) murmur
CHEST: (+) wheezes, (+) rhonchi; decreased breath sounds, (−) rales
ABD: (+) Spleen tip, LLQ MASS consistent with hard stools
GU: Boggy hard prostate
RECT: Guaiac negative
EXT: (+) Tremor
NEURO: Oriented x 1, lethargic but responsive to deep pain

Results of Laboratory Tests

Na 132	Hct 33.2	AST 40	FBG 200	PT 11.1
K 3.0	Hgb 11.6	ALT 37	Ca 8.5	PTT 39
Cl 101	WBC 15.8k	LDH 120	PO_4 3.1	
HCO_3 22	Plts 40k	Alk Phos 348	Mg 2.0	
BUN 45	MCV 100	Alb 2.5	Chol 173	
Cr 2.0	MCHC 32	T.Bili 0.9	TG 94	

WBC differential: 75 P, 13 B, 8 L, 4 M
ABGs: PO_2 60, PCO_2 45, pH 7.30
Urinalysis: pH 6, 1% glucose, 0-4 WBC, 0-3 RBC, Gram stain (−) organisms
CSF: 1000 WBC, 80% polys, Glu 54, Gram stain: Gram (+) diplococci
Sputum Gram stain: + polys, Gram (+) diplococci
Chest x-ray: RML infiltrate

Problem

S:

O:

A:

P:

Problem

S:

O:

A:

P:

Problem

S:

O:

A:

P:

Problem

S:

O:

A:

P:

Problem

S:

O:

A:

P:

Problem

S:

O:

A:

P:

Problem

S:

O:

A:

P:

Problem

S:

O:

A:

P:

Questions

1. Evaluate the appropriateness of the pain regimen. Justify and list all concerns and considerations supporting use of these agents. What changes, if any, would you recommend?
2. The intern wants to empirically start cefotaxime since it has good CNS penetration and is the best drug for his meningitis.
   a. Explain why you agree or disagree with the intern's rationale and choice of antibiotic for meningitis. Justify your conclusions.
   b. If you agree, recommend an appropriate dosing regimen and treatment duration.
   c. If you disagree, recommend appropriate antibiotic(s) choice(s), dosing regimen(s), and treatment duration. Justify your antibiotic selection(s).
3. Three days after completion of antibiotic therapy, a urinalysis from the indwelling Foley catheter shows:

   pH 7, 20-25 WBC, 5-10 RBC, Gram stain: many Gram (+) and Gram (−) organisms

   Physical Examination:

   VS: T 37° BP 130/80 HR 70 Rectal: tender prostate
   WBC 8.5 w/normal differential

   The intern wonders whether other antibiotics should be added to cover the UA and Gram stain findings. What treatment regimen, if any, would you recommend and why?
4. On Day 8 of antibiotic treatment, A.H. spikes a 40° temperature from a phlebitic intravenous site and vancomycin is to be started. Recommend a dose and dosing interval to give a steady-state Cp_{min} of 10 and a nontoxic peak. A.H.'s creatinine is still 2.0. Justify your recommended dosing regimen.
5. Recommend an appropriate regimen to treat A.H.'s constipation.
6. Despite the narcotic analgesics, A.H. is experiencing increasing bone pain, thus he decides to receive chemotherapy. He is continued on narcotics and scheduled to begin chemotherapy as follows:

   Cisplatin 100 mg/M^2 i.v. q 3 weeks
   Etoposide (VP 16) 100 mg/M^2 i.v. bolus q 3 weeks
   Vincristine 2 mg i.v. bolus q 3 weeks

   a. A.H. comes to the oncology clinic to begin day 1 of chemotherapy. After he receives the chemotherapy, he stands up to leave and feels dizzy, requiring that he sit back down. The nurse takes his blood pressure and finds that it has fallen from 127/81 (taken prior to chemotherapy administration) to 85/50. What is the most likely cause? How might it be prevented in the future?
   b. His CBC and platelet count show a decrease in WBCs, HCT, and platelets. Which two agents are most likely producing the myelosuppression?
   c. Three hours after receiving the chemotherapy A.H. develops severe nausea and vomiting. Which chemotherapeutic agent is most likely responsible? Suggest an appropriate antiemetic regimen.

CASE 98

CC: D.C. is a 40-year-old premenopausal female who underwent a right modified radical mastectomy 12 months ago for removal of an ER+ 3-cm breast cancer; no regional lymph nodes were involved and no metastatic disease was apparent at the time of surgery. She is now admitted to the hospital with complaints of rib pain, dry mouth, urinary frequency, dysuria, and fatigue.

Past Medical History

D.C. has fibrocystic breast disease. She has had hypertension for 5 years and diabetes mellitus since age 7. She has recurrent UTIs (five to six per year). She has had seizures beginning at age 10 and had breast cancer (12 months ago).

Problem List

1. Metastatic breast cancer with bone pain
2. Hypercalcemia with dehydration
3. Urinary tract infection
4. Fibrocystic breast disease
5. Hypertension
6. Diabetes mellitus
7. Seizures

Medication History

Triphasil 1 p.o. qd according to 28-day regimen
HCTZ 50 mg p.o. qd
Phenytoin 300 mg p.o. qd
NPH Insulin 20 U sq qAM and 10 U qPM
Reg Insulin 10 U sq qAM and 10 U qPM

Allergies

Penicillin (anaphylaxis)
Erythromycin (rash)

Social History

D.C. is divorced and raising two children, ages 4 and 6. Her mother had history of HTN and breast cancer; she died age 65 of CVA. Her father has HTN, but is alive and well. She drinks alcohol moderately and smokes one pack per day of cigarettes.

OB/GYN History

Menarche at age 10; G_2P_2; birth control pills x 15 years.

Physical Examination

VS: BP 85/60 (standing) 123/85 (lying) HR 95 T 37 Wt 65
HEENT: WNL

COR: WNL
ABD: WNL
GU: WNL
RECT: WNL
EXT: Poor skin tugor; no CVA tenderness
NEURO: WNL

Results of Laboratory Tests

Na 136	Hct 42	LDH 127	PO_4 3.0
K 3.7	Hgb 14	Alk Phos 210	Mg 2.2
Cl 101	WBC 11k	Alb 3.4	Phenytoin 18
HCO_3 30	Plts 167	T. Bili 0.9	PT 11.2
BUN 10	AST 31	Glu 95	PTT 33
Cr 1	ALT 27	Ca 15.5	

Urinalysis: WBC esterase positive; RBCs: A few, otherwise WNL
ECG: WNL
Brain CT: WNL
Abdominal CT: WNL
Bone scan: Multiple bone metastases
Chest x-ray: No pulmonary metastases present.
Urine culture: >100,000 cfu/ml of *E. coli*

Problem

S:

O:

A:

P:

Problem

S:

O:

A:

P:

Problem

S:

O:

A:

P:

Problem

S:

O:

A:

P:

Problem

S:

O:

A:

P:

Problem

S:

O:

A:

P:

Problem

S:

O:

A:

P:

Problem

S:—————————————————
—————————————————
—————————————————

O:—————————————————
—————————————————
—————————————————
—————————————————

A:—————————————————
—————————————————
—————————————————
—————————————————

P:—————————————————
—————————————————
—————————————————

CASE 99

CC: V.P. is a 69-year-old female who is stable after right total-knee arthroplasty on July 10 for the treatment of chronic right-knee pain. The patient was hospitalized 1 week ago from the orthopedic clinic. She was treated with meperidine 25 mg i.m. q 3–4 h prn postoperatively to control her pain, but she still continued to complain of pain in the right knee and low back. Two days ago she began to experience shortness of breath (SOB), difficulty breathing, chest pain without radiation when she got out of bed, and she coughed up blood-tinged sputum. She has complained of painful urination since yesterday. The Foley catheter was removed 2 days ago.

Past Medical History

V.P. has a 12-year history of Crohn's disease with numerous exacerbations and remissions. Her typical complaints during an acute attack have been severe abdominal pain, diarrhea, and low-grade fever. Colonoscopy and x-rays have shown ileocolitis. She has a 10-year history of coronary artery disease. She usually experiences dull, squeezing substernal chest pain radiating down her left shoulder and arm approximately once a month. Usually the chest pain is relieved by two to three sublingual nitroglycerin tablets. She had a left-leg deep venous thrombosis (DVT) in 1980.

Problem List

1. Coronary artery disease (CAD)—s/p MI 1977
2. Degenerative joint disease (DJD) of both knees for 20 years
3. Crohn's disease for 12 years
4. Essential hypertension for 15 years
5. Hypercholesterolemia—well controlled with medication
6. Recurrent urinary tract infection (one to two times per year)
7. Pain management
8. Pulmonary embolism

Medication History

Sulfasalazine 1 g t.i.d. ×3 years
Prednisone 40 mg qd × 2 years
Metoprolol 100 mg b.i.d. × 5 years
Isosorbide dinitrate 40 mg q.i.d. × 10 years
NTG s.l. 0.6 mg for acute anginal attack
Probucol 500 mg b.i.d. × 2 years

Medications on Admission

Meperidine i.m. 25 mg q 3–4 h prn
Acetaminophen/codeine #3 1–2 tablets q4–6h prn
Triazolam 0.125 mg hs prn
Mylanta 15 cc prn
Docusate 250 mg b.i.d. prn in addition to the above outpatient medications

Allergies

None.

Social History

V.P. is married and has two children (29 and 34 years old). She has smoked one pack per day for 35 years. She drinks occasionally, one–two glasses of wine per week.

Family History

Her father died of MI at age of 67; she has a brother who has hypertension.

Physical Examination

GEN: Moderate truncal obesity with abdominal striae
VS: BP 140/95 HR 90 RR 22 T 38.5 Wt 90 kg
HEENT: Slight arteriolar narrowing, no exudates, or hemorrhages
COR: WNL
CHEST: Faint breath sounds, no rales or wheezing.
ABD: No pain on deep palpation.
RECT: Guaiac negative.
EXT: Swelling, pedal edema, erythema of right knee, several ecchymoses.

Results of Laboratory Tests

Na 141	Hct 38	AST	Glu 97	PT 12.1
K 3.8	Hgb 12	ALT	Cholesterol	PTT 32
Cl 102	WBC 12.5k	Alk Phos 68	(fasting) 190	ESR 5
HCO₃ 24	Plts 250k	Alb 3.8	Triglyceride	
BUN 14	MCV 90	Bili 0.3	140	
Cr 1.1	MCH 33			

Urinalysis: 10–15 WBC/HPF, 25 RBC/HPF, Urine culture—1 million CFU/ml − enterococci
ECG: ST and T wave abnormalities, possibility of lateral ischemia but no changes from previous ECG taken on admission
Barium enema: No evidence of Crohn's disease
Endoscopy: Acute and chronic esophagitis without stricture
V/Q scan: PE positive at 95% level

Problem 8. Pulmonary Embolism

S: V.P. has SOB, difficulty in breathing, tightness in the chest without radiation, and hemoptysis.

O: Increases in heart rate, RR, and temperature, V/Q scan positive, faint breath sounds

A: The patient is in acute respiratory distress and therefore needs to be treated. Risk factors for the development of PE in this patient are obesity, advanced age, major knee surgery, immobilization, and a history of DVT. The patient needs to be treated immediately to prevent further thrombosis and emboli, to resolve the clot, and to restore normal hemodynamics. However, thrombolytic agents, such as streptokinase or urokinase are not indicated due to the non-life-threatening PE and her recent surgery. Heparin and warfarin therapy need to be initiated. Drug interactions with anticoagulant therapy should be avoided.

P: Prior to initiation of anticoagulation therapy, check baseline PTT and PT, platelets, and CBC. Begin with 50–70 U/kg of heparin loading dose and then 15–25 U/kg/hour heparin maintenance dose for 7–10 days. Start warfarin 1–2 days after heparin initiation and continue for 3–6 months. Heparin and warfarin therapy should overlap at least for 4–5 days. Monitor HCT, platelets, guaiac, hematuria, bleeding, and bruises during anticoagulation therapy. Check PTT 4–6 hours after initiation of heparin and maintain 1.5–2.5 times control values. Also maintain PT between 16–22 for full anticoagulation therapy. Educate the patient with respect to side effects, compliance, clinic visits, ASA products, and diet.

Problem 7. Pain Management

S: V.P. has continuous pain in the right knee and lower back

O: None

A: V.P.'s pain is poorly controlled at present secondary to a low dose of meperidine. Meperidine 25 mg i.m. is a subtherapeutic dose to control pain postoperatively.

P: Increase the meperidine dose to 50–75 mg i.m. q 2 to 3 hours prn to control severe pain. Encourage patient to take acetaminophen w/ codeine 1–2 tabs q4–6h prn to control mild to moderate pain. Monitor the patient closely for possible mental status changes such as hallucinations, confusion, and disorientation secondary to narcotic pain medications. Monitor CNS excitation and/or seizures due to accumulation of normeperidine, a metabolite of meperidine although this is less likely to occur in this patient with good renal function.

Problem 1. Coronary Artery Disease/ Angina Pectoris

S: V.P. has dull, squeezing substernal chest pain radiating down her left shoulder and arm that occurs once a month. Chest pain is usually relieved by sublingual nitroglycerin.

O: ECG shows abnormal ST and T waves, possible lateral ischemia but no acute changes.

A: Her angina pectoris is fairly well controlled at present considering her number of risk factors for CAD. The risk factors in this patient are cigarette smoking, hypercholesterolemia, advanced age, obesity, poor control of hypertension, and a family history of heart disease. The combination of oral nitrate and metoprolol has a beneficial hemodynamic effect.

P: Continue metoprolol 100 mg b.i.d. and isorsorbide dinitrate 40 mg q.i.d. for the prevention of anginal attacks. Treat acute anginal chest pain with sublingual nitroglycerin. Give her information regarding the correct use of sublingual tablets for chest pain. Instruct her regarding correct storage and handling of nitroglycerin. Discuss with the patient the side effects of NTG such as headache, dizziness, and possible syncope.

Problem 6. Recurrent Urinary Tract Infection (UTI)

S: V.P. has had painful urination since yesterday.

O: V.P. has fever. U/A shows 10–15 WBC/HPF; urine culture shows 1 million cfu/ml enterococci.

A: The UTI needs to be treated. Risk factors associated with a UTI are her advanced age, female genitalia, and a foley catheter. She needs to be treated for approximately 10–14 days.

P: Begin ampicillin 500 mg p.o. q.i.d. for approximately 2 weeks. May treat with phenazopyridine 100 mg t.i.d. for 1–3 days for painful urination. Avoid TMP/SMX since it inhibits the metabolism of warfarin (see Problem 8). Monitor for signs and symptoms of UTI and side effects of the antibiotic. Educate the patient regarding side effects of ampicillin compliance, and signs and symptoms of UTI.

Problem 4. Essential Hypertension

S: None.

O: Her BP = 140/95. Fundoscopy revealed slight arteriolar narrowing.

A: Risk factors that predispose her to hypertension are advanced age, obesity, smoking, and a family history of hypertension. V.P. is currently taking metoprolol for the treatment of hypertension and CAD but may benefit from the addition of diuretics.

P: Add hydrochlorothiazide (HCTZ) 25 mg q.d. p.o. to metoprolol. Monitor side effects of HCTZ (hypokalemia, hyperglycemia, hypovolemia, hypercholesterolemia, hyperuricemia, and hypercalcemia). Consider ordering a potassium supplement since the patient's potassium level is 3.8 (low end of normal range). Educate the patient regarding salt restriction, weight reduction, regular exercise, and sodium content in drugs. Try to get V.P. to discontinue smoking.

Problem 3. Crohn's Disease

S: Severe abdominal pain, diarrhea, low-grade fever

O: Guaiac-negative; barium enema shows no evidence of active disease; no abdominal pain on deep palpation. ESR NL, Alb 3.8.

A: No evidence of active disease. Prednisone and sulfasalazine are ineffective during the remission phase. Prednisone and sulfasalazine need to be discontinued.

P: Discontinue sulfasalazine. Give prednisone 40 mg qd then taper by 5 mg/week until dose 7.5–10 mg/day. Then decrease dose by 0.5–1.0 mg/week or change to hydrocortisone 30 mg/day and then decrease dose by 2.5 mg/week until morning cortisol level is >10. Monitor for a flare of her Crohn's disease by abdominal pain, diarrhea, guaiac, fever, weight loss, nutrition, and ESR. Monitor for symptoms of adrenal insufficiency including electrolytes, BP, HR, blood glucose, anorexia, arthralgia, nausea, vomiting, and a flu-like illness. Educate the patient regarding symptoms of adrenal insufficiency, reasons of tapering, and the need for stress coverage up to 1 year after steroid taper. Instruct her to tell health care providers about her steroid history and to obtain a Medi-Alert bracelet.

Problem 2. Degenerative Joint Disease

S: V.P. complains of chronic knee pain and low back pain.

O: None

A: V.P. has undergone total-knee arthroplasty for chronic right-knee pain and the surgery should relieve her right-knee pain. NSAID may help to relieve her pain in other joints. Ibuprofen would be appropriate since the patient will be receiving long-term anticoagulation therapy (see Problem 8). An agent with the least antiplatelet and GI irritant properties is needed. Choline salicylate and other nonaspirin salicylates are acceptable alternatives.

P: Begin ibuprofen 600 mg p.o. q.i.d. Educate patient regarding weight reduction, rest, exercise, and applying local heat.

Problem 9. Steroid Side Effects

S: None.

O: Patient has truncal obesity, abdominal striae, ecchymoses, and increased WBC

A: The steroids should be tapered since they are not effective during the maintenance of Crohn's disease

P: Taper as in Problem 3.

Problem 5. Hypercholesterolemia

S: None.

O: Cholesterol (fasting) 190, triglycerides 140.

A: V.P.'s hypercholesterolemia is well controlled with her current therapy, and she is not suffering any side effects of the probucol although probucol has caused serious toxicity in animals.

P: Continue probucol 500 mg b.i.d.

CASE 100

CC: R.H. is a 35-year-old woman who comes to the gynecology clinic complaining of mood swings leading to violent aggression towards her co-workers and especially her husband, for the last 6 months. She was diagnosed 2 months ago as having premenstrual syndrome and has been treated. She also complains of breast swelling and tenderness, headache, nausea, and urinary frequency. After intercourse, she has noticed a homogeneous, grey vaginal discharge that gives off a "fishy" odor. Since she has had a 12-pound weight gain over the last 2 months, she fears that she may be pregnant due to her reliance on the rhythm method of contraception and the fact that her periods have been irregular for the last 6 months. She would require a therapeutic abortion, if she were pregnant, due to a previous spinal cord injury. She also complains of rectal soreness and flatulence for the last 2 months.

Past Medical History

R.H. had rheumatic heart disease at age 12, and grand mal seizures since age 20, which are treated with carbamazepine and diazepam. Her last seizure was 6 years ago. A hang-glider accident 2 years ago resulted in a spinal bleed at L3, and she has been warned that any further spinal trauma, even that caused by childbearing, may lead to paralysis or death.

Ob/Gyn History

G2P2; last menstrual period was 6 weeks ago. Recurrent vaginal infections led the patient to have her IUD removed 2 months ago. PMS was diagnosed 2 months ago; it begins with ovulation and ends at the end of menses. She is now using the rhythm method of contraception.

Past Surgical History

Exploration of lumbar vertebrae and fusion 6 years ago.

Problem List

1. PMS for 6 months, worsening
2. Vaginal discharge coating vulva, with "fishy" odor after intercourse
3. Seizure disorder
4. Chronic back pain
5. Possible, contraindicated pregnancy

Medication History

Progesterone supp 400 mg pr b.i.d. ×2 months
FDS Feminine Hygiene Spray daily ×2 weeks (self-medication)
Tap water douches after intercourse (self-initiated)
Carbamazepine 200 mg p.o. b.i.d. × 6 years
Diazepam 2 mg b.i.d. × 6 years
Oxycodone HCl 5 mg/acetaminophen 325 mg p.o. 5 times daily × 6 years.

Allergies

Penicillin (anaphylaxis)
Detergents and latex (husband also).

Social History

Smokes 1½ ppd × 12 years.

Physical Examination

GEN: Well-developed, well-nourished woman who is very irritable and a poor historian due to lack of concentration.

VS: BP 145/95 RA (sitting) HR 80 T 37 RR 18 Ht 5'6" Wt 67 kg

HEENT: WNL

COR: WNL

CHEST: Breasts swollen and tender to palpation

ABD: Slightly distended, nontender to palpation

GU: Grey, homogeneous vaginal discharge, coating the labia

RECTAL: Perianal erythema, flautulence, no hemorrhoids.

EXT: Vertical scar on lumbar region, 6 inches

NEURO: WNL

Results of Laboratory Tests

Na 141	BUN 15	WBC 11k
K 4.1	Cr 0.8	Plts 220k
Cl 100	Hct 34	Carbamazepine 2
HCO$_3$ 25	Hgb 11	Guaiac (+)

Vaginal fluid: Normal saline wet mount "clue cells"; pH = 5, KOH sniff test (+)

Urine culture (−)

Pregnancy test: (+)

EEG: Within normal limits

Problem 1. Premenstrual Syndrome

S: She complains of mood swings leading to violent aggression toward co-workers and especially her husband, breast swelling and tenderness, headache, and urinary frequency. Her symptoms begin at the onset of ovulation each month and resolve by the end of menses.

O: She is very irritable and a poor historian due to lack of concentration. She was diagnosed 2 months ago with PMS.

A: Since the patient is pregnant, PMS should clear; however, pregnancy termination is necessary. Since the etiology of PMS is unknown, and therapies are empiric, it is not unusual for even successful therapies to fail after several months, as has happened with the progesterone suppositories in this patient. The external rectal erythema, flatulence and guaiac positive stool may be due to the progesterone suppositories.

P: Begin spironolactone 25 mg po q.i.d. days 14–28 of each cycle. Counsel patient regarding stress reduction, diet modification, and appropriate exercise programs. Patient education should include information on the empirical nature of the various therapies, with the positive reinforcement that some patients have responded very well to any given drug or ancillary treatment, or combination thereof. Monitoring the efficacy of PMS therapies requires interviewing the patient's co-workers

and spouse as well as the subjective response of the patient herself.

Problem 5. Rectal Symptoms

S: Patient complains of rectal soreness and flatulence.

O: Perianal erythema; guaiac (+) without hemorrhoids.

A: Patient is experiencing side effects to progesterone rectal suppository.

P: Discontinue progesterone rectal suppositories.

Problem 6. Elevated BP

S: Asymptomatic.

O: BP 145/95 RA sitting.

A: May be due to anxiety component of PMS.

P: Monitor BP three times on subsequent visits every 3 months. Urge patient to discontinue smoking and counsel her regarding weight reduction, exercise, and low sodium diet.

Problem 2. Vaginal Discharge

S: Patient complains of homogeneous, grey vaginal discharge coating vulva plus "fishy" odor after intercourse.

O: KOH added to discharge gives off "fishy" odor; normal saline wet mount shows "clue cells" present; vaginal pH 5.

A: Nonspecific vaginosis, also known as *Gardnerella* vaginitis, which is actually a polymicrobial infection. Feminine hygiene sprays may further the vulvar irritation. Douching after intercourse is never recommended and may lead to alteration of the normal vaginal flora as well as pregnancy. Metronidazole is the drug of choice. There is no need to treat the partner in the index case. If the infection recurs, both the patient and her partner should be treated with the same regimen simultaneously.

P: Begin metronidazole 500 mg b.i.d. for 7 days. Instruct the patient to avoid alcohol until 24 hours after the last dose and that a metallic taste in the mouth and brownish discoloration of the urine may occur. Intercourse should be avoided during therapy. Monitoring of drug efficacy can be done by the patient's observation of vaginal discharge and dysuria. No follow-up visit is necessary unless symptoms persist.

Problem 3. Seizure Disorder

S: Onset age 20; grand mal; no seizures for the last 6 years.

O: EEG WNL; carbamazepine level = 2.

A: The carbamazepine could be discontinued since the level is subtherapeutic, the patient has had no seizure activity for 6 years, and the brain electrical activity is normal. Oral diazepam has not been proven to be beneficial for seizures and therefore should be discontinued.

P: Taper the carbamazepine over 2 weeks. Decrease to 200 mg qd for 1 week, then 100 mg qd ×1 week, then discontinue. Discontinue diazepam. Reassure the patient that her seizures should not recur, but if it does, it could lead to spinal injury. Monitoring of discontinuation of seizure medications should consist of phone calls to the patient over the next several weeks to check for any seizure activity and to give further reassurance.

Problem 7. Chronic Back Pain

S: Oxycodone HCl 5 mg/acetaminophen 325 mg p.o. 5 times daily for 6 years.

O: The patient did not complain of back pain today.

A: The patient may be habituated to oxycodone, which may no longer be required for adequate analgesia.

P: Discontinue oxycodone/acetaminophen and substitute ibuprofen 400 mg p.o. q.i.d. Discuss the desirability of stopping oxycodone/acetaminophen with the patient and that she should do so by tapering off by 1 tablet a day over a week and substituting ibuprofen 400 mg to a maximum of q.i.d. The patient should be monitored for any signs of withdrawal from oxycodone and the efficacy of the ibuprofen. Phone calls, in a frequency determined by patient need, should give needed reassurance during the transition. The ibuprofen should be taken with food or milk.

Problem 8. Contraindicated Pregnancy

S: Breast tenderness and swelling; nausea; last menstrual period was 6 weeks ago.

O: IUD removed 2 months ago; using the rhythm method for contraception; serum pregnancy test (+).

A: The patient is pregnant. Severe spinal injury history gives poor prognosis for mother during pregnancy, therefore the pregnancy should be terminated.

P: Therapeutic suction abortion should be initiated as soon as possible. Since the patient has a history of rheumatic heart disease, prophylaxis against bacterial endocarditis is needed. Since the patient has a severe penicillin allergy, administer vancomycin 1 g i.v., infused slowly over 1 hour to prevent the "red man syndrome," beginning 1 hour before procedure. Also give gentamicin 1.5 mg/kg i.m. or i.v. 30 minutes before procedure. The patient should be instructed that she should consider having a tubal ligation or that her husband should have a vasectomy. Information on male

and female sterilization should be provided so that the wife and husband can make a decision before her follow-up visit. BCPs, barrier methods, and IUDs are all contraindicated in this patient. Barrier methods cannot be used since both the patient and her husband are allergic to detergents and latex. The active ingredients in contraceptive jellies, creams, foams, suppositories, and sponges are detergents such as nonoxynol-9. Condoms, other than those from animal sources, and diaphragms are made of latex. Monitoring consists of having the patient return in 3 weeks for a pelvic examination to check for bleeding or infection. Note: If the patient elected to maintain her pregnancy, the drugs and chemicals to which she has been exposed during the pregnancy must be evaluated as to their teratogenic potential. The exact date of the first day of the last menstrual period must be known in order to determine which developing organ systems were exposed to these agents. The exact exposure dates and amounts must also be identified. Teratogenicity references must be consulted, and the patient must be advised appropriately. Finally, smoking may be detrimental to the fetus, and the patient should be encouraged to quit.

CASE 101

CC: J.A. is a 26-year-old woman who comes to the gynecology clinic complaining of a severe vaginal itch with malodor, dysuria, and menstrual cramps which have resumed during the last several months and are not relieved by aspirin. She also complains of midcycle abdominal cramping.

Past Medical History

J.A. has had hypertension since age 20; it is controlled by diet and biofeedback. She had peptic ulcer disease (PUD) at age 24, now resolved. She had pelvic inflammatory disease (PID) at age 25.

Past Surgical History

She had a right salphingectomy resulting from an ectopic pregnancy, at age 23.

Ob/Gyn History

G2P1Ectopic1
LMP 7 days ago
Dysmenorrhea began at menarche and is usually moderate
Postpartum 4 months; discontinued breast feeding 2 months ago.

Problem List

1. Primary dysmenorrhea
2. Secondary dysmenorrhea
3. Monilia vaginosis
4. Trichomonas vaginitis
5. Contraception

Medication History

ASA 650 mg q 4 h while awake beginning 3 days before menses is expected.

Allergies

None known.

Social History

J.A. is recently divorced; her latest boyfriend has moved away.

Family History

Her mother has Type II diabetes and hypertension (HTN); her father also has HTN.

Physical Examination

VS: BP 120/80 LA (sitting) HR 75 T 37.1 RR 19 Ht 5′4″ Wt 52 kg

GEN: WDWN

HEENT: WNL

COR: WNL

ABD: WNL

GU: Vulvar erythema with white patches; intertrigo with satellite lesions; green, frothy vaginal discharge; meatal erythema; "strawberry cervix."

RECT: WNL

EXT: WNL

NEURO: WNL

Results of Laboratory Tests

Na 142	HCO$_3$ 26	Hct 39	OGTT NL
K 4.3	BUN 14	Hgb 13	Guaiac (−)
Cl 101	Cr 0.9	FBG 85	

Vaginal fluid: KOH slide: pseudohyphae, Nickerson's media (+), NS slide: motile protozoans

Problem 1. Primary Dysmenorrhea

S: Menstrual cramps have resumed over the last several months with midcycle abdominal cramping.

O: History of primary dysmenorrhea since menarche.

A: The patient may have been amenorrheic during the 2 months of breast feeding, although this does not always occur. Primary dysmenorrhea usually occurs in ovulatory cycles and for this patient ovulation is evidenced by midcycle abdominal cramping or "mittleschmerz" due to prostaglandin release by the ruptured ovarian follicle. Aspirin should be discontinued since salicylates work poorly in the prevention of endometrial prostaglandin synthesis. It was unnecessary for the patient to take aspirin 3 days prior to menses since prostaglandins have half-lives of usually less than 1 minute. Therefore, any NSAID need only be initiated at the onset of cramping. Ibuprofen is now generic and inexpensive as well as one of the drugs of choice. If ibuprofen fails, the other drugs of choice for dysmenorrhea may be tried in the following order: naproxen, naproxen sodium, and finally, mefenamic acid. If NSAIDS fail, oral contraceptives are the usual second choice. However, this patient should not take oral contraceptives due to her family history of cardiovascular disease and diabetes, as well as her own hypertension history. She may have secondary dysmenorrhea.

P: Begin ibuprofen 800 mg p.o. at the onset of cramping, and 400 mg q4h prn dysmenorrhea or "mittleschmerz" symptoms. Patient education should include instructions to discontinue aspirin. The ibuprofen should be taken with food or milk, especially in this patient with a history of PUD. Monitoring the efficacy of the drug therapy relies on the subjective response of the patient.

Problem 3. Secondary Dysmenorrhea

S: Failure of NSAIDS to relieve dysmenorrhea or midcycle cramping.

O: Right salphingectomy to remove ectopic pregnancy at age 23; PID age 25.

A: Pelvic surgery and PID may have left adhesions.

P: Acetaminophen 325 mg/codeine 30 mg p.o. q4h prn pain. Patient education should contain an explanation of the possibility of adhesions causing the pain. They could be detected by laparoscopy and surgically lysed, but they often recur. Use as little narcotic as possible.

Problem 3. Vaginal Candidosis

S: J.A. has severe vaginal itch and dysuria.

O: Vulvar erythema with white patches; intertrigo with satellite lesions; KOH slide: psuedohyphae; Nickerson's media (+).

A: J.A. has vaginal candidosis. If clotrimazole fails, it may be tried again or miconazole or butoconazole may be used, which are the other drugs of choice. If recurrent episodes ensue for several months, an intestinal reservoir of monilia may be to blame which may be treated with the following: If not pregnant, ketoconazole 200 mg p.o. b.i.d. × 3 days; if pregnant, nystatin 500,000 U p.o. t.i.d. × 14 days along with vaginal therapy for 14 days. Since 5−25% of male partners of infected females may asymptomatically carry penile yeast, some clinicians recommend treatment of the male partners with an antifungal cream for 7 days.

P: Clotrimazole vaginal cream 1% 2 × 45 gm: Apply one applicatorful p.v. hs ×7 days and apply externally BID to areas involved. The patient should be told to use the medication for the entire 7 days, even if the vaginal and vulvar symptoms disappear and the satellite lesions clear, since the infection may still be present. Therapy should continue during menses. Monitoring for treatment efficacy does not require a follow-up visit unless there is a therapeutic failure.

Problem 4. Trichomonas Vaginitis

S: J.A. complains of vaginal itching, vaginal malodor, and dysuria.

O: Normal saline slide shows motile protozoans; meatal erythema; vaginal malodor; "strawberry cervix;" green, frothy discharge.

A: J.A. has trichomonas vaginitis.

P: Start metronidazole 2 g p.o. stat for both the patient and her partner. Patient education: Warn the patient of the possible disulfiram reaction if taken with alcohol, the possible metallic taste in the mouth, and the possible brown urine due to the metabolites of metronidazole. All those involved should take the metronidazole simultaneously. Monitoring of therapeutic success consists of resolving of symptoms. Follow-up visits are only required in the case of therapeutic failures. If therapy fails, many practitioners suggest getting liver function tests before repeating therapy, although this is controversial and should probably be reserved for patients already at risk for hepatic disease. The CDC now recommends metronidazole 2 g p.o. × 3 days for resistant cases for both the patient and partner.

Problem 5. Contraception

S: J.A. is sexually active and has vaginal infections.

O: J.A. is sexually active; will probably have other sexual partners.

A: Although the recurrent yeast infections may indicate colonization as the source, the trichomonas vaginitis is probably sexually transmitted. Her dysmenorrhea rules out the use of an IUD as would the possibility of multiple sexual partners. Her family history of cardiovascular disease and diabetes along with her history of hypertension rules out the use of oral contraceptives. Condoms and foam would afford the best contraceptive effect while protecting her from sexually transmitted diseases, especially AIDS.

P: Discuss the use of condoms including the choice of products and the advisability of always using condoms and the substantial contraceptive effectiveness when used with contraceptive foam. Monitoring of all female patients should consist of yearly pap smears, blood pressure, and the patient's reports of any abnormalities discovered during monthly breast self-examination.

CASE 102

CC: D.J. is a 14-month-old female who is admitted to University Medical Center after arriving in the emergency room in status epilepticus.

History of Present Illness

D.J. was in good health until 24 hours prior to admission when she became less playful. At bedtime she was upset, crying and would not sleep. Several hours later her mother heard noises and found D.J. arching her back and posturing. She was then noted to have tonic-clonic movements of her arms and legs, urinary incontinence, and vomiting. This lasted approximately 2 minutes and was followed by 60 minutes of sleeping. At 4:30 AM D.J. began screaming. She vomited twice, started to seize again, and was brought to the ER.

Past Medical History

D.J. was the 8 lb 5 oz product of a full-term, uncomplicated pregnancy. She has been a healthy baby with the exception of otitis media (OM) diagnosed 2 weeks ago. She was treated with ampicillin 125 mg p.o. t.i.d. ×10 days. Her mother states that she discontinued the antibiotics after 4 days because the baby developed a maculopapular rash and diarrhea. She was no longer symptomatic from the OM. The parents have a history of poor compliance with clinic visits.

Problem List

1. Meningitis
2. Seizures
3. Meningitis prophylaxis
4. Otitis media
5. Fever
6. Incomplete immunizations

Immunization History

DPT, TOPV at 2 months only

Social History

D.J. has a 3-year-old healthy brother; both children attend day care 5 days/week.

Allergies

Ampicillin (maculopapular rash, diarrhea)

Physical Examination

VS: BP 106/74 HR 150 RR 54 T 40.2 Wt 10 kg

HEENT: Erythematous right tympanic membrane, mucous membranes moist, PERRL

NECK: Stiff, unable to flex

CHEST: Clear

CV: RRR, no murmur

NEURO: listless, irritable when aroused, + Brudzinski's

Results of Laboratory Tests

Na 133	BUN 16	WBC 18k	Alb 4.0
K 3.3	Cr 0.7	Plts 417k	T. Pro 7.2
Cl 103	Hct 35.5	AST 33	Ca 9.8
HCO₃ 17	Hgb 12	ALT 8	

Urinalysis: WNL
WBC Differential: 83% polys, 10% lymphs, 5% monos, 2% eos
LP: CSF cloudy; Gram stain positive for small, Gram-negative rods, WBC 18.4 K (100% polys), RBC 0, protein 113, glucose 52

D.J.'s seizure was controlled with lorazepam 0.5 mg i.v. × 2. She was admitted and placed on the following:

Phenobarbital 25 mg i.v. b.i.d.
Lorazepam 0.5 mg i.v. prn seizure
ASA 120 mg p.o./p.r. q4–6h prn T >38.5°
Ampicillin 500 mg i.v. q6h

D.J. had a normal EEG. Blood cultures × 2 were negative. The CSF culture revealed H. influenza, type B, lactamase positive.

Problem 1. Meningitis

S: D.J. was less playful 24 hours prior to admission, listless, posturing, irritable, screaming, and vomiting.

O: Febrile to 40.2°C; seizure × 2; + Brudzinski's; CSF Gram stain positive for small, Gram-negative rods; stiff neck, cloudy CSF with WBC (100% polys); CSF glucose <50% of serum glucose; CSF protein elevated. CSF culture positive for H. influenza, type B, lactamase positive.

A: D.J. has bacterial meningitis secondary to inadequately treated OM. D.J. is currently on ampicillin 200 mg/kg/day; the antibiotic regimen is inadequate for the CSF culture results. Therapy is imperative because of the high morbidity and mortality of meningitis.

P: Evaluate D.J.'s allergy to ampicillin. Add chloramphenicol 100 mg/kg/day i.v. divided q 6 or discontinue ampicillin and begin cefotaxime 200 mg/kg/day divided q 6 or Ceftriaxone 100 mg/kg/day divided q 12. Antibiotics should be continued for 14 days. Repeat the lumbar puncture 24–48 hours after beginning therapy to monitor clinical and bacteriologic response. Monitor for side effects of therapy; monitor signs and symptoms of meningitis; consider prophylaxis for the patient and close contacts to eradicate the carrier state.

Problem 2. Seizures

S: By history tonic-clonic movements of arms and legs; postictal state lasting 60 minutes.

O: Status epilepticus on admission. EEG—normal; febrile 40.2°C; CSF positive for meningitis.

A: The seizures are secondary to elevated temperature and/or the meningitis. Status epilepticus was controlled with two doses of lorazepam 0.5 mg (0.05 mg/kg). D.J. had a complex seizure (long duration, focal characteristics, more than one) and is currently receiving phenobarbital 25 mg i.v. b.i.d. (5 mg/kg/day). D.J. should have received a loading dose of 15 mg/kg i.v. × 1 prior to beginning the maintenance dose.

P: Continue phenobarbital 5 mg/kg/day for prophylaxis. Monitor phenobarbital level (therapeutic = 15–40 μg/ml). Continue for 30 months (patient had complex seizure therefore is at risk for recurrence of febrile seizures). Monitor for side effects of phenobarbital (sedation, paradoxical hyperactivity, and respiratory depression with rapid i.v. administration). Patient education: Educate parents with respect to phenobarbital prophylaxis and side effects of phenobarbital.

Problem 3. Meningitis Prophylaxis

S: None.

O: 14-month-old infant with H. influenza meningitis

A: The current antibiotics will not eradicate the carrier state. Prophylaxis with rifampin is required for D.J. and all close contacts to eradicate the carrier state.

P: Rifampin 20 mg/kg p.o. q.d. × 4 days to be given to D.J. prior to discharge. D.J.'s parents, 3-year-old brother, and day-care class (both children and adults) should also receive rifampin 20 mg/kg p.o. q.d. × 4 days (maximum of 600 mg/day). Patient education: Educate parents with respect to side effects of rifampin (red secretions, nausea, vomiting); administration to children (suspension compounded by pharmacy or as powder packets sprinkled on a small amount of applesauce); and compliance.

Problem 4. Otitis Media

S: By history, OM diagnosed 2 weeks ago.

O: Right tympanic membrane erythematous; febrile to 40.2°C

A: The OM was diagnosed 2 weeks ago and was inadequately treated with ampicillin 125 mg p.o. t.i.d. (37.5 mg/kg/day) ×4 days. An appropriate regimen would have been 125 mg p.o. q.i.d. ×10 days (50 mg/kg/day). Her mother discontinued the ampicillin after 4 days, when D.J. developed a rash and diarrhea. The antibiotic therapy for D.J.'s meningitis will treat her OM.

P: Antibiotics as outlined for meningitis. Monitor signs and symptoms of OM. Recheck her ears at the end of therapy. Evaluate D.J.'s ampicillin "allergy". Educate parents as to D.J.'s ampicillin reaction and the importance of compliance with therapy.

Problem 5. Fever

S: D.J. is a 14-month-old baby with history of OM, now presenting with meningitis, elevated temperature, and seizures.

O: T 40.2°C

A: Her temperature is elevated because of the bacterial meningitis. Normal oral temperatures for this age group range from 36.5 to 37.5°C. Rectal temperatures are >0.5°C higher than oral temperatures. Axillary temperatures are >0.5°C lower than oral temperatures. The fever should be treated because an elevated temperature will put D.J. at risk for another seizure, dehydration, and discomfort. She is currently on ASA 120 mg p.o./p.r. q 4–6 h prn. Begin APAP 10–15 mg/kg/dose. APAP is available as drops (80 mg/0.8 ml) and elixir (160 mg/5 ml). APAP is relatively nontoxic in therapeutic doses.

P: Discontinue ASA. ASA is not available in a convenient liquid preparation for children. ASA has a higher frequency of side effects than acetaminophen (APAP). May also try alternating APAP with ASA if APAP alone does not control the fever. Cooling blankets may also be helpful. Patient Education: Educate parents with respect to appropriate dosing of antipyretic agents. Also caution against use of ASA in children with viral infections (especially chicken pox) secondary to the association of ASA and Reye's syndrome.

Problem 6. Incomplete Immunizations

S: By history: DPT, TOPV at 2 months of age only.

O: Not available

A: D.J. should receive appropriate immunizations. Must consider potential side effects of the pertussis component of DPT (seizures, neurologic changes). D.J. has received one dose of DPT without any apparent problems. She now has a history of seizures, either febrile or secondary to meningitis. Her seizures occurred when she was >12 months in age but also prior to completion of the DPT series. Her EEG study was normal; therefore further immunization with DPT is not an absolute contraindication.

P: When D.J.'s current febrile illness resolves bring her immunizations up to date. D.J. should receive a TB skin test; she should also receive DPT and TOPV in 2 weeks (age 15 months). One month later (age 16 months) she should receive MMR. In two months (age 17 months) she should receive her third dose of DPT and TOPV. D.J.'s immunization will now be up to date. At 18 months she should receive her fourth dose of DPT and TOPV. At 4 years she should receive her fifth dose of DPT and TOPV. At age 14 years and q 10 years thereafter she should receive Td. Patient Education: Educate parents with respect to the importance of immunizations. Check 3-year-old brother's immunization records. Discuss side effects (risk vs benefit) of DPT with parents. Ensure that D.J.'s seizures have been adequately evaluated. Discuss contraindications of immunization with parents.

CASE 103

CC: J.D. is a 72-year-old woman who is brought to the clinic by her son because of increasing confusion and forgetfulness, polyuria and right lower abdominal pain with constipation. J.D. has not been doing well the last month at home, and her son is considering nursing home placement.

Past Medical History

Parkinson's disease was diagnosed 8 years ago and is moderately well controlled but contributes to J.D.'s inability to care for herself. She has chronic bronchitis/emphysema; her major complaint is shortness of breath with moderate exertion. She had three exacerbations during the last year that required hospitalization and steroids but she has not been intubated. J.D. also has rheumatoid arthritis, diagnosed 15 years ago. J.D. was treated with ASA for 9 years but it was discontinued because of disease progression; prednisone was started 6 years ago. She has type II diabetes mellitus, onset 6 years ago. J.D. has never been tightly controlled but was asymptomatic on tolbutamide 750 mg t.i.d. In an attempt to simplify her drug regimen, her physician changed to glyburide 5 mg qd 1 month ago. Diverticulosis was diagnosed 4 years ago after a lower GI bleed. J.D. has anemia of chronic disease and open-angle glaucoma, which is adequately controlled.

Social History

J.D. is widowed and lives alone. She drinks two glasses of sherry daily; she used to smoke (75 pack-years) but stopped 6 years ago.

Pastsurgical History

Total abdomial hysterectomy and bilateral salpingoophorectomy, 20 years ago.

Problem List

1. Parkinsonism
2. Chronic bronchitis/emphysema
3. Rheumatoid arthritis
4. Type II diabetes mellitus
5. Diverticulosis with constipation
6. Anemia
7. Glaucoma

8. Mental deterioration, rule out dementia
9. Dry skin
10. Prednisone toxicity
11. Osteoporosis
12. Seborrhea

Medication History

Sinemet 25/100 t.i.d. ×1 year
Benztropine 1 mg b.i.d. ×4 years
Theophylline Elixir 30 ml q.i.d. ×4 years
Terbutaline 5 mg tablet q.i.d. ×4 years
Albuterol inhaler prn
Prednisone 20 mg q.d. ×6 years
Glyburide 5 mg q.d. ×1 month
Hydroxyzine 25 mg q.i.d. for itching ×1 month
Diazepam 10 mg hs for sleep ×1 month
Hydrocodone 5 mg and 500 mg acetaminophen 1 or 2 tablets q6h 1 month for pain of arthritis
Thioridazine 50 mg q.i.d. for confusion ×1 month
Timolol 0.5% 2 drops both eyes qd

Allergies

PCN (rash)
Codeine (nausea and vomiting)

Review of Systems

J.D. complains of back pain, dry skin, increased thirst, difficulty swallowing large pills, and morning stiffness.

Physical Examination

GEN: Small, thin, frail woman with lack of spontaneous movements
VS: BP 110/70 HR 100 RR 24 T 37.5 Wt 45 kg Ht 5′6″
HEENT: Mask-like facies, seborrhea of scalp and brow, normal intraocular pressure.
COR: WNL
CHEST: Rales and rhonchi, few expiratory wheezes.
ABD: Right lower abdominal pain on palpation without rebound tenderness
GU: WNL
RECT: WNL, guaiac-negative
EXT: Swollen bilateral MTP, wrists and ankles, very dry, thin skin.
NEURO: + Cog wheeling, resting hand tremor

Results of Laboratory Tests

Na 138	Hct 29.9	ALT 33	Ca 8.9	Sed Rate 75
K 4.0	Hgb 10.3	LDH 99	PO_4 2.6	Theophy-
Cl 103	WBC 13.8k	Alk Phos 75	Mg 1.3	lline 6
HCO_3 20	Plts 202k	Alb 3.7	Uric Acid 6	(drawn 2 hours
BUN 24	MCV 90	T bili 1.1	Hgb_{A1c} 11	after the dose)
Cr 0.8	AST 30	Glu R 380	RF 1:512	

WBC differential: WNL
Urinalysis: Glu neg ketones neg (by Ketodiatix)
CHEST X-RAY: no pneumonia, severe osteoporosis of spine
PFT's: Pre-bronchodilator $FEV_1 = 1000$ ml; post-bronchodilator $FEV_1 = 1500$ ml.

Problem 8. Mental Deterioration

S: Patient is experiencing increasing confusion and forgetfulness.
O: Son is considering placing patient in a nursing home.
A: J.D. is on multiple medications that could be contributing to her mental deterioration including theophylline elixir, which contains 20% ethanol, hydroxyzine, hydrocodone, and thioridazine. Diazepam has a long half-life, particularly in the elderly, and may accumulate. The dose of diazepam is large for a small, elderly patient. Thioridazine is not useful for confusion, and neuroleptics are frequently used inappropriately in elderly patients. Hypoxemia, hyperglycemia, and ethanol may also be contributing to her confusion. J.D. lives alone, and isolation may be an additional contributing factor. No drug treatment is required until further workup is completed.
P: Discontinue the diazepam, hydroxyzine, thioridazine, and hydrocodone and monitor for signs and symptoms of withdrawal. Change the theophylline elixir to a product that does not contain alcohol. Obtain TFTs to rule out hypothyroidism and VDRL and B_{12} levels to exclude reversible causes of dementia. Other common causes of mental deterioration in the elderly, including depression and fecal impaction, will be excluded or treated if present. Discuss with the family the dangers of CNS depressants including ethanol and overcompliance in elderly patients. A day-care center for the elderly or a senior's community could be sought as alternatives to a nursing home.

Problem 1. Parkinsonism

S: J.D. has difficulty swallowing and is unable to care for herself.
O: J.D. has cog wheeling, lack of spontaneous movements, resting tremor, and mask-like facies
A: The treatment for her parkinsonism has been inadequate, and the signs and symptoms are not controlled. The dose of Sinemet is very low and should have been increased soon after the drug was started. The dose of benztropine is also low. Anticholinergics are safe in open-angle glaucoma that is being adequately treated but may be contributing to her constipation. Anticholinergics are more effective for tremor and rigidity while levo-dopa is more effective for akinesia. A dose of 75 mg carbidopa per day saturates the enzymes. Terbutaline may be worsening the tremor.
P: Increase Sinemet 25/100 by one tablet per day until J.D. is taking two tablets q.i.d. Then switch to Sinemet 25 mg/250 qid and increase by one tablet per day until J.D. is taking 2 tablets q.i.d. or her signs and symptoms are controlled. In-

crease the benztropine slowly by 0.5 mg every 5–7 days to a maximum of 6 mg/day, or until there are disabling side effects or control of the disease. Monitor for an increase in movements, ability to care for herself, more facial animation, and a decrease in tremor and cog wheeling. For Sinemet monitor pulse, ECG, BP, nausea, vomiting, diarrhea, end-of-dose phenomena, on/off effect, nightmares, and psychosis. For benztropine monitor constipation, intraocular pressure, dry mouth, and pulse rate. Educate the patient and family about the disease and the drugs.

Problem 2. Chronic Bronchitis/Emphysema

S: J.D. is experiencing SOB on exertion.

O: PO_2 56; PCO_2 42; rales/rhonchi, wheezes

A: Treatment has not been optimal and CNS depressants could be depressing her respiration. Oral β_2 agonists are not superior to the inhaled form of these drugs and have more side effects. The terbutaline may be contributing to her tremor and increased heart rate. β-agonist inhalers should be administered on a regular schedule in this symptomatic patient. Bronchodilators are indicated in J.D. because she has a reversible component as evidenced by improvement in pre- and post-FEV_1 by 50%. The use of an inhaler will be difficult for a patient with parkinsonism so a spacer should be used. J.D.'s theophylline level is below the therapeutic level because of the low content in the elixir. The elixir is rapidly absorbed so that J.D. is experiencing large peak-to-trough fluctuations. Ipratropium may be additive with the bronchodilators and is particularly useful in chronic bronchitis. Inhaled steroids are not very effective in COPD but may be tried. J.D. has a decreased O_2-carrying capacity because of her anemia. Her pH is within the normal range, which indicates the chronicity of her blood gases.

P: Discontinue oral terbutaline. Begin albuterol or metaproterenol 2 puffs q.i.d. and prn with an Aerochamber. Change the theophylline elixir to Slobid, which can be sprinkled on applesauce or jam for easy swallowing. Increase the theophylline dose until a therapeutic level between 10 to 20 mg/liter is obtained. If J.D. is still symptomatic, add ipratropium 2 puffs q.i.d. 10–15 minutes after the β_2-agonist is administered. If the prednisone cannot be tapered because of exacerbations, institute triamcinolone 2 puffs b.i.d. Administer a yearly influenza vaccine and a pneumococcal vaccine once. Decrease the theophylline dose by one-half for 1 day after the flu vaccine. Give J.D.'s family a supply of tetracycline or cotrimoxazole to be given if sputum production increases or sputum color becomes green. Monitor ABGs, SOB, pulse, FEV_1, PFTs, theophylline level, and chest examination. Educate J.D. on the proper use of her inhalers with the Aerochamber: (a) Attach inhaler to Aerochamber; (b) exhale normally and slowly, (c) activate the inhaler into the Aerochamber; (d) place Aerochamber in mouth making a tight seal with lips; (e) inhale slowly; (f) hold breath for 10–15 seconds, (g) exhale slowly; (h) repeat in 5–10 minutes. Follow with triamcinolone inhalations. Triamcinolone inhaler has a spacer already attached. Wash inhalers daily.

Problem 4. Type II Diabetes Mellitus

S: J.D. is experiencing increased thirst and polyuria.

O: Random glucose 380, Hgb_{A1c} 11%

A: J.D. was previously asymptomatic on tolbutamide 750 mg t.i.d. The current glyburide dose does not equal the previous tolbutamide dose. Very tight control is not desired in a 72-year-old patient with no serious complications of diabetes since hypoglycemia could cause serious problems. However, the elevated Hgb_{A1c} level indicates that J.D.'s diabetes has been uncontrolled for some time. J.D.'s glucose may decrease as steroids are tapered. Levodopa causes a false-negative test with the glucose oxidase method for urine testing.

P: Increase the glyburide to 7.5 mg/day and reassess in 2 weeks. If J.D.'s blood glucose is still not controlled, continue to increase by 2.5 mg/day every 2 weeks until a maximum of 20 mg/day. Doses >10 mg/day should be administered as twice daily. Keep the FBS less than 180 mg/100 ml and random blood glucose <220 mg/100 ml. J.D. should not have any symptoms of hyperglycemia or hypoglycemia. Keep the urine glucose negative or trace (+), monitor FBS, Hgb_{A1c}, urine glucose, signs and symptoms of hypoglycemia (irritability, confusion, fainting, and feeling hungry) and of hyperglycemia (polyuria, polydipsia, fatigue, and blurred vision). Teach the patient and the family how to recognize and treat hypoglycemia with 4 oz orange juice or 2 teaspoons sugar followed by a light snack such as a sandwich, how to test the urine with Tes-tape and read the results at the border because of the levodopa, and how to maintain a diabetic diet with no concentrated glucose and 50% calories from complex carbohydrates, 30% from fats and 20% from protein. Also instruct them on proper foot care and how to obtain a Medi-Alert bracelet for J.D.

Problem 3. Rheumatoid Arthritis

S: J.D. is experiencing morning stiffness.

O: Swollen MTP, wrists and ankles, anemia, sed rate = 75, RF 1:512

A: Initial therapy with aspirin was appropriate, but the prednisone was inappropriate; the dose was very high, and it has caused J.D. problems. (See Problem 10.) A remitting agent should have been initiated 6 years ago when the disease began progressing. Penicillamine is not contraindicated in a patient with a rash to PCN but it has more adverse effects than gold. Narcotics should be avoided if possible in chronic diseases since tolerance and dependence will develop. It will take 6–9 months for a response to gold therapy.

P: Begin gold aurothioglucose since the oil form has less nitritoid reactions. Give a 1-mg test dose intramuscularly followed 10 mg the next week, and 25 mg the next week. Then give 50 mg q week until a total dose of 1 g is reached or the disease is controlled. If a response is obtained and can be maintained, increase the interval between injections by 1 week at a time until injections are given each month. Institute a NSAID such as sulindac 100–200 mg b.i.d. for 2 weeks to 1 month. If no response, try another NSAID such as naproxen 375 mg b.i.d. for 2 weeks to 1 month. Acetaminophen in doses less than 4 g/day may be used for pain relief. Monitor joint inflammation and swelling, walking time, grip strength, duration of morning stiffness, sedimentation rate, and activities of daily living. Before each injection of gold, obtain CBC, platelets, and a urinalysis for proteinuria. Look for rashes and stomatitis and inquire about diarrhea. Check a stool guaiac and inquire about GI distress from the NSAID. Monitor RF and liver function tests every month for 3 months. Provide physical therapy and education about rest, exercise, heat, paraffin baths, etc.

Problem 10. Prednisone Toxicity

S: J.D. has back pain.

O: She has severe osteoporosis of the spine by x-ray, glaucoma, thin skin, an elevated glucose, and an elevated WBC with normal differential.

A: Prednisone has caused severe osteoporosis, in a predisposed patient which is a reason to discontinue it. Because the prednisone is being used to treat rheumatoid arthritis, it must be tapered very slowly. J.D. will require steroid stress coverage for up to 1 year after the steroids are discontinued.

P: Taper prednisone by 1 mg/day every 2 weeks until the dose is 10 mg/day. Then taper by 1 mg/day/month until J.D. is off prednisone or the AM cortisol is >10. Test adrenal reserve in 9–12 months with a cortrosyn stimulation test. Monitor for a flare of her rheumatoid arthritis and her chronic bronchitis and any signs or symptoms of adrenal insufficiency, including a flu-like syndrome, an elevated K, decreased

BP, and decreased glucose, although the latter three are seen very late in adrenal insufficiency. Educate J.D. and her family about the signs and symptoms of adrenal insufficiency, compliance with the taper, and the need for steroid coverage for 1 year. They should also inform all health care providers about her steroid use. Add the steroid information to her Medi-Alert bracelet.

Problem 11. Osteoporosis

S: J.D. has back pain.

O: Chest x-ray reveals severe osteoporosis.

A: J.D. has osteoporosis induced by steroids as above. J.D. is postmenopausal by more than 20 years. Estrogens may not be effective at this late date, however, estrogens do decrease the rate of bone loss, and J.D. has no contraindication to their use. Calcium supplements and vitamin D have not proven to be of benefit, and calcium would worsen her constipation. Sodium flouride results in the formation of fragile bones.

P: Begin conjugated estrogens 0.625 mg qd for 21 days/month. Monitor for DVT and PE.

Problem 5. Diverticulosis/Constipation

S: J.D. has constipation.

O: J.D. has right lower abdominal pain without rebound; she is guaiac negative and afebrile.

A: J.D. should be treated for her constipation, and the pain should be relieved. Various drugs with anticholinergic activity including hydroxyzine, thioridazine, and benztropine, and the narcotics may be causing the constipation. Parkinsonism may also be contributing to her constipation.

P: Administer a Fleets enema or a glycerin suppository for immediate relief. Begin a sugar-free bulk laxative such as psyllium 1 teaspoonful t.i.d. in 8 oz water. Increase the fiber in her diet by providing assistance such as delivery of meals by an agency or meals at a seniors' center. Monitor relief of pain and constipation. Teach J.D. about mixing the laxative and drinking an additional glass of liquid with each dose. Warn J.D. that she should avoid other laxatives and that the bulk laxative may take several days to have an effect and increase flatulence. Assess whether immobility or restricted range of motion is interfering with normal bowel habits. Advise her to place a footstool in front of the toilet if this makes her more comfortable.

Problem 9. Dry Skin with Itching

S: J.D. is experiencing itching.

O: J.D. has dry skin.

A: Sebum production decreases with age. Drugs with anticholinergic activity can decrease sweating. Excessive bathing or soaps may cause dry skin.

P: Assess the frequency and duration of her bath or shower and brand of soap. Change if necessary. Begin Eucerin; it should be applied liberally after bathing or showering. Monitor symptomatic relief.

Problem 12. Seborrhea

S: None.

O: J.D. has seborrhea of scalp and brow.

A: Parkinson's patients frequently have seborrhea. It should be treated because it is a cosmetic problem.

P: Use zinc pyrothinate or selenium sulfide shampoo every two days. Lather hair, cover with shower cap, and leave on 5–10 minutes, then rinse. Begin hydrocortisone 1% cream; it should be applied sparingly to the brow and the area around the eyes should be avoided. Once controlled, decrease the frequency of application or the strength of the steroid to avoid the effects of steroids on the face.

Problem 7. Open-Angle Glaucoma

S: None.

O: J.D. has normal intraocular pressure

A: This problem may be steroid induced as above (Problem 10). Timolol, a nonselective β-antagonist, is not the drug of choice in a patient with bronchospastic lung disease.

P: Discontinue timolol. Begin pilocarpine 1% 1 drop in each eye twice a day.

CASE 104

CC: J.S. is a 2-week-old male infant brought to the clinic. His mother states that he has been unusually lethargic with diarrhea for 2 days and vomiting for 1 day. Although today he has not had a wet diaper for 4 hours, he has developed a diaper rash over the last several days. His mother states that she has tried to treat the rash with a variety of agents including corn starch and A & D ointment. She has also been using talc powder to make him more comfortable. He has been breastfeeding without difficulty until yesterday.

Past Medical History

J.S. is the 7 lb 3 oz product of an uncomplicated pregnancy to a G1P1, 26-year-old, married female. The mother has a history of migraine headaches that improved during pregnancy. Over the last week, J.S.'s mother has felt increasing anxiety that she attributes to having a new baby at home. Two days ago she felt the prodrome of a migraine and started taking diazepam 5–10 mg p.o. q.i.d. Her headache progressed and yesterday she added ergotamine 2 mg × 1 and than 1 mg qh × 4 with resolution of her headache. She intends to continue the diazepam for several more days, as recommended by her neurologist.

Problem List

1. Dehydration
2. Diarrhea/vomiting
3. Positive toxicology screen
4. Diaper rash
5. Nutrition

Allergies

NKA

Physical Examination

GEN: Lethargic, but arousable, 2-week-old male infant in Pampers

VS: BP 80/60 HR 160 RR 30 T 38.6 Wt 2.5 kg (birth weight = 3.3kg)

HEENT: Depressed fontanel, sunken eyes, dry mucous membranes

CV: Tachycardia

CHEST: WNL

SKIN: Erythematous, macerated genital region with satellite lesions

NEURO: Lethargic

Results of Laboratory Tests

Na 132	Cr 0.9	AST 30	Glu 80
K 3.4	Hct 50	ALT 25	Ca 7.8
Cl 96	Hgb 18	Alb 3.4	PO_4 4.5
HCO_3 16	WBC 7.8k	T. Bili 3.5	Mg 1.5
BUN 18	pHs 595k		

WBC Differential: WNL
Urinalysis: no urine available
LP: WNL
Blood cultures: pending
Toxicology screen: (+) benzodiazepines, (+) ergotamines

Problem 1. Dehydration

S: J.S. has had diarrhea for 2 days, vomiting for 1 day and no wet diaper for 4 hours.

O: J.S. has a depressed fontanel, sunken eyes, dry mucous membranes; his weight decreased 0.8 kg from birth weight. No urine is available for urinalysis. He has decreased Na, K, Cl, CO_2, Mg and elevated BUN, serum Cr, bilirubin, Hct, Hgb, WBC, HR.

A: J.S. has severe dehydration (25%) secondary to diarrhea and vomiting and needs replacement of the amount of fluid lost in addition to the amount required for maintenance. He also needs replacement of electrolytes lost plus maintenance requirements.

Fluids lost: 800 g = 800 ml
Maintenance fluids: 3.3 kg × 120 ml = 400 ml
Normal serum Na: = (140 mEq/liter)(0.6 liter/kg)(3.3 kg) = 278 mEq
Observed serum Na = (132 mEq/liter)(0.6 liter/kg)(2.5 kg) = 198 mEq.
Replacement Na = 278 − 198 = 80 mEq
Maintenance Na = 3 mEq/kg × 3.3 kg = 9.9 mEq

Total Na required = 80 + 9.9 = 90 mEq
K is > 3 mEq/liter therefore provide maintenance K only.
K requirement = 2 mEq/kg/day = 6.6 mEq
Replacement + maintenance = 1200 ml fluid + 90 mEq Na + 7 mEq K

P: Replace fluids and electrolytes lost secondary to diarrhea, vomiting and fever. Provide maintenance fluids and electrolytes.
Run 50% over 8 hours (75 cc/hour) and remainder over next 16 hours (40 cc/hour). Replace diarrhea losses milliliter for milliliter with D5W 0.45 NaCl. Reassess fluid/electrolyte status in the morning. Monitor diarrhea, intake/output, daily weight, electrolytes (Na, K, Cl, CO_2, Mg, PO_4), and temperature.

Problem 2. Diarrhea/Vomiting

S: J.S. has had diarrhea for 2 days and has been vomiting for 1 day

O: J.S. has dehydration as outlined above. Positive toxicology screen for ergotamines. LP is within normal limits. Blood cultures are pending. WBC 7.8 with normal differential.

A: The sepsis workup for J.S. is pending. Ergotamine toxicity is the likely cause for his diarrhea and vomiting.

P: Rule out an infectious etiology for the diarrhea. Replace lost fluids as above. Monitor diarrhea for signs of improvement. Obtain a stool to rule out parasites and infectious diarrhea. Monitor serum electrolytes.

Problem 3. Positive Toxicology Screen

S: J.S. has history of unusual lethargy, vomiting, and diarrhea.

O: Toxicology screen is positive for benzodiazepines and ergotamine. J.S. has slightly elevated bilirubin.

A: J.S. has ingested diazepam and ergotamine via mother's breast milk. J.S. now presents with side effects of both drugs. Diazepam side effects include sedation, lethargy, and elevated bilirubin. Ergotamine side effects include diarrhea, vomiting, and decreased BP.

P: Discontinue mother's breast milk. Assess mother's requirements for diazepam and ergotamine. Select an alternate nutrition source for J.S. if his mother requires these drugs. Monitor signs and symptoms of drug toxicity in J.S. Monitor bilirubin for signs and symptoms of jaundice and hyperbilirubinemia. Patient education: Counsel mother with respect to drugs excreted in breast milk.

Problem 4. Diaper Rash

S: J.S. has had diarrhea for 2 days. J.S.'s mother is taking diazepam to decrease her anxiety associated with having a new baby.

O: J.S. has an erythematous, macerated genital region. Satellite lesions are present. The baby is wearing Pampers. J.S.'s mother has been treating his diaper rash with corn starch and A & D ointment. She is also using talc powder for comfort.

A: J.S. has a severe diaper rash secondary to diarrhea or infrequent diaper changes. The satellite lesions indicate a *Candida* infection.

P: Clean diaper area with plain water. Treat the *Candida* infection with nystatin (powder, ointment or cream) or clotrimazole (cream) q.i.d. May also use 0.5% hydrocortisone cream b.i.d. for up to 7 days for severe irritation. Use cloth diapers; allow the baby to have diaperless periods. Change diapers frequently. Use vaseline as a moisture barrier. Use zinc oxide as a protectant. Avoid talc powder due to risk of aspiration. Avoid corn starch as it is a good medium for fungal growth. Educate parents with respect to changing the baby's diaper as soon as it is wet; avoiding overnight use of plastic pants and disposable diapers; exposing the diaper area to air whenever possible; rinsing diapers with diluted vinegar (½ cup vinegar in half-filled washing machine for 30 minutes); avoiding use of talc powder and corn starch.

Problem 5. Nutrition

S: J.S. is currently receiving 100% of nutritional needs from breast milk. His mother has a history of migraines.

O: J.S. has a positive toxicology screen

A: Mother requires drugs excreted in breast milk to control her migraine headaches. J.S. is currently symptomatic with side effects attributed to diazepam and ergotamine. The baby ingested the drugs via breast milk. J.S. will need an alternative nutritional source when his mother requires these drugs.

P: Select an alternative nutrition source to begin when the diarrhea and vomiting resolve. Enfamil and Similac are nutritional products formulated to resemble breast milk. Caloric intake for J.S. should be approximately 100–120 kcal/kg/day with protein 1–2g/kg/day for the first year (first 10 kg). Monitor J.S. for tolerance of new formula and appropriate weight gain. Educate mother about nutritional needs and about avoiding breast feeding when she is taking medication for her migraine headaches.

CASE 105

CC: G.S. is a 38-year-old woman who is brought to the emergency room at 1 PM because her husband says "she has lost her mind". G.S. has been hearing voices and thinks that she has a new purpose in life to save the world from the devil. She has been preaching nonstop at a mall for the last 4 hours. He also thinks that she has been sexually active with strangers. She has never done anything like this before.

Past Medical History

G.S. has had type I diabetes since age 18; it has been controlled fairly well in the past. She monitors her blood glucose and adjusts her insulin dose. She has asthma; onset was 8 years ago with one to two mild attacks per year. Asthma is seasonal, occurs in the cold winter months; her last attack was 6 months ago. She also has migraine headaches (four headaches per month) which are controlled on current regimen. G.S. has Crohn's disease, which flared 4 months ago, and she was started on treatment to induce a remission; ileal involvement was shown. G.S. did not require hospitalization for this flare. She has had hypothyroidism secondary to thyroiditis for 5 years.

Problem List

1. Acute psychosis
2. Type I diabetes mellitus
3. Asthma
4. History of migraine headaches
5. Hypothyroidism
6. Crohn's disease
7. Pubic lice

Social History

G.S.'s mother has schizophrenia; her father has ulcerative colitis. G.S. does not drink ethanol, smoke, or use recreational drugs.

Allergies

None known.

Medication History

NPH/regular insulin 12/4 U 7 AM and NPH/regular 5/10 U at 7 PM. (She administered her AM dose today.)
Theophylline SR 450 mg b.i.d. ×8 years
Albuterol inhaler 2 puffs q.i.d. and prn ×8 years
Cromolyn 2 puffs q.i.d. added 6 months ago
Atenolol 50 mg p.o. q.d. for migraine headache ×3 years
Prednisone 60 mg p.o. q.d. ×4 months
Metronidazole 500 mg p.o. q.i.d. ×4 months
Levothyroxine 0.15 mg p.o. q.d. ×5 years

Review of Systems

G.S. has itching in pubic area; she has had one to two loose nonbloody bowel movements per day.

Physical Examination

GEN: Agitated young woman in minor distress
VS: BP 130/85 HR 60 RR 18 T 37.8 Wt 60 kg
Ht 5'5"
HEENT: Thyroid normal
CHEST: Few rhonchi, no wheezes or rales
ABD: No abdominal tenderness, guaiac (−)
GU: Deferred, (+) for pubic lice
EXT: WNL, good pulses in feet bilaterally
NEURO: NL DTRs, decreased sensation in both lower extremities
MENTAL STATUS: Oriented × 3, delusions, auditory hallucinations, loose associations

Results of Laboratory Tests

Drawn at 2:30 PM:

Na 141	Cr 1.7	MCV 98	Glu 60	PTT P
K 3.1	Hct 43	AST 15	Ca 9.3	Hgb$_{A1c}$ 7%
Cl 108	Hgb 14.3	Alk Phos 67	PO$_4$ 3.6	ESR 18
HCO$_3$ 24	WBC 12.8k	Alb 4	Mg 2.1	Theophy-
BUN 16	Plts 362k	T.Bili 0.6	PT 11.2	lline 15

TFTs: RT$_3$ 31, TSH 4, T$_4$ 6.3
ABGs: pH 7.41, PO$_2$ 80, PCO$_2$ 34
Urinalysis: P

Problem 1. Acute Psychosis

S: Husband says G.S. has "lost her mind" and is sexually active with strangers.

O: G.S. is experiencing auditory hallucinations (hearing voices) and delusions; she thinks she must "save the world from the devil." She has been preaching at a mall, and is agitated and combative. She is engaging in inappropriate sexual behavior and makes loose associations.

A: Steroids may have precipitated acute psychosis in this woman with a positive family history of schizophrenia. Steroid psychosis may occur at any time during therapy and is more common at doses of prednisone >40 mg/day. This bizarre behavior requires treatment, parenteral therapy may be necessary since G.S. is agitated and combative. A high-potency neuroleptic is needed. Both haloperidol and fluphenazine are equally effective and have high EPS but are low for sedation, cardiovascular, and anticholinergic side effects. Prophylaxis of EPS is controversial and could wait until she has a reaction or benztropine 1 mg p.o. b.i.d. could be initiated.

P: Begin haloperidol 5–10 mg i.m. q 30–60 minutes until calm. Switch to the oral route when the patient will take oral medication. The acute dose will probably be in the range of 40–100 mg/day. Decrease the dose, if possible, to a maintenance dose of 5–40 mg/day. Neuroleptic therapy may no longer be required if the steroids are discontinued. If not, the duration of treatment will be 4–6 months. Monitor for a decrease in agitation and combative behavior. The psychotic thought process will resolve much more slowly. Watch for EPS, dystonia, akinesia, akathisia, orthostatic hypotension, dizziness, and anticholinergic effects such as dry mouth and constipation. Explain everything carefully to G.S. so that she will not feel threatened. Increase the fiber in her diet to alleviate the constipation and offer sugarless gum or saliva substitute for dry mouth.

Problem 2. Type I Diabetes Mellitus

S: None.

O: Her laboratory results shows glucose = 60 mg/100 ml and Hgb_{A1c} = 7%.

A: While G.S. has no current complaints, she gave herself her insulin at 7 AM and she is likely to become very hypoglycemic when her NPH insulin peaks at 4 PM. Otherwise, her insulin dosing appears appropriate and she is well controlled. However, since G.S. is psychotic at this time, it would be prudent to treat her DM with a sliding scale until adequate nutritional intake is assured.

P: Ascertain if she has eaten anything in the last 4 hours. If G.S. will take anything orally, give 4 oz orange juice and a snack now. If G.S. will not take orange juice orally, begin D5 0.45NS with 20 mEq KCl at 100 ml/hour. Discontinue previous insulin dosing and begin a sliding scale based on q4h blood glucose determinations. Give 1–2 U regular insulin for each 30–50 mg >120 mg/100 ml blood glucose. Keep blood glucose >80 and <140 mg/100 ml. Monitor for signs and symptoms of hypoglycemia including hunger, irritability, dizziness, and sweating. Atenolol may mask other signs and symptoms of hypoglycemia except sweating. Monitor signs and symptoms of hyperglycemia such as polydipsia, polyuria, blurred vision, and fatigue. Continue patient education regarding diabetes once acute psychosis has resolved.

Problem 7. Lice

S: G.S. has itching in pubic area

O: Physical examination revealed pubic lice.

A: Pregnancy must be ruled out since gamma benzene should not be used in the first trimester. Otherwise G.S. requires treatment after she is calm.

P: Have nursing service initiate Lindane after a warm bath and when skin is dry and cool; apply 1% lindane thinly to pubic area, thighs, trunk, and axillae. Rub in and leave on for 8–12 hours. Then wash off thoroughly. Sexual contacts should also be treated. Clothing should be washed in hot water. A nit comb may be used to remove nits from pubic hair. Reapply in 7 days only if still infected. Do not apply to the face.

Problem 6. Crohn's Disease

S: G.S. has had one to two loose bowel movements per day; there are no complaints of pain.

O: Physical examination showed no abdominal tenderness; G.S. is guaiac-negative. Her ESR = 18.

A: G.S. had a flare of her Crohn's disease 4 months ago and was started on prednisone and metronidazole to induce a remission. Steroids are effective for inducing remissions in Crohn's disease. The dose of prednisone was higher than the recommended 0.75 mg/kg. Metronidazole is also effective for inducing remissions in Crohn's disease but both agents were not required since G.S. did not require hospitalization. The dose of metronidazole was >20 mg/kg. Sulfasalazine would not work in G.S. since she does not have colonic involvement. A remission normally requires 2 to 4 weeks for induction and G.S. appears to be in remission now. Neither agent is effective for maintenance therapy in Crohn's disease. Steroids may be causing her psychosis but cannot be abruptly discontinued because of 4 months of treatment at a high dose which probably has caused HPA axis suppression.

P: Discontinue metronidazole. Begin a rapid steroid taper because of the psychosis. Decrease the dose of prednisone by 5 mg/day every 3–4 days until 10 mg/day is reached. Then continue taper by 1 mg/day/week until 8 AM cortisol is >10 or G.S. is off prednisone. In 9–12 months, perform a cortrosyn stimulation test to document adequate adrenal recovery and remove the need for stress coverage. Monitor for a flare of her asthma (see below) and a flare of her Crohn's disease by bloody diarrhea, abdominal pain, and ESR. Monitor for signs and symptoms of adrenal insufficiency (flu-like illness myalgias, arthralgias, BP, electrolytes, and glucose). Patient education for a later date would include recognizing signs and symptoms of adrenal insufficiency, the need for steroid stress coverage for up to 1 year after the prednisone is discontinued, and obtaining a Medi-Alert bracelet.

Problem 3. Asthma

S: No complaints.

O: Chest ascultation revealed no wheezes. Laboratory data revealed: PO_2 = 80, PCO_2 = 34, RR = 18.

A: G.S. had seasonal asthma that is under control and appears to have been overtreated for only one to two mild attacks per year. While the theophylline level is within the therapeutic range of 10–20, it is not needed at this time and may only be needed during the cold winter months. Atenolol is a β_1 selective beta-blocker and is probably not contributing to G.S.'s asthma. Since G.S. is hospitalized, it will be safe to discontinue the asthma medications under medical supervision. If G.S. becomes symptomatic during the acute psychosis, she may be unable to use the metered dose inhaler correctly. A spacing device or a nebulizer may be required.

P: Discontinue theophylline and cromolyn. Keep albuterol on an as-needed basis. Monitor shortness of breath, cough, wheezing, and respiratory rate. After resolution of the acute psychosis, check on ability to use inhaler correctly and continue education regarding inhalers.

Problem 4. Migraine Headache

S: None.

O: History.

A: G.S. had headaches at such a frequency as to require prophylactic therapy. Ergotamine compounds would be relatively contraindicated in a patient with diabetes who is likely to have peripheral vascular disease although pedal pulses are good bilaterally. Atenolol may mask signs and symptoms of hypoglycemia except for sweating and may prolong recovery from hypoglycemia. While relatively contraindicated in this patient, it appears to be controlling her headache. There is no need to change therapy at this time while G.S. is being closely monitored.

P: Continue atenolol for now. Consider amitriptyline or verapamil later.

Problem 8. Hypokalemia

S: None

O: K = 3.1

A: G.S. has steroid-induced hypokalemia.

P: Administer KCl 40 mEq p.o. × 1 dose. Monitor K.

Problem 5. Hypothyroidism

S: None

O: Thyroid normal by palpation, $T_4 = 6.3$, $RT_3U = 31$, NL DTRs, TSH = 4

A: By both subjective and objective assessment, G.S. appears to be euthyroid. Dose is slightly >1 μg/lb, but there is no evidence of hyperthyroidism.

P: Continue levothyroxine 0.15 mg p.o. q.d. Monitor signs and symptoms of hypothyroidism and hyperthyroidism. Monitor TFTs every 6 months.

CASE 106

CC: A.D. is a 24-year-old female found nearly comatose in her apartment with an empty prescription bottle of amitriptyline 50 mg tablets that was filled 3 days ago.

History of Present Illness

A.D. was found by a friend, who was able to briefly arouse her. A.D. vomited once, "passed out" and seized, at which time the paramedics were called. In the ambulance, she seized one more time. Upon arrival to the emergency room, she was comatose and began seizing again during the physical examination. According to the friend, A.D. has a long history of severe depression and had appeared to be more despondent recently.

Problem List

1. Tricyclic antidepressant (TCA) overdose
2. Seizures
3. Metabolic acidosis
4. Hypotension
5. Tachycardia
6. Cardiac conduction disturbances

Physical Examination

VS: BP 80/58 HR 150 irreg RR 20 T unable to obtain

HEENT: Pupils 6 mm, equal and reactive to light; dry oral mucous membrane; no abnormal breath odor detected

COR: Tachycardia

CHEST: Clear to auscultation, shallow respirations

ABD: Absent bowel sounds

RECTAL: Guaiac negative

SKIN: Warm, dry; no obvious signs of external trauma

NEURO: Positive response to painful stimuli

ABGs: pH 7.20, Pco_2 28, Po_2 70, HCO_3 18

ECG: Supraventricular tachycardia, right bundle branch block, QRS 0.14 seconds, QTc prolonged

Problem 1. Tricyclic Antidepressant Overdose

S: A.D., according to friend, was increasingly despondent.

O: Comatose state, empty amitriptyline bottle, dilated pupils, tachycardia, warm, dry skin, dry mucous membrane, absent bowel sounds, QRs 0.14, QTc prolonged.

A: A.D. has suffered a serious overdose from an unknown number of amitriptyline tablets and needs to be monitored in an ICU for at least 24 hours. A gastric emptying procedure will only be effective if the suspected time since ingestion is less than 24 hours. This should be undertaken only after the basic life support measures have been instituted.

P: Prevent aspiration during lavage by inserting an endotracheal tube and then inflating the cuff. Lavage the gastric contents by inserting a 40 French orogastric hose and irrigating with several liters of normal saline until clear fluid is returned. Pour a slurry of 1 g/kg of activated charcoal plus a cathartic (saline or sorbitol) down the lavage tube. Repeat the activated charcoal/cathartic regimen every 3–4 hours to decrease the enterohepatic circulation of the tricyclic antidepressants. Assure the presence of bowel sounds before additional doses are given. Order a urine toxicity screen and stat blood acetaminophen and aspirin levels to rule out multiple drug overdose.

Problem 2. Seizures

S: None.

O: Seizure activity was observed by medical personnel.

A: Seizure activity is frequently seen with TCA

overdose. True seizure activity must be distinguished from choreoathetotic and myoclonic movements, which can occur in about 50% of TCA overdoses. Seizures must be treated to prevent exacerbation of acidosis, hyperthermia, and rhabdomyolysis.

P: Initially control seizure activity with i.v. diazepam 5–10 mg given over 5 minutes. Load with i.v. phenytoin 15–20 mg/kg (up to 1 g). Run at a rate no greater than 50 mg/minute.

Problem 3. Metabolic Acidosis

S: None

O: Arterial blood pH 7.20

A: A.D. has metabolic acidosis from tissue hypoxia secondary to hypotension and seizures. In addition to its effect on correcting acidemia, alkalinization with sodium bicarbonate to a blood pH of 7.4–7.5 has been shown to aid in the management of conduction blocks, ventricular arrhythmias and hypotension from tricyclic overdoses. The mechanism is not well understood.

P: Administer a bolus of 1–2 mEq/kg of sodium bicarbonate i.v. As determined by serial blood pH measurements, readminister the bolus or begin a continuous infusion of sodium bicarbonate. Maintain the arterial pH between 7.45 and 7.5. Monitor ABGs every 2 hours. Monitor fluid status, electrolytes, BUN, and Cr.

Problem 4. Hypotension

S: None.

O: BP 80/58

A: Hypotension subsequent to TCA overdose may be due to several different mechanisms: decreased peripheral vascular resistance from the α-blocking effects; direct myocardial depression, and/or poor cardiac filling due to tachycardia. This patient's hypotension must be treated as it is compromising cardiac output and leading to tissue hypoxia and subsequent acidemia.

P: Administer normal saline or lactated Ringer's solution at a rate determined by responses in blood pressure, pulse and fluid status. A Swan-Ganz catheter may be necessary to deliver sufficient fluids without causing pulmonary edema. If blood pressure does not respond to the fluid challenge, a pressor agent should be used. Because of the α-blocking effects of TCA, predominantly α-adrenergic agents such as norepinephrine or phenylepherine may be preferred, although dopamine has worked well clinically.

Problem 5. Tachycardia

S: N/A

O: Supraventricular tachycardia of 150 beats/minute

A: Tachycardia following TCA overdose is due to the anticholinergic properties as well as a heightened adrenergic response from the inhibition of norepinephrine uptake. As long as adequate blood pressure and perfusion are maintained, tachycardia does not require treatment. In this patient, hypotension should first be corrected before the tachycardia is treated.

P: Correct hypotension as described in Problem 4. If hypotension and poor perfusion persist despite adequate therapy, propranolol may be used to decrease the heart rate. Propranolol must be used cautiously as it may increase cardiac depression.

Problem 6. Cardiac Conduction Disturbances

S: N/A

O: QRS interval 0.14 seconds, prolonged QTc, right bundle branch block

A: "Quinidine-like" properties of TCAs are responsible for the conduction defects seen after serious TCA overdoses. These defects are manifest on the ECG as increases in PR interval, QRS complex, and QT interval. This patient is predisposed to re-entry arrhythmias such as ventricular tachycardia and fibrillation. Phenytoin for seizure control may also serve to protect against arrhythmias. Avoid using quinidine, procainamide, and disopyramide.

P: Correct the acidemia with sodium bicarbonate. Maintain pH between 7.45 and 7.5. Consider placing a temporary pacemaker.

CASE 107

CC: M.P. is a 19-year-old male who comes into the emergency room complaining of nausea and vomiting.

History of Present Illness

M.P. states that he took between 30 and 35 acetaminophen tablets (500-mg acetaminophen per tablet) about 8 hours ago. Within a few hours he became nauseated and vomited three times. He also complains of feeling "bad" all over. He says that he had a fight with his girlfriend and took the tablets in front of her to "show her". Neither was too concerned about potential toxicity since "it was only Tylenol."

Past Medical History

M.P. has no other medical problems. He denies previous suicide attempts and denies recreational drug use and intravenous drug abuse.

Physical Examination

GEN: WDWN anxious-looking male in moderate distress.

VS: BP 100/75 HR 100 RR 18 T 37 Wt 73 kg

HEENT: Unremarkable

COR: Sinus tachycardia

CHEST: Lungs clear

ABD: No masses or organomegaly, no guarding, moderate midepigastric tenderness, + bowel sounds

RECTAL: Guaiac negative

SKIN: Pale, diaphoretic

NEURO: Cranial nerves grossly intact, alert and oriented × 3

Results of Laboratory Tests

Na 147	Cr 1.0
K 4.5	Hct 42.0
Cl 100	Hgb 14.4
HCO$_3$ 29	WBC 10.5k
BUN 15	Glu 95

Acetaminophen (APAP) 200 μg/ml (8 hours post-ingestion)

Aspirin < 20 μg/ml

LFTs: pending

Problem

S:

O:

A:

P:

Problem

S:

O:

A:

P:

Problem

S:

O:

A:

P:

Questions

1. Is this a serious APAP overdose?
2. What is the significance of the serum APAP level?
3. What is the rationale for N-acetylcysteine therapy in APAP overdose?
4. How should N-acetylcysteine be administered?

CASE 108

CC: M.H. is a 32-year-old female hospitalized for lower quadrant abdominal tenderness, chills, vomiting, and fever for 1 week. She also admits to problems with weight gain, breast tenderness, spotty periods, acne, fatigue, and depression since she started taking birth control pills.

Past Medical History

M.H. has history of gestational hypertension and diabetes, recurrent cystitis, acne, pain due to vaginal fibroids, and fibrocystic breast disease.

Medications History

Loestrin 1.5/30 for 5 months (ethinyl estradiol 30 μg, norethindrone acetate 1.5 mg)
Cotrimoxazole 160/800 mg 1 tablet hs prior to intercourse, last dose 7 days ago
Tetracycline 250 mg q.i.d. for acne $\times$ 3 years
Metronidazole 2 g stat p.o. 1 week prior to admission for asymptomatic trichomonas

Allergies

None known

Ob/Gyn History

M.H. has menstrual cramps and has been spotting early in her cycle. Her last menstrual period was 6 weeks ago.

Social History

M.H. is an unmarried graduate student who lives with her 3-year-old daughter. She smokes (2 ppd for 10 years) and drinks alcohol (three to four glasses wine per night).

Family History

She has a family history of atherosclerotic cardiovascular disease (ASCVD), hypertension (HTN) and adult onset diabetes mellitus.

Review of Systems

($-$) dysuria, ($+$) early morning nausea
($+$) constipation, ($+$) pelvic and abdominal pain

Physical Examination

GEN: WDWN young woman in moderate distress
VS: BP 140/96 HR 96 T 39.8 RR 20 Wt 55 kg Ht 5'1"
HEENT: WNL
COR: WNL
CHEST: WNL
BREAST: Multiple cysts bilaterally with one dominant lump
ABD: ($+$) rebound tenderness
GU: ($-$) CVAT
RECT: WNL
PELVIC: ($+$) bilateral cervical adnexal tenderness
EXT: ($+$) varicose veins
NEURO: WNL

Results of Laboratory Tests

Na 136   Hct 33.8
K 4.0   Hgb 11.2
Cl 100   WBC 28.8k
HCO$_3$ 28   Plts P
BUN 10   MCV 78
Cr 1.0

Urinalysis: pH 6.0, 10–20 WBC/HPF, 10 RBC/HPF, Gram stain: ($+$) GNR

Problem

S:

O:

A:

P:

Problem

S:

O:

A:

P:

Problem

S:

O:

A:

P:

Problem

S:

O:

A:

P:

Problem

S:

O:

A:

P:

Problem

S:

O:

A:

P:

thiazides. If you agree, recommend a thiazide drug and dose. If you disagree, explain why and recommend an alternative treatment.

7a. M.H. decides to have a therapeutic abortion as well as a vaginal hysterectomy for her fibroids. Recommend a prophylaxic antibiotic regimen (drug, dosage, duration, rationale) for her hysterectomy.

7b. Explain the risks versus benefits of estrogen replacement therapy in M.H. after hysterectomy and defend your decision to treat/or not treat.

8. Her breast biopsy is positive for breast cancer and she undergoes a modified radical mastectomy. Pathology reveals a 5-cm ER-positive mass and 3/10 positive lymph nodes. Adjuvant chemotherapy with tamoxifen is prescribed. Explain why you agree or disagree with this therapy. If you agree, recommend a dose and duration for tamoxifen therapy. If you disagree, recommend alternative drug and dose.

CASE 109

CC: R.R. is a 70-year-old female brought to the ER on March 3 by her family because of slurred speech, mental status changes and ataxia.

History of Present Illness

Mental status changes: R.R. has been alert and active until approximately 6 months ago (clinic visit on October 4) when her family noted increased forgetfulness. About 1 month ago (clinic visit on February 7) the family noted increased confusion with routine activities along with headaches and dizziness. By 3 weeks ago (clinic visit February 14) the family felt that R.R. had become "senile" or "demented" and were afraid to leave her alone at home. Slurred speech began 2–3 days ago, and paranoid ideation with visual hallucinations began today.

Past Medical History

Peptic ulcer disease (PUD): Diagnosed in June 1984, at which time it was treated with sucralfate and presumably it resolved. One month ago, a guaiac-positive stool was noted on a clinic visit and cimetidine was prescribed.

Hypertension (HTN): For many years that has been relatively well controlled on triamterene/hydrochlorothiazide.

CHF: Mild pedal edema was noted about 10 years ago and it has been well controlled on current regimen.

Type II diabetes mellitus: Elevated fasting blood sugars have been noted on each clinic visit during the last year. Diet and weight loss have been prescribed.

Chronic renal failure secondary to HTN and dia-

Questions

1. Evaluate the hormonal balance of the birth control pill (BCP) used in M.H. and list evidence to support your answer. Recommend an alternative birth control pill (progestin and estrogen) and explain your selection rationale.

2. What patient education information can you give M.H. regarding missed pills and warning signs for pill side effects. Identify any patient specific factors that can decrease BCP efficacy.

3. Recommend a complete treatment regimen for management of the cervical motion tenderness. State your rationale for selection. (Include drug, dosage, duration, route.)

4. The pregnancy test returns positive. Identify and explain the potential teratogenic risks that M.H. has presented to her pregnancy prior to her hospital admission.

5a. The intern wants to treat the UTI with single-dose therapy since M.H. is totally asymptomatic and the intern does not want to give her any more teratogens. How do you respond and give reasons to support your decision to the intern.

b. Recommend an empiric regimen (drug, dose, duration) for her abnormal UA and defend your antibiotic selection.

6. Defend or refute the following: M.H.'s BP should be treated now and be treated with

betes: Baseline Cr≅2.3 as was documented on clinic visits during last year.

Osteoarthritis of knees and hips: Indomethacin SR 75 mg b.i.d. began 1 month ago in an effort to encourage her ambulation. The only other drug treatment that has been tried was an appropriate regimen of acetaminophen which failed.

Chronic anemia: Documented as iron deficiency thought to be secondary to PUD and treated with FeSO₄.

Depression with complaints of difficulty sleeping and expression of feelings of worthlessness and guilt: Her family reports that R.R. has lost all interest in her usual activities, refuses to participate in social activities, and does little more than sit around all day. They also note that R.R. talks frequently about death recently.

Medication History

R.R. is compliant with all her drugs because the family administers them. She takes the following:

Indomethacin SR 75 mg b.i.d. began January 31
Cimetidine 400 mg qid began January 31
Flurazepam 30 mg qhs not prn may repeat ×1 began September 23
Doxepin 25 mg q AM began three years ago
FeSO₄ 300 mg p.o. tid for 4 years
Dyazide b.i.d. for 7 years
Digoxin 0.25 mg po qd for 10 years

Allergies

None known

Review of Systems

Per family: R.R. has had no bowel movement in 3 days and has had a decreased appetite for last month.

Physical Examination

GEN: Elderly woman who is agitated, confused, shouting and screaming

VS: BP 145/80 (lying), 135/65 (standing) HR 50 T 36 RR 18 Wt 65 kg Ht 5'0"

HEENT: Moderate AV nicking, normal thyroid, periorbital edema, moderate alopecia

COR: Normal S_1 and S_2, no S_3, S_4, murmur or rub

CHEST: No rales, ronchi, or wheezes

ABD: No masses or tenderness, normal liver size

GU: WNL

RECT: Guaiac positive

EXT: No edema, decreased ROM in hips, no inflammation of joints

NEURO: Oriented ×1, ataxia, decreased reflexes

SKIN: Dry, coarse, cold

Results of Laboratory Tests

Na 146	Cr 4.6	MCV P	T.Bili 0.3	PT 12.6
K 4.4	Hct 38.5	MCHC 31.9	Glu 402	PTT 38
Cl 119	Hgb 12.8	AST 47	Ca 7.9	
HCO₃ 18	WBC 7.7k	Alk Phos 79	PO₄ 4.8	
BUN 80	Plts 191k	Alb 3.8	Mg 3.1	

ABGs (on room air): PO₂ 84, PCO₂ 29, pH 7.29
TFTs: T4 (D) 3.3, RT₃U 21, TSH>20
Urinalysis: WNL
ECG: Normal sinus rhythm with no LVH
Chest x-ray: Clear, no evidence of pneumonia or CHF

Problem

S:

O:

A:

P:

Problem

S:

O:

A:

P:

Problem

S:

O:

A:

P:

Problem

S:

O:

A:

P:

Problem

S:

O:

A:

P:

Problem

S:

O:

A:

P:

Problem

S:

O:

A:

P:

Problem

S:

O:

A:

P:

Problem

S:

O:

A:

P:

Questions

1. Recommend drug treatment for her paranoid ideation and visual hallucinations. Give drug, dose, route, schedule, and duration. Discuss your reasons for selecting this drug for this patient over available alternatives.
2. Recommend a new drug treatment regimen for her depression. Be specific, give drug, dose, schedule, how you would titrate the dose and how long you would treat. State goals and monitoring parameters. Give the time course for resolution of signs and symptoms.
3a. Identify four drugs that may be causing R.R.'s 6-month history of mental status changes. Explain the mechanism of these adverse effects if they are known.
  b. Recommend appropriate alternatives in her drug regimen to eliminate these four possible drug-related mental status changes. Alterations must include either acceptable alternative treatments or reasons why this problem should not be treated with drugs at this time. For alternate therapy, give drugs, doses, route, schedule, and your reason for selection.
4. R.R. is diagnosed as being hypothyroid based on her laboratory thyroid function tests. Are any drugs affecting the interpretation of her thyroid function tests? Recommend treatment for her hypothyroidism. Give drug, dose, route, schedule, and titration. State your goals and monitoring parameters. Discuss any drug interactions between thyroid replacement and the drugs that R.R. was on prior to admission.
5. Prior to discharge, it is documented that R.R.'s blood glucose levels are consistently within the 320–400 range. Design an appropriate drug regimen for the treatment of her diabetes. Give drug, dose, and schedule. State your goals and monitoring parameters. Give your reasons for selection.

CASE 110

CC: J.J. is a 15-month-old baby boy who is brought into the emergency room by his mother, who states that J.J. developed a cold 5–6 days ago and diarrhea yester-day but was otherwise doing well until this morning when he developed a fever and began tugging at his right ear. She also tells you that one of the employees at J.J.'s day-care was diagnosed with TB 3 weeks ago and that a child at the day-care was diagnosed with *Haemophilus influenzae* B meningitis yesterday.

Past Medical History

J.J. was a full-term baby who was the product of a normal vaginal delivery. He had otitis media twice, at ages 6 and 12 months. He also had measles at age 13 months.

Allergies

Ampicillin (rash)
Sulfa (Steven Johnson Syndrome)

Social History

J.J. lives with his mother, father, and 4-year-old brother. He has attended day-care since the age of 12 months.

Physical Examination

VS:	BP 106/64 HR 120 T 39.9 (rectal) RR 28 Wt 10 kg
HEENT:	Otoscopic exam: bulging erythematous right TM
COR:	tachycardia
CHEST:	Clear
ABD:	Benign
GU:	WNL
RECT:	Diarrhea in diaper heme (+)
EXT:	WNL
NEURO:	WNL

Results of Laboratory Test

Na 137	Cr 0.5	MCV 78	Alk Phos 113
K 3.9	Hct 38	MCHC 32	Alb 3.6
Cl 101	Hgb 12	AST 28	T Bili 0.7
HCO_3 22	WBC 23k	ALT 20	Glu 80
BUN 10	Plts 201k	LDH 121	Ca 8.6

Urinalysis: WNL
Stool culture: pending
Chest x-ray: Normal
PPD: Induration 12 mm (48-hour reading)
LP: RBC 1, WBC 0, gluc 40, prot 10

Problem

S:

O:

A:

P:

Problem

S:

O:

A:

P:

Problem

S:

O:

A:

P:

Problem

S:

O:

A:

P:

Problem

S:

O:

A:

P:

Problem

S:

O:

A:

P:

Questions

1. Recommend an appropriate treatment regimen for J.J.'s otitis media. Include drug(s), dose(s), route(s), frequency of administration, and duration of treatment. Justify your recommendation.
2. Explain why J.J. should or should not receive any prophylactic treatment for his exposure to *Haemophilus influenzae* B meningitis. If he should receive treatment, give drug(s), dose(s), route(s), and duration of treatment.
3. What, if any, treatment should J.J. receive at this time for his positive PPD? Be specific; include drug(s), dose(s), route(s), and duration. Justify your answer.
4. The intern wishes to prescribe antipyretic therapy for J.J. Recommend an appropriate regimen including drug(s), dose(s), and route(s). Justify your selection.
5. The stool culture returns and is positive for Campylobacter. Recommend appropriate therapy for J.J.'s Campylobacter including drug(s), dose(s), route(s), and duration.
6. Recommend a complete vaccination schedule for the completion of J.J.'s normal childhood vaccinations. Include time sequence and specific vaccinations.
7. J.J. recovers from his otitis media and URI. One week later, you are working in the poison control center and J.J's mother calls you and states that J.J. has just swallowed a whole bottle of iron tablets. Recommend acute treatment that J.J.'s mother should perform prior to bringing J.J. to the hospital. Explain the rationale and, if appropriate, give drug(s), dose(s), route(s), and frequency of administration.

CASE 111

CC: R.C. is a 49-year-old female who was admitted to the emergency room on June 29 with chief complaints of nausea, vomiting, diarrhea, severe rib spasm, low back pain, anorexia, and abdominal cramps for 12 hours. The patient states that the muscle spasm and low back pain have increased in severity for a week, and that she took more ASA/oxycodone and diazepam than was prescribed. She ran out of ASA/oxycodone tablets 2 days ago. The patient was transferred from the ER to the general medicine service for further workup after receiving morphine 10 mg i.m. stat.

Past Medical History

R.C. has numerous medical and surgical problems. R.C. has urinary incontinence due to a neurological dysfunction, and performs straight intermittent catherization at home. The patient has undergone four lumbar surgeries for the treatment of chronic back pain, and has been treated with a number of narcotic analgesics. She developed a DVT after one of the surgeries. Because of muscle spasm with unknown etiology she was prescribed diazepam. R.C. has had diabetes for 6 years and has been fairly well controlled with insulin in two daily doses. She occasionally tests her urine for glucose but is very reluctant to do blood glucose monitoring.

Medication History

ASA/oxycodone (approximately 10 tablets/day) for 1 year

Diazepam 10 mg q.i.d. prn for muscle spasm for 3 years

Warfarin 5 mg hs for 3 months

Mylanta II 15 ml prn for ulcer for 5 years

Human insulin NPH/regular 10 U/5 U q AM and 5 U/5 U q PM

Vitamin C 6 g q.d.

Allergies

Procaine (severe nausea)

Ampicillin (skin rash)

Social History

R.C. has smoked 2 ppd for 20 years. She has had two to four drinks of whiskey per day for 15 years.

Physical Examination

GEN: Ill appearing female complaining of severe pain

VS: BP 140/95 RR 22 HR 110 T 40.5 Wt 55 kg

HEENT: Scleral icterus, mild gum bleeding, sialorrhea, lacrimation, rhinorrhea

COR: Sinus tachycardia

CHEST: Some tenderness of the right rib muscles, CVA tenderness, otherwise WNL

ABD: Pain on palpation and tenderness

RECTAL: Guaiac positive

EXT: Several bruises on legs, muscle twitching in legs, hot dry skin with decreased skin turgor

ENDOSCOPY: 2-cm duodenal ulcer with oozing blood

Results of Laboratory Tests

Na 134	Cr 1.2	MCV 102	T.Bili 3.4
K 3.4	Hct 34	AST 102	FBS 320
Cl 98	Hgb 11	ALT 47	PT 28
HCO_3 26	WBC 12.5k	Alk Phos 95	PTT 35
BUN 18	Plts 185k	Alb 3.2	Hgb_{A1c} 12%

Urinalysis: 5–10 WBC/HPF, 15–20 RBC/HPF, urine Clinitest = 2%

Urine culture: 1 million cfu/ml *Proteus mirabilis*

Problem

S:

O:

A:

P:

Problem

S:

O:

A:

P:

Problem

S:

O:

A:

P:

Problem

S:

O:

A:

P:

Problem

S:

O:

A:

P:

Problem

S:

O:

A:

P:

Problem

S:

O:

A:

P:

Problem

S:

O:

A:

P:

Problem

S:

O:

A:

P:

Problem

S:——————————————————————

O:——————————————————————

A:——————————————————————

P:——————————————————————

Problem

S:——————————————————————

O:——————————————————————

A:——————————————————————

P:——————————————————————

CASE 112

CC: L.C. is a 30-year-old female who is admitted to general hospital with complaints of shortness of breath (SOB), fever, pleuritic chest pain, watery diarrhea, abdominal pain, and a cough productive of green sputum for 3 days. She also notes nausea and weight gain the last month, which she attributes to birth control pills.

Past Medical History

L.C. has had asthma for 15 years. She has pustular acne and is status post S/P splenectomy secondary to motor vehicle accident (MVA) 1 year ago. She has seizures secondary to head trauma from MVA.

Medication History

Tetracycline 250 mg b.i.d. × 5 years
Theodur 400 mg b.i.d.
Tri-Norinyl-28 1 tablet hs × 3 months
Phenytoin 300 mg q.d. × 1 year

Allergies

Penicillin ("maculopapular rash," no SOB)

Social History

L.C. is unmarried and is employed as a cocktail waitress. She smokes (2 ppd for 10 years) and drinks alcohol (approximately four rum and cokes per night).

Family History

L.C.'s mother is alive and suffers from Type II diabetes mellitus and hypertension. Her father had hypertension and died of myocardial infarction at age 50.

Physical Examination

VS:	BP 140/70 HR 80 T 38 RR 20 Wt 65 kg (60 kg 2 months ago) Ht 5′2″
HEENT:	WNL
COR:	NL S1S2 (−)S3 (−)murmurs
CHEST:	(+) wheezes, (+) rhonchi, (−) rales, (+) echophony
ABD:	Benign, (−) rebound tenderness
GU:	(+) CVAT (+) dysuria
RECT:	WNL
EXT:	WNL
NEURO:	WNL

Results of Laboratory Tests

Na 140	Cr 1.5	Theophylline 15
K 3.5	Hct 15	Phenytoin 15
Cl 100	Hgb 35	Pregnancy Test (+)
HCO_3 20	WBC 20.3k	
BUN 30	FBG 250	

WBC differential: 80P, 10B, 7L, 3M
ABGs: pH 7.54, PO_2 60, PCO_2 30
Stool Examination: Many WBCs, RBCs, no organisms seen on Gram stain
Sputum Gram stain: (+) polys, Gram (+) diplococci
Urinalysis: Sp gr 1.015, pH 7, 10–20 RBC, 25–50 WBC, 4+ Bacteria Gram Stain: (+) GNR, 2% glucose, protein (+)
Chest x-ray: RML infiltrate

Problem

S:

O:

A:

P:

Problem

S:

O:

A:

P:

Problem

S:

O:

A:

P:

Problem

S:

O:

A:

P:

Problem

S:

O:

A:

P:

Problem

S:

O:

A:

P:

Problem

S:

O:

A:

P:

CASE 113

CC: H.L. is a 70-year old, 53-kg man who comes to clinic today for follow-up of his multiple medical problems.

Past Medical History

H.L. has insulin dependent diabetes mellitus. He also has a history of sustained ventricular tachycardia (S/P MI × 2) that failed all available antiarrhythmics and was placed on amiodarone. H.L. suffers from hypertension, emphysema, and depression.

Medication History

Insulin NPH 25 U regular 10 U q AM
HCTZ 50 mg b.i.d.
L-thyroxine 0.05 mg q AM
Clonidine 0.2 mg b.i.d.
KCl 20 mEq b.i.d.
Metaproterenol 2 puffs 6 ×/day
Theophylline 200 mg q.i.d.
Amiodarone 200 mg b.i.d. × 2 years

Allergies

None known

Social History

H.L. lives with his adult daughter, who is responsible for administering his medications, and who monitors his urine glucose only occasionally. H.L. does not drink ethanol. H.L. smoked cigarettes (80 pack-years) but quit 10 years ago.

Review of Systems

H.L. complains of dyspnea, weakness, fatigue, constipation, insomnia, and frequent urination. All of his other complaints relate to his feeling worthless, depressed, and that he is a burden to his family. He is not suicidal, but feels that life is not worth living, and he has become difficult for his child to manage at home because of irritability. He is not eating and sleeps little. These problems are of 2 months duration and are getting worse.

Physical Examination

GEN: Elderly gentleman in no apparent distress
VS: BP 140/85 HR 60 T 36.8 RR 25 Wt 53 kg Ht 5'6"
HEENT: Senile cataracts in both eyes, normal thyroid
COR: NL S1 and S2, no S3, S4 or (m)
CHEST: Decreased breath sounds
ABD: No masses or tenderness, normal size liver
RECT: Moderate BPH
EXT: WNL
NEURO: Decreased DTRs

Results of Laboratory Tests

Na 142	Cr 1.2	AST 18	PO_4 3.5	Theophy-
K 4.2	Hct 46.2	Alk Phos 50	Mg 1.8	lline 15
Cl 106	Hgb 15.3	Alb 4.0	PT 10.8	Stool gua-
HCO_3 31	WBC 6k	FBG 318	PTT 31.9	iac (−)
BUN 15	Plts 200k	Ca 9.0	Hgb_{A1c} 18	

TFTs: TT_4 4.1, T_3RIA 90, RT_3U 22, TSH 24.7
ABG: PO_2 65 PCO_2 35 pH 7.40

Urinalysis: glucose 1%, ketone (−), protein (−)
PFTs: Prebronchodilator, FEV_1/FVC = 800/1200; postbronchodilator, FEV_1/FVC = 900/1300.
ECG: Normal sinus rhythm

Problem
_____

S: _____
_____
_____

O: _____
_____
_____

A: _____
_____
_____
_____

P: _____
_____
_____

Problem

S:

O:

A:

P:

Problem

S:

O:

A:

P:

Problem

S:

O:

A:

P:

Problem

S:

O:

A:

P:

Problem

S:_____

O:_____

A:_____

P:_____

Problem

S:_____

O:_____

A:_____

P:_____

CASE 114

CC: K.L. is a 67-year-old male who comes to clinic today for follow-up of multiple medical problems. Today, he complains of nausea, vomiting, heart palpitations, and he is very depressed.

Past Medical History

K.L. has chronic bronchitis and emphysema secondary to cigarette smoking. He is short of breath on minimal exertion such as walking 1 block. He has a 100 pack-year smoking history and, although he stopped smoking last year, he has continued to feel short of breath with minimal exercise. He has had increased sputum production in the last week. R.L. has rheumatoid arthritis, which was initially treated with aspirin but this led to a GI bleed. He is currently treated with naproxen 250 mg b.i.d. He complains of worsening morning stiffness and arthralgias with swelling in most joints. R.L. has type II diabetes mellitus (DM), which is currently treated with tolbutamide. He is noncompliant with his diet and has refused to lose any weight. He does not check his urine as prescribed. He has some of the complications of DM but is particularly troubled by the neuropathy, which has led to orthostatic hypotension, gastric paresis, and impotence. He also has psoriasis with scaly patches on his elbows, knees, and scalp. He has tried various nonprescription medications without success.

Medication History

Theodur 400 mg q.i.d.
Metaproterenol 20 mg q.i.d.
Albuterol 2 puffs q 4–6 h prn
Cromolyn 20 mg inhaled q.i.d.
Erythromycin 500 mg q.i.d. started 8 days ago
Dyazide 1 b.i.d.
Naproxen 250 mg b.i.d.
Tolbutamide 1500 mg t.i.d.
Flurazepam 30 mg q hs prn insomnia
Hydrocortisone cream 0.5% to scalp

Allergies

None known

Review of Systems

K.L. has increasing insomnia with late-morning awakening, decreased interest in daily living, thoughts of suicide because of his poor health although he has no firm plan at this time. He has increased polyuria, polydipsia, and nocturia.

Physical Examination

GEN: Elderly gentleman in no apparent distress who is leaning forward on elbows and is breathing through pursed lips.

VS: BP 120/85 HR 120 irreg T 37.6 RR 33 Wt 88 kg Ht 5'11"

HEENT: Patches of scale in scalp, + JVD

COR: Distant S1, split S2, no S3, + S4

CHEST: Distant breath sounds and scattered rhonchi throughout all lung fields

ABD: (+) Hepatojugular reflex, ? hepatomegaly, no fluids waves

RECT: Guaiac-negative

EXT: Fine tremor in both hands, normal deep tendon reflexes, diminished pedal pulses bilaterally, 3+ pitting edema to the midcalf

NEURO: WNL

Results of Laboratory Tests

Na 133	Cr 1.2	T.Bili 1.1
K 4.7	Hct 44.7	FBG 385
Cl 90	Hgb 15.1	Uric Acid 8.7
HCO$_3$ 32	WBC 10.9k	Theophy-
BUN 37	Plts 229k	lline 32

ABGs (on room air) pH 7.44, PCO2 42, PO2 49

Urinalysis: 2% glucose

Pulmonary function test:
Prebronchodilator, $FEV_1/FVC = 0.8/1.2$ liter;
Postbronchodilator, $FEV_1/FVC = 0.9/1.5$ liter

Problem

S:

O:

A:

P:

Problem

S:

O:

A:

P:

Problem

S:

O:

A:

P:

Problem

S:

O:

A:

P:

Problem

S:

O:

A:

P:

Problem

S:

O:

A:

P:

Problem

S:

O:

A:

P:

CASE 115

CC: D.P. is a 46-year-old woman with a long psychiatric history characterized as unipolar depression who is brought to the ER with a probable polydrug overdose.

History of Present Illness

D.P. was a heroin shooter, but has been in a methadone maintenance program. She was found unconscious with empty prescription bottles for diazepam, Percodan (oxycodone and aspirin), and Tylenol #3 (acetaminophen and codeine 30 mg). Her friend states that D.P. also took 20 methadone 10-mg tablets.

Past Medical History

D.P. has a depressive disorder. She also has a history of intravenous drug abuse, several suicide attempts by drug overdoses, and GI bleeding secondary to duodenal ulcer (February 1986). She had rheumatoid arthritis diagnosed in November 1985; therapy was started with Piroxicam 40 mg qd. She has type IV hyperlipidemia and is status post pancreatitis ($\times 2$, 1979 and 1980) and hysterectomy and bilateral salpingo-oophorectomy in 1982.

Medication History

Tranylcypromine 30 mg q AM $\times$ 3 years
Trazodone 100 mg qhs $\times$ 3 years
Gemfibrozil 600 mg b.i.d. $\times$ 4 years instituted after attempts at nondrug treatment had failed
Ranitidine 150 mg bid since February 1986
Piroxicam 40 mg qd since November 1985
Conjugated estrogens 2.5 mg q.d. since 1982
Percodan 1–2 q6h prn $\times$ many years
Tylenol #3 1–2 q 4–6 h prn many years
Diazepam 20 mg q.i.d. $\times$ many years
Methadone 40 mg q.d.

Allergies

None known

Social History

D.P. reports alcohol use (one to two drinks per day) and cigarettes (one to two packs per day).

Physical Examination

GEN: Female responsive only to deep pain
VS: BP 80/50 P 103 RR 10 T 37 Wt 82 Kg
HEENT: Pinpoint pupils, icteric sclera, no gag reflex
COR: NL S1 and S2; no murmurs, rubs, or gallops
CHEST: Clear to ascultation
ABD: Soft, nontender
EXT: Fresh needle tracks, no inflammation, erythema or tenderness of any joints
NEURO: Responsive only to deep pain

Results of Laboratory Tests

Na 138	Hct 36	AST 58	Glu 80	PT 12.5
K 4.2	Hgb 11.2	ALT P	Ca 9.3	PTT 36
Cl 106	WBC 5.8k	LDH 246	PO_4 2.0	Amylase 100
HCO_3 24	Plts 193k	Alk Phos 60	Mg 1.7	ESR 5
BUN 24	MCV 70	Alb 3.2	Chol 206	
Cr 1.3	MCHC 24	T.Bili 2.5	Trigyclerides P	

ABGs: PO_2 40, PCO_2 50, pH 7.3
Urinalysis: P
Stool guaiac (+), NG aspirate (+) heme
ECG: Normal
Toxicity screen:
Ethanol—negative
Acetaminophen—60 μg/ml
Diazepam—6,000 ng/ml
Desmethyldiazepam—positive
Salicylate—25 μg/ml
Barbiturates—negative
Methadone—2,800 ng/ml
Oxycodone—positive

Problem

S:

O:

A:

P:

Problem

S:

O:

A:

P:

Problem

S:

O:

A:

P:

Problem

S:

O:

A:

P:

Problem

S:

O:

A:

P:

Problem

S:

O:

A:

P:

Problem

S:

O:

A:

P:

Problem

S:

O:

A:

P:

Problem

S:

O:

A:

P:

APPENDIX A

Answers

In addition to providing answers, we refer the reader to the corresponding section in the textbook for a more detailed discussion.

SECTION 1
Nutrition
CASE 3

1. J.L. has a current weight of 40 kg while she is 5'5" tall. Ideal body weight would be approximately 57 kg. She also has evidence of an iron deficiency anemia (MCV = 78) and her albumin is 3.1. It is likely that J.L. also has other vitamin deficiencies.

   For a more detailed discussion of the signs and symptoms of malnutrition see Section I, Chapter 2, and Chapter 3, page 42.

2. Provide enteral nutrition to prevent further weight loss and repair current deficits. J.L. does not require parenteral nutrition. As J.L.'s GI problems are at, or proximal, to the gastroduodenal junction, a feeding tube should be inserted into the jejunum. A predigested, isotonic tube feeding product in a quantity to meet needs should be initiated. Vitamins and minerals at the recommended daily allowance will be added. Monitor weight, urinary input and output (I/O), blood sugar, serum electrolytes, MCV, blood cell smear, albumin, and diarrhea.

   For an explanation of enteral nutrition see Section 1, Chapter 3, pages 49–50.

SECTION 2
Diseases of the Blood
CASE 7

1. Quinine sulfate or aspirin may cause hemolysis in a patient who is glucose-6-phosphate dehydrogenase deficient. Methyldopa may cause a Coomb's positive hemolytic anemia. E.T.'s peripheral blood smear shows hemolyzed RBCs and the Coomb's test is positive. Aspirin, ethanol, and naproxen can cause GI blood loss, his stool is guaiac positive, and he shows evidence of iron deficiency anemia. His alcoholism may be contributing to his folate deficiency. See Section 2 Chapter 4 page 76. Drugs causing iron deficiency anemia are discussed in Section 2, Chapter 4, page 62.

Drugs causing hemolytic anemia are presented in Section 2, Chapter 4, Tables 4.17, and 4.21.

2. Discontinue the agents causing the hemolysis, i.e., methyldopa and quinine; also discontinue the drugs that can cause GI blood loss including the aspirin and naproxen. Begin ferrous sulfate 325 mg p.o. t.i.d. for 3–6 months. Also begin folic acid 1 mg p.o. q.d. for 2–3 weeks. The treatment of iron deficiency anemia is discussed in Section 2, Chapter 4, page 64–66. The treatment of folate deficiency anemia is discussed in Section 2, Chapter 4, pages 77–78.

3. The monitoring parameters for E.T.'s anemia would include hemoglobin, which should increase by 2 mg % in 3 weeks; hematocrit, which should increase by 6% in 3 weeks; and reticulocyte count, which should increase in 7 days and return to normal within 2–3 weeks. The peripheral blood smear and the red blood cell indices such as MCV, MCH, and MCHC should return to normal in 3 months. Patient education: The ferrous sulfate should be taken on an empty stomach if it does not cause too much GI discomfort. If E.T. cannot tolerate taking the ferrous sulfate on an empty stomach, he should take it with food but not antacids. The iron may cause constipation and turn his stools dark. To avoid the constipation, E.T. should increase the amount of fresh fruits and vegetables in his diet. E.T. needs to improve his nutritional intake and decrease his alcohol consumption, but this may be difficult because of the history of alcoholism. Counseling or Alcoholics Anonymous may help him to stop drinking and his roommate may help with compliance with the regimen. E.T. should continue to take the iron for the full 6 months even though he may begin to feel better sooner. The iron should be stored out of the reach of children. E.T. should not take any drugs (OTC or prescription) without consulting his pharmacist because of his G-6-P-D deficiency. Monitoring parameters for anemia are presented in Section 2, Chapter 4, Table 4.3. Patient education regarding iron is discussed in Chapter 4, page 64.

4. E.T.'s fluid and electrolyte problems are complex. E.T. has hypovolemia and hypernatremic dehydration as evidenced by the orthostatic blood

pressure changes, increased BUN/Cr, increased serum sodium, decreased weight, and poor skin turgor. However, E.T. has total body fluid overload with third spacing, which is shown by the ascites on physical examination. In addition, E.T. has metabolic acidosis; his pH is less than 7.35 and his HCO_3 is less than 20. He has partial respiratory compensation with a PCO_2 of 35. The assessment of fluid and electrolyte problems is discussed in Section 1, Chapter 1.

5. E.T. has lost 5 kg (75–70 kg = 5 kg) and has a 5-liter fluid deficit. However, his blood pressure is within normal limits in the supine position. Give E.T. 5% dextrose in 0.45% normal saline at a rate of 500 ml/hour for 2 hours and monitor BP, orthostatic BP, serum electrolytes, and arterial blood gases. If his blood pressure still shows orthostatic changes and the serum sodium is within the normal range, give 5% dextrose in 0.9% sodium chloride at 500 ml/hour until the blood pressure is stable. The replacement fluids should not contain potassium until his serum potassium is less than 4. The acidosis should correct with adequate fluid replacement; E.T. does not require any additional treatment at this time for the acidosis. Once the fluid deficit is corrected, E.T. will require maintenance fluid therapy. Replace the phosphorus with 8 mMol given as an infusion over 8 hours and remeasure the PO_4. The treatment of fluid and electrolyte imbalance is discussed in Section 1, Chapter 1.

SECTION 3
Endocrine and Metabolic Disease
CASE 13

1. Physical Examination: Hypertension, moon facies, posterior subcapsular cataract, truncal obesity, muscle wasting, poor muscle tone, edema, transparent skin, striae and ecchymoses.
Laboratory Tests: Increased RBC, HCT, Hgb, WBC, PMN, FBS, and Na, and decreased K and Lymphs.
   The signs and symptoms of steroid excess are discussed in Section 3, Chapter 6, pages 121–3.

2. Pharmacokinetic: Cimetidine: enzyme inhibition decreases clearance of steroids.
Pharmacologic: Naproxen: additive Na/water retention. Triamcinolone Cream: percutaneous absorption through excoriated skin increases steroid effect.
Drug interactions with steroids are discussed in Section 3, Chapter 6, page 133 and in a drug interaction textbook.

3. Abdominal surgery represents major stress. This patient has evidence of HPA axis suppression: a long history of steroid use and a clinical presentation consistent with the use of steroids in pharmacologic doses.

Preoperative: Hydrocortisone (HC) 100 mg i.v. as the Na succinate or Na phosphate salt. Dosing should start approximately 8 hours before the surgery.
Perioperative: Continue hydrocortisone 100 mg q8h for an additional 24–72 hours, depending on the status of the patient.
Postoperative: Taper steroid doses and change to oral dosing as soon as the patient can tolerate it.
   Sample tamper schedule: after 100 mg HC IV q8h for several days.

   HC 50 mg i.v. or p.o. q8h for 1–2 days
   HC 50 mg p.o. q12h or b.i.d. for 1–2 days
   Prednisone 10 mg p.o. t.i.d.

The treatment of a patient with HPA axis suppression who has undergone major stress is presented in Table 6.4 in Section 3, Chapter 6.

4. a. Consolidate prednisone 10 mg t.i.d. to 30 mg qd; this should take about 1 week. Using 5 mg/day increments, first decrease the evening dose and then the afternoon dose to 0, while increasing the morning dose by an equal amount.
   b. Decrease the dose by 5 mg/day every week until the dose is 10 mg qAM (the dose on admission).
   c. Slow the taper; decrease the dose by 1 mg/day every 2–4 weeks. This final phase of the steroid taper should be guided by the clinical presentation of the patient and the AM cortisol levels, which should be obtained just prior to each dose adjustment once the dose has been reduced to 10 mg or less qd.
   Iatrogenic HPA suppression is discussed in Section 3, Chapter 6, pages 129–30.

5. Monitoring for a too-rapid taper of the steroid dose must include attention to the disease for which the steroids were prescribed.
   a. Flare of the rheumatoid arthritis;
   b. Signs and symptoms of cortisol deficiency:
   Flu-like symptoms: nausea, vomiting, anorexia, muscle weakness or aches
   Abdominal pain
   Orthostatic hypotension
   Decreased blood glucose or serum electrolytes;
   c. Cortisol levels below 10 μg/ml
   The signs and symptoms of adrenal insufficiency are presented in Section 3, Chapter 6, pages 130–1.

SECTION 4
Renal Disease
CASE 18

1. Vd = (0.3 liter/kg)(60 kg) = 18.0 liter
LD = (Vd)(Cp) = (18 liter)(60 mg/liter) = 1080 mg
   The equations for calculating initial doses in patients with renal failure are presented in Section 4, Chapter 11, page 234.

2. Vd = dose/Cp = 1080 mg/64 mg/liter = 16.9 liter

We will assume that the volume of distribution remains constant throughout the case. In reality, the volume is affected by multiple factors and may be altered by hemodialysis. Therefore the true volume of distribution may fluctuate during dialysis. The discussion of calculating pharmacokinetic parameters in patients with renal failure is presented in Section 4, Chapter 11, page 234.

3. During intradialytic period:

$$k = \frac{\ln Ci/C}{t} = \frac{\ln 64/45}{16 \text{ hour}} = 0.022$$
$$Clp = kV = (0.022)(16.9) = 0.37 \text{ liter/hour}$$
$$t_{1/2} = 0.693/k = 0.693/0.022 = 31.5 \text{ hour}$$

With these calculations alone we can see that a maintenance interval of 72 hours is reasonable. The half-life is 31.5 hour. After 72 hours about 2.3 half-lives will have passed and the level will have dropped by approximately 80% (50% after one half-life, 75% after two half-lives, 87.5% after three half-lives). For example, given a peak of 55 mg/liter we would expect a trough of approximately 11 mg/liter (55 mg/liter times 20% remaining after two half-lives). We can verify this expectation by solving for final concentration and an interval of 72 hours using Equation 3:

$$\frac{\ln 55 - \ln x}{(0.37)/(16.9)} = 72 \text{ hour} \quad x = 11.25$$

Given a level of 55 mg/liter and a 72-hour interval we would expect a trough of 11.25 mg/liter. Since both this peak and trough are within the therapeutic range and a 72-hour interval is a workable dosing interval, we will calculate our maintenance dose based on this interval and this peak.

Using Equation 4 we calculate the maintenance dose as follows:

$$MD = \frac{(55 \text{ mg/liter})(16.9 \text{ liter})}{[1 - e^{-(0.37/16.9)/(72 \text{ hour})}]} = 734 \text{ mg}$$

Since 734 mg is an impractical dose we would round off to 750 mg and recheck our expected peak and trough using Equations five and six. Doing so we find that 750 mg q72h should give us a peak of about 55.8 mg/liter and a trough of about 11.45 mg/liter.

The calculation of doses in patients on dialysis is discussed in Section 4, Chapter 11, pages 234–5.

4. During dialysis:

$$k = (\ln 45/6)/4 \text{ hour} = 0.5$$
$$Cl = (0.5)(16.9 \text{ liter}) = 8.45 \text{ liter/hour}$$
$$Cl = Cld + Clp, \quad 8.45 = Cld + .37$$
$$Cld = 8.08$$

Using Equation 8

$$CaD = (11.45 \text{ mg/liter})(e^{-(8.08 + 0.37)/16.9(4 \text{ hour})}) = 1.55 \text{ mg/liter}$$

This equation is presented on page 234, Section 4, Chapter 11.

5. Using Equation 11:

$$\text{Infusion rate} = (11.45 \text{ mg})(8.08 + .37) = 96.75 \text{ mg/hour}$$

(We can round this rate to 100 mg/hour for ease of administration and will change the expected Css to 11.8 mg/liter, [(100 mg/hour)/8.08 + .37 = 11.8 mg/liter])

This equation is discussed in Section 4, Chapter 11, page 235.

6. Yes, it would be expected that AB 77 would be dialyzed because it meets all the criteria for dialyzable drugs (low molecular weight, low protein binding, rapid distribution, little elimination via routes other than the kidney, a small volume of distribution and, a high water solubility). The characteristics of drugs that predict whether the drug is dialyzed are discussed in Section 4, Chapter 11, page 233.

7. AB 77 100 mg/hour via continuous i.v. infusion for 4 hours during each hemodialysis period and AB 77 750 mg i.v. push q72h immediately posthemodialysis.

SECTION 5
Gastrointestinal Diseases
CASE 24

1. a. Vancomycin 125–500 mg p.o. q.i.d. ×10–14 days.

   b. Vancomycin is effective against *C. difficile*. Metronidazole is also effective but the patient is on warfarin. Metronidazole stereoselectively inhibits the metabolism of the S-isomer of warfarin, resulting in a significant increase in the anticoagulant effect. Avoid this combination of drugs if possible. Antimotility agents are contraindicated in the treatment of diarrhea due to infectious agents and have been reported to worsen pseudomembranous colitis (PMC), avoid these agents in this patient.

   The treatment of PMC is discussed in Section 5, Chapter 16, page 310.

2. The goal of fluid replacement in the treatment of diarrhea is to avoid dehydration and electrolyte abnormalities, which can result from the loss of fluid, potassium bicarbonate, and NaCl. The patient should be instructed to avoid drinking large amounts of free water; frequent small quantities of a fluid containing electrolytes should be used. Canned soft drinks, chicken or beef bouillon, fruit juices, or Gatorade are all good sources of sodium, chloride, and potassium. This patient has evidence of mild dehydration and needs fluid replacement (thirst, elevated BUN/Cr ratio, Na = 143, Cl = 105).

Fluid and electrolyte replacement is discussed in Section 1, Chapter 1 as well as Section 5, Chapter 16, page 308.

3. Vancomycin is not absorbed to any significant extent when given orally. Large quantities of the drug reach the colon; this property is the rationale for the use of this drug in the treatment of PMC. Measurable systemic serum concentrations have been reported in patients with renal failure in the presence of an acutely inflamed bowel but most clinicians consider the absorption of vancomycin to be negligible. Consult a pharmacology text for information on the absorption of vancomycin.

CASE 25

1. Hepatitis B immune globulin (HBIG), 0.06 ml/kg i.m. within 24 hours of exposure is recommended for prophylaxis.

2. It is not necessary to give F.A.'s husband HBIG at this time, as he was not exposed and it is not known if his wife will become positive for HBsAG.

3. Children born to mothers who are HBsAG positive at delivery should receive the following:
   a. HBIG 0.5 ml i.m. within 24 hours of delivery. Immune globulin must be given to provide immediate passive immunity.
   b. Recombivax 0.5 ml i.m. should be given within 7 days of birth. Recombivax may be given at the time HBIG is given, but should be administered in the opposite thigh. Recombivax 0.5 ml i.m. should be repeated at 1 month and 6 months of age. The vaccine is necessary to stimulate the child's immune system to produce hepatitis B antibodies and to provide long-term protection against infection.

   The treatment of hepatitis B exposure is discussed in Chapter 14, Section 5, pages 277–278.

SECTION 6
Rheumatic Diseases
CASE 32

1. a. J.C. should receive oral gold therapy as a remitting agent because giving her intramuscular gold would risk hematoma formation because of her anticoagulation therapy. The anticoagulant cannot be discontinued. In addition, J.C. has a history of rashes with both chloroquine and penicillamine, so hydroxychloroquine and penicillamine should be avoided unless the history of allergy is clarified to suggest that these drugs would not pose a risk to the patient. Begin auranofin 3 mg

b.i.d. and increase to 9 mg/day in 6 months if there is no response. If there is no response after 9 months of therapy, then discontinue the gold. The choice of treatment at that point will be difficult because J.C. is a poor candidate for treatment with methotrexate since she drinks ethanol and would have increased risk of hepatotoxicity. Monitoring parameters for oral gold include monthly CBC with differential, platelets, and urinalysis for proteinuria, as well as questions about GI distress, diarrhea, rash, stomatitis, fever and shortness of breath. The use of oral gold in rheumatoid arthritis is discussed in Section 6, Chapter 18, page 327–328.

b. J.C. is taking low-dose aspirin, which could increase her uric acid level. In addition, anti-inflammatory doses of aspirin were previously ineffective and aspirin increases the risk of bleeding in a patient on warfarin. Discontinue the aspirin. The piroxicam has not been effective in relieving her complaints of swelling and pain and may cause peptic ulcer disease. She has failed trials with ibuprofen and naprosyn at maximal doses. Another NSAID could be started to relieve her complaints until the gold becomes effective. However, it is unlikely that another NSAID will be effective. A reasonable alternative for an elderly patient taking anticoagulants is sulindac 200 mg b.i.d., which is unlikely to worsen her impaired renal function. The use of NSAIDs in rheumatoid arthritis is discussed in Section 6, Chapter 18, pages 323–326.

2. Low-dose aspirin, furosemide, ethanol ingestion, poor renal function, and obesity are contributing factors to her hyperuricemia. Contributing factors to hyperuricemia are discussed in Section 6, Chapter 19, page 332.

3. Probenecid is not effective in this patient whose creatinine clearance is less than 30 ml/minute. J.C.'s Cr Cl is approximately 20 ml/minute. In addition, probenecid should not be used in patients with a history of uric acid stones because it may worsen gouty nephropathy. Allopurinol is effective in patients with decreased renal function. Begin allopurinol 100 mg p.o. qd. The dose should be decreased in renal impairment. Discontinue the probenecid. Continue the prophylactic colchicine 0.5 mg p.o. qd for 3–6 months. The treatment of gout and hyperuricemia is discussed in Chapter 19, pages 335–341.

4. $$\text{Cl} = \frac{\text{FD}}{\tau \text{Css}} = \frac{0.7 \times 62.5 \ \mu\text{g}}{1 \ \text{day} \times 0.6 \ \text{ng/liter}} = 72.9 \ \text{liter/day}$$

$$\text{New dose} = \frac{\text{Cl} \times 2 \times \text{Css}}{\text{F}}$$

$$= \frac{72.9 \ \text{liter/day} \times 1 \ \text{day} \times 1.2 \ \text{ng/liter}}{0.7}$$

$$= 124 \ \mu\text{g/day}$$

New dose = 0.125 mg qd

The calculation of digoxin doses is presented in Section 8, Chapter 26, pages 460–461.

SECTION 7
Respiratory Disease
CASE 37

1. Make sure the canister is properly inserted into the plastic shell by gently twisting it back and forth.

   Remove the cap.

   Use in the upright position.

   Shake before each puff.

   Hold the mouthpiece 1½ inches away from your open mouth for the β_2-agonist inhaler.

   Use the closed-mouth technique and close your eyes with ipratropium bromide inhaler.

   Breath out normally.

   As you begin to take a slow, deep breath, firmly depress the top of the canister. Hold your breath as long as comfortable (up to 10 seconds) to let the medication settle. Breathe out slowly through pursed lips.

   Use the β_2 inhaler first. Wait 5–20 minutes between puffs.

   If breathing difficulty persists, consult a physician.

   Do not overuse your inhaler.

   Clean canister and mouth piece daily with hot soapy water.

   The use of inhalers is discussed in Section 7, Chapters 21, pages 370–372 and 22 page 379.

2. C.T. is requiring greater than 15 mg prednisone per day so he should be started on 8 puffs b.i.d. or 4 puffs q.i.d. Both regimens are equally effective, so C.T. could choose the one that is most convenient for him. C.T. may not be compliant with this type of therapy so compliance should be carefully assessed at follow-up visits. The onset of action of the inhaled steroids is from 2 to 4 weeks so the systemic and inhaled steroids should overlap by about 2 weeks before the systemic steroids are slowly tapered. The inhaled steroids should be preceded by the β_2-agonist inhaler. The use of inhaled steroids in asthma is discussed in Section 7, Chapter 21, pages 368–369.

3. Yes. This patient has increased sputum production, his sputum is green and purulent, and his WBC is elevated. While this has been a controversial area, antibiotics have recently been shown to decrease the frequency of respiratory failure and to prevent deterioration in lung function. C.T. has not recently received antibiotics so any of the following would be acceptable: cotrimoxazole 160/800 mg 1 b.i.d., tetracycline 500 mg q.i.d. or doxycycline 100 mg q.d. Therapy should continue for 10 days. C.T. should not receive ampicillin, which would be appropriate for his condition, but he has an allergy to penicillin. The treatment of acute exacerbations of COPD with antibiotics is discussed in Section 7, Chapter 22, pages 381–382.

4. $$Css = \frac{SFD/\tau}{Cl}$$

   $$8 \text{ mg/liter} = \frac{(1)(1)(300)/12 \text{ hours}}{Cl}$$

   $3.1 \text{ liter/hour} = Cl$

   $Vd = (0.48 \text{ liter/kg})(78.3 \text{ kg})$

   $Vd = 37.6 \text{ liter}$

   $$t_{1/2} = \frac{0.693}{Cl/V}$$

   $$t_{1/2} = \frac{0.693}{3.1 \text{ liter/hour}/37.6 \text{ liter}}$$

   $t_{1/2} = 8.4 \text{ hours}$

   Revised dose:

   $$Css = \frac{SFD/\tau}{Cl}$$

   $$13 \text{ mg/liter} = \frac{(1)(1)(D)/12 \text{ hour}}{3.1 \text{ liter/hour}}$$

   $D = 484 \text{ mg}$

   Since C.T. has a long half-life, a sustained release formulation is not necessary. However, Theodur 500 mg q12h would be an acceptable regimen that may increase compliance. Consult a pharmacokinetic text for calculating theophylline doses.

SECTION 8
Cardiovascular Disorders
CASE 42

1. C.K. is experiencing cardiovascular signs of digoxin toxicity including second degree AV block and PVCs; gastrointestinal symptoms including nausea, decreased appetite, and diarrhea; and CNS symptoms of confusion and lethargy. C.K. also has a digoxin serum level of 2.7 ng/ml which is in the toxic range.

   The presentation of digoxin toxicity is discussed in Section 8, Chapter 26, page 462.

2. Verapamil was added to C.K.'s drug regimen 10 days ago to control his hypertension. Verapamil decreases the clearance of digoxin by 20%–30% but has no effect on the volume of distribution. In response to this decrease in digoxin clearance, the serum digoxin level will increase. This effect is usually seen within 1 week of therapy.

   Hypokalemia is also a major factor contributing to C.K.'s digoxin toxicity. C.K. increased his furosemide dose and has been experiencing diarrhea—both of which can cause a decrease in serum potassium and thus potentially increase the uptake of digoxin by the myocardial tissues. C.K. is not receiving a potassium supplement. The predisposing factors for digoxin toxicity are discussed in Section 8, Chapter 26, page 462, Table 26.4.

3. Colchicine is the drug of choice for an acute gouty attack. It is most effective when given within the first 24–36 hours of the attack. The usual dose of colchicine is 0.5 or 0.6 mg: 2 tablets immediately, then 1 tablet every 1–2 hours until relief. The maximum amount of colchicine per attack is 6–8 mg. Since C.K. has had previous gouty attacks, he should take one-half of the total dose of colchicine needed in his previous attack immediately. He should then titrate colchicine to effect by taking 1 tablet every 1–2 hours.

   The treatment of acute gout is discussed in Section 6, Chapter 19, pages 335–338.

4. C.K. was started on allopurinol for gout approximately 2 months ago. Allopurinol decreases the elimination of warfarin, thus an increase in anticoagulant effect can be seen. C.K. also was taking cotrimoxazole for 10 days. Cotrimoxazole stereoselectively inhibits metabolism of the S isomer of warfarin, thus an increased anticoagulant effect is seen.

   In addition C.K. has had diarrhea, which may decrease vitamin K absorption and he has had a decreased appetite.

   The drug interactions with warfarin are discussed in Section 8, Chapter 23, pages 394–395.

5. Stress compliance with warfarin since C.K. is at risk of thromboembolic complications secondary to his prosthetic valve. C.K. should watch for signs and symptoms of bleeding; he should check for bruises, bleeding from his mouth, or nose, blood in his urine or stools, and dark tarry stools. C.K. should use a soft-bristle toothbrush to avoid gum bleeding, have a stable diet (in terms of vitamin K intake), and check with a physician or pharmacist before using nonprescription drugs. Remind him to avoid alcohol.

   Adverse reactions to warfarin are discussed in Section 8, Chapter 23, page 394.

6. Since C.K. has congestive heart failure (CHF), verapamil may or may not be a good choice. Calcium channel blockers have peripheral arterial vasodilating properties, thus they can decrease afterload. However, calcium channel blockers (especially verapamil) are negative inotropes and thus they can decrease contractility. Calcium channel blockers should not be used in patients with CHF if the left ventricle ejection fraction is ≤30%. Verapamil may also decrease conduction by its effects on the SA and AV nodes.

   The treatment of hypertension is discussed in Section 8, Chapter 24, pages 405–421.

CASE 43

1. In atrial fibrillation associated with nonvalvular heart disease and coronary artery disease, the data is inconclusive on whether anticoagulant therapy should be used. Long-term warfarin therapy may be considered in young patients who are not at increased risk of hemorrhagic complications.

   S.L. is elderly, complains of abdominal pain, and has a positive stool guaiac and an ulcer on endoscopy. She has been in atrial fibrillation for 10 years without a thromboembolic problem; therefore, she is not a candidate for warfarin therapy.

   The indications for anticoagulant therapy in patients with atrial fibrillation are discussed in Section 8, Chapter 25, page 442.

2. The distribution of digoxin in the body must be considered when interpreting plasma levels. Digoxin follows a two-compartment model of distribution. Digoxin is initially distributed into the plasma compartment and then into the tissue compartment, where the pharmacological effects on the myocardium occur. As plasma samples are obtained from the initial compartment, plasma digoxin levels do not accurately reflect the pharmacologic effects of digoxin until complete distribution into both compartments has occurred. Because the initial volume of distribution is small, high plasma levels are commonly reported immediately after a dose is administered. Since the heart is in the second compartment, these levels are not representative of the level in the heart itself and the levels do not represent therapeutic or toxic effects. To evaluate serum digoxin levels, obtain levels at least 6 hours after an oral dose. The kinetics of digoxin in S.L. are determined as follows:

   Estimate of renal function: CrCl =

   $$\frac{(140-71)}{(72)(1.6)}(0.85) = 0.6 \text{ ml/min/kg}$$

   Cl = 0.6 ml/min/kg + 0.8 = 1.4 ml/min/kg
     (48 kg) = 96.8 liter/day
   Vd = 3.8 + 3.1(0.6 ml/min/kg) = 5.66 liter/kg
     (48 kg) = 272 liter
   $$k = \frac{96.8 \text{ liter/day}}{272 \text{ liter}} = 0.36 \text{ day}^{-1}$$
   $$t_{1/2} = \frac{(0.693)(272 \text{ liter})}{96.8 \text{ liter/day}} = 1.95 \text{ days}$$
   Cpss expected =
   $$\frac{SFD}{Cl} = \frac{(0.8)(125 \ \mu g/day)}{96.8 \text{ liter/day}} = 1.0 \ \mu g/liter$$

   As S.L. takes her digoxin every morning, the plasma level of 5.2 ng/ml at the 9 AM blood draw is due to sampling before the drug has completely distributed throughout the body. Also, S.L. does not have any signs of digoxin toxicity and therefore, she does not need therapy with digoxin antibody fragments. The expected Cpss level of digoxin is calculated to be 1.0 μg/liter, and this amount of digoxin appears to be controlling the ventricular rate adequately. The use of digoxin antibody fragments and digoxin pharmacokinetics are discussed in Section 8, Chapter 26 page 463.

3. *Problem 5: Chronic Atrial Fibrillation.* S.L. is currently on digoxin, at an appropriate dose that is controlling her heart rate. Therefore continue digoxin at the current dose.

The treatment of atrial fibrillation with digoxin is discussed in Section 8, Chapter 25, pages 438–440.

Problems 1, 2: Coronary Artery Disease-Angina. S.L.'s angina is uncontrolled on the current regimen:

a. Sublingual isosorbide dinitrate is no more effective than sublingual nitroglycerin; there is little evidence in the literature supporting the claims that the former has a prolonged action. Change the isosorbide dinitrate to 20 mg p.o. q 4–6 h, and titrate up if S.L.'s angina does not decrease in frequency after an adequate trial.

b. It is appropriate to add a calcium channel blocker to this patient's regimen; however, nifedipine has the most vasodilating properties, which lead to Na^+ and water retention. Nifedipine should be avoided in patients with atrial fibrillation. The combination of diltiazem with digoxin may help control S.L.'s atrial fibrillation. The clinical significance of the drug interaction between diltiazem and digoxin is questionable because of inconsistency in the literature and the limited increase in serum digoxin when the interaction does occur. Verapamil will increase S.L.'s digoxin level; however, as her expected level is 1.0 μg/liter this may not be a problem.

S.L. has 2+ pitting edema at the ankles and has a history of problems with constipation. Therefore change the nifedipine to diltiazem 30 mg p.o. q6h.

c. S.L. has asthma, which seems to be out of control; a nonspecific β-blocker should not be used in this patient. If a β-blocker is used, a β_1-specific blocker may be tried with caution. Discontinue the propranolol and add metoprolol 50 mg p.o. q12h.

d. Continue with the sublingual nitroglycerin.

The treatment of angina is discussed in Section 8, Chapter 27, pages 478–85.

Problem 3: Hypertension. S.L.'s hypertension is well controlled, and her current BP is 160/80.

a. Hydrochlorothiazide (HCTZ) has decreased efficacy when the CrCl is less than 30 ml/min. S.L.'s estimated CrCl is 0.6 ml/min/kg = 29 ml/min. This is a gray area on whether or not the HCTZ will be effective, would continue the HCTZ; however, 50 mg p.o. b.i.d. is too high a dose and same efficacy occurs with 25–50 mg p.o. qd. Change the HCTZ to 25 mg p.o. qd and monitor S.L.'s BP.

b. Propranolol should not be used in a patient with uncontrolled asthma. Discontinue the propranolol as above.

c. S.L.'s serum potassium is 5.4 mEq/liter; she probably does not need to be on the potassium supplement, especially when the dose of the HCTZ is decreased. Discontinue the potassium supplement.

The treatment of hypertension is discussed in Section 8, Chapter 24, pages 405–421.

Problem 6: Asthma. S.L.'s asthma is not well controlled.

a. Discontinue the propranolol as above.

b. S.L.'s theophylline level is therapeutically low, 5.4 mg /liter.

Theophylline Kinetics

$Vd = (0.48 \text{ liter/kg})(48 \text{ kg}) = 23 \text{ liter}$
$Cl = (0.04 \text{ liter/hour/kg})(48 \text{ kg}) = 1.9 \text{ liter/hour}$
$k = \dfrac{1.9 \text{ liter/hour}}{23 \text{ liter}} = 0.08 \text{ hour}^{-1}$
$t_{1/2} = \dfrac{(0.693)(23 \text{ liter})}{1.9 \text{ liter/hour}} = 8.3 \text{ hours}$
Expected Cpss =
$\dfrac{FSD}{CL} = \dfrac{(200 \text{ mg})/(12 \text{ hours})(1)}{1.9 \text{ liter/hour}} = 8.7 \text{ mg/liter}$
Observed Cpss = 5.4 mg/liter
Revised $Cl = \dfrac{(200 \text{ mg})/(12 \text{ hours})}{5.4 \text{ mg/liter}} = 3.1 \text{ liter/hour}$

New Dose = (15 mg/liter) (3.1 liter/hour) (12 hour) = 558 mg

Change Theodur to 500 mg p.o. b.i.d. (expected level 13.4 mg/liter)

c. S.L. is steroid dependent as she has been admitted to the hospital numerous times for acute exacerbations requiring treatment with intravenous steroids and is currently on 15 mg of prednisone daily. As S.L. is not currently in a acute attack, add triamcinolone acetonide 1 puff b.i.d., wait 2 weeks and then start a slow taper of the prednisone. Triamcinolone is a better choice as the triamcinolone inhaler comes with its own spacer attached and she would require 4 puffs four times daily of beclomethasone. The triamcinolone inhaler would be more convenient. Add albuterol 2 puffs q6h, to be used prior to the triamcinolone to enhance penetration of the triamcinolone into the bronchial tree and to prevent the triamcinolone from inducing bronchospasm.

The treatment of asthma is discussed in Section 7, Chapter 21, pages 356–370.

Problem 8: Peptic Ulcer Disease. S.L. has a duodenal ulcer that requires therapy; it may have been caused by the prednisone. Taper the prednisone as above, if possible. Start ranitidine 150 mg p.o. qhs (lower dose as calculated CrCl is 29 ml/min). Avoid cimetidine as it will decrease the clearance of the theophylline.

The treatment of peptic ulcer disease is discussed in Section 5, Chapter 12, pages 247–252.

Problem 7: Constipation. S.L. is currently without complaints of constipation. To prevent constipation from occurring she should increase the fiber intake in her diet. Psyllium 1 tablespoon b.i.d. can be added if necessary. The treatment of constipation is discussed in Section 5, Chapter 16, pages 302–5.

4. There is a lot of information that S.L. needs to learn to enable her to use her nitroglycerin (NTG) effectively:
   a. When experiencing chest pain, S.L. should sit down and dissolve 1 NTG tablet under her tongue. The tablet should not be swallowed and she should not have food in her mouth at the same time.
   b. Sublingual NTG rapidly relieves the chest pain, usually within 3–5 minutes. She should take 1 tablet; if the pain has not resolved in 5 minutes, she should take another tablet. If the pain has not resolved in an additional 5 minutes, S.L. should take a third NTG tablet and proceed to an emergency room.
   c. S.L. may observe that when she takes the NTG she may develop a headache. This may be relieved with acetaminophen (she should take the acetaminophen after the episode of chest pain has resolved).
   d. The NTG may make S.L. dizzy and light-headed, and increase her heart rate. Therefore she should sit down when taking the medication.
   e. The NTG may produce a burning sensation under the tongue when taken. This is not an indication of potency.
   f. S.L. can take the NTG prophylactically 5–10 minutes before activities that usually precipitate anginal attacks (i.e., climbing stairs).
   g. S.L. should take her NTG with her at all times.
   h. After each use, the cap of the bottle should immediately be closed tightly.
   i. The cotton filler should be discarded after the initial opening of the bottle.
   j. The NTG should be kept away from hot, humid places to prevent a loss of potency.
   k. The NTG should be kept in the original container, without other medications in the same bottle.
   l. S.L. should get a new bottle of NTG 6 months after opening the bottle for the first time.

   Patient education concerning nitroglycerin is discussed in Section 8, Chapter 27, pages 478–479.

SECTIONS 9 AND 10
Skin and Eye Diseases
CASE 51

1. H.S. is hypothyroid.

   Subjective findings that support this include depression, constipation, paleness, muscle weakness and pain, tingling sensations, fatigue, and weight gain despite loss of appetite (13 kg in 1 month).

   Objective findings include ptosis, palpable thyroid, enlarged tongue, increased TSH, and decreased TFTs.

   The signs and symptoms and laboratory diagnosis of hypothyroidism are presented in Section 3, Chapter 7, page 154.

2. H.S. needs thyroid replacement.
   Sodium levothyroxine (synthetic, chemically pure T_4) is the agent of choice.

   It has a long half-life, smooth onset of action, contains a reliable amount of thyroxine, is standardized, and is inexpensive.

   Dessicated thyroid (defatted, dried pig thyroid powder, containing 0.17–0.23% iodine) is inexpensive but is poorly standardized with variable hormonal content and T_4/T_3 ratio. It deteriorates during storage, and some people have allergic reactions to the animal protein.

   Thyroglobulin (partially purified pig thyroglobulin) is biologically standardized but there is a variable T_3/T_4 ratio. It is hard to monitor, unreliable and more expensive.

   Sodium Liothyronine (synthetic, chemically pure T_3) is well absorbed and fast acting, but is expensive, has a short half-life and is difficult to monitor.

   Liotrix (4:1 mixture of T_4 and T_3) has both short- and long-acting effect, but it is expensive and has a variable formula. Since T_4 is converted to T_3, there is no rationale for the mixture except in the rare individual who is unable to convert T_4 to T_3.

   The choice of a thyroid replacement product is presented in Section 3, Chapter 7, pages 156–158.

3. Estrogens can increase serum T_4 and T_3, with normal serum free T_3, free T_4, and TSH, due to increased serum TBG concentration.

   Phenytoin can decrease serum T_4 and T_3, decrease serum free T_4, and increase tissue T_4 uptake.

   Drug interference with thyroid function test is discussed in Section 3, Chapter 7, page 141.

4. Do not agree with systemic steroid therapy.

   Patients often rebound after therapy. Discontinuation results in prompt relapse, frequently with severe exacerbations of the psoriasis.

   The use of systemic steroids in psoriasis is discussed in Section 9, Chapter 29, page 524.

5. Potent topical steroids e.g., TAC, Lidex, Halog, Diprosone or other steroids, should be first line of treatment in this newly diagnosed psoriasis patient.

   TAC 0.5% or any other appropriate strength for steroid chosen. Apply TAC ointment twice or three times per day.

Rationale: The steroid will suppress inflammation and prevent cell division.

Should use with a keratolytic agent.

Salicylic acid 2–5%. Apply at bedtime or two to three times a day.

Rationale: To remove scales, for keratolytic effect.

or

Coal Tar 2–5%. Apply at bedtime or two times a day.

Rationale: Used to remove scales, for keratolytic effect, and to decrease epithelial cell division.

or

Zetar Bath 2 capfuls in bath water every night.

Hydroxyzine 10–25 mg p.o. q4–8h for itching.

or

Diphenhydramine 25–50 mg p.o. q6h.

Should not use Goeckerman treatment, PUVA, or MTX in this patient since the patient is newly diagnosed and the psoriasis is not that severe. These forms of treatment have more potential adverse effects and should be reserved for patients who have failed the previously outlined regimen.

The treatment of psoriasis is discussed in Section 9, Chapter 29, pages 520–524.

6. Patient education:

There is no cure, but remission can occur.

Do not use topical steroids in areas without lesions.

Do not use topical steroids near eyes, mouth, ears, or other mucous membranes.

Do not keep occlusive wrap on for too long—maceration can occur.

Dab steroid cream on and then spread thin layer thoroughly.

One-half to 1 oz should be enough to cover the entire body.

The effect of steroid is enhanced with occlusion—use ointment, Saran wrap, Baggies, "space suit".

Cover with Saran wrap overnight.

Leave Coal Tar on for about 24 hours.

Do not occlude coal tar as this can cause burning.

Wipe off excess coal tar with mineral oil.

Salicylic acid should only be applied to lesions.

Hydrate by bathing skin prior to application to increase absorption of the salicylic acid.

Hydroxyzine/diphenhydramine can make you drowsy or sleepy.

Be careful when driving or operating heavy machinery.

Patient education for topical medications is presented in Section 9, Chapter 29, pages 524–525.

7. Kwell (Lindane, Gamma Benzene 1%) lotion:

Apply to skin from neck down.

Leave on overnight or for 8–12 hours.

Wash off next morning.

Repeat in 1 week to get the eggs that may have hatched.

8. Patient education:

Wash bedding and clothes in the hot-cycle wash.

Take a warm bath; allow the skin to dry and cool.

The itching may continue for a few days even after you have been treated, due to an allergic reaction to the bugs.

Treat all infected members of the household.

Caution: Keep out of reach of children. Lindane may be toxic in infants and young children if used incorrectly.

Frequent use may cause skin irritation or contact dermatitis.

Avoid contact with eyes or mucous membranes.

Shake well before using.

For questions 7 and 8 consult a reference on the treatment of scabies and the use of Lindane.

SECTION 11
Neurological and Psychological Disorders
CASE 56

1. Phenytoin→decreased levodopa effect

Metoclopramide→dopamine receptor antagonism

Carbamazepine→mechanism unknown

Reserpine→depletion of CNS dopamine

Drugs that decrease the effect of levodopa are discussed in Section 11, Chapter 33, pages 599–600.

2. No. Anticholinergics are effective for mild Parkinson's disease and are appropriately used as an adjunct to levodopa therapy; *however*, levodopa should be used in conjunction with carbidopa (peripheral dopa-decarboxylase inhibitor) to reduce the peripheral effects of dopamine excess.

Recommend one of the following:

a. Change to Sinemet; wait 6–8 hours after last dose of levodopa then start Sinemet 25/100–1 p.o. t.i.d. Increase by 1 tablet every 3–4 days as tolerated to optimal antiparkinsonian effect. Change to 10/100 strength of Sinemet when daily carbidopa dose of 75–100 mg can be maintained.

b. Discontinue levodopa and begin bromocriptine 1.25 mg p.o. b.i.d., increasing by 1.25–2.5 mg every 2–3 days as tolerated to the minimum dose to provide adequate anti-parkinsonian effects. Average daily doses range from 30–70 mg and should be divided into three or four doses throughout the day. Bromocriptine and Sinemet are of equal efficacy.

Bromocriptine, however, is expensive, and has a higher rate of adverse effects (30–50%). For these reasons, bromocriptine is usually reserved for severely disabled patients who no longer respond adequately to levodopa therapy. Sinemet is, therefore, preferred to bromocriptine for treatment of this patient.

The treatment of Parkinsonism is discussed in Section 11, Chapter 33, pages 595–601.

3. Nausea: will improve by changing to Sinemet. Postural hypotension: will improve by changing to Sinemet.
CNS side effects (vivid dreams, anxiety): no effect by changing to Sinemet.
Dyskinesias (restlessness, facial grimace, rhythmic jerking movements of the extremities): no effect or worsened by changing to Sinemet.

The side effects or adverse reactions of Sinemet are presented in Section 11, Chapter 33, pages 598–599.

4. Recommend zinc pyrithione 2% shampoo. Over-the-counter products are just as effective as prescription shampoos if used properly. Zinc pyrithione products are less expensive than selenium sulfide products.

Instructions for use: (a) Shampoo at least every other day. (b) Leave on scalp at least 2 minutes (up to 30 minutes) before rinsing thoroughly. (c) If initial treatment fails, cover head with shower cap after lathering and leave in place for 30 minutes to 2 hours; remove cap, then rinse.

Consult a book on over-the-counter drugs for the treatment of dandruff.

SECTION 12
Psychiatric Disorders
CASE 65

1. Subjective observations include feeling worthless, stupid, self-pity, changes in life style, loss of interest in usual activities (anhedonia), recurrent thoughts of death and suicide, anorexia/weight loss, and insomnia.

The signs and symptoms of depression are discussed in Section 12, Chapter 35, page 624.

2. Trimpramine is not appropriate because it has high anticholinergic side effects and the patient has chronic constipation. The initial dose was too high (50 mg t.i.d.). Large quantities (#100) should not be dispensed to a suicidal patient, especially since this patient was to be followed in 1 week. Three-times-a-day dosing may interfere with the patient's daily activity, especially for patients who are working. The treatment of depression is discussed in Section 12, Chapter 35, pages 629–635.

Methyldopa was not appropriate because it can cause depression and the patient's BP has been controlled with HCTZ and diet. The increase in BP may have been related to her current problem and hypertension should not be treated based on a single reading.

HCTZ is appropriate because the patient's BP was controlled with HCTZ.

The treatment of hypertension is discussed in Section 8, Chapter 24, pages 405–421.

3. The patient experienced anticholinergic side effects and sedation; therefore, discontinue trimpramine. Begin desipramine because it has less sedative, anticholinergic, and cardiovascular side effects. Give 25–50 mg hs, increase by 25–50 mg every 3–7 days up to a maximum of 300 mg/day. Other reasonable approaches: (a) Even though it may not be the drug of choice, can continue trimpramine but decrease the dose. (b) Although not approved for the treatment of depression alprazolam may also be considered because it is effective. The treatment of depression and the side effects of antidepressants are discussed in Section 12, Chapter 35.

4. The patient is hyperactive, speaks rapidly, dresses inappropriately, has thought disorders, grandiosity, a decreasing need for sleep, distractability.

The signs and symptoms of mania are discussed in Section 12, Chapter 35, pages 629–635.

5. Lithium therapy: Starting dose 900–1200 mg/day (b.i.d. dosing), may go up to 1800 mg/day in divided doses. B.D. may require a lower dose because of HCTZ therapy. Adjust the dose according to the lithium level (acute, 0.8–1.5 mg/dl; maintainance, 0.6–1.2 mg/dl). Continue lithium therapy for 3–6 months. The lag time for lithium to work is 5–10 days; therefore, the patient needs initial neuroleptic therapy: haloperidol 20–40 mg/day p.o. q6h. Decrease to half the dose in 3–5 days and discontinue in 7–10 days. As long as B.D. is continued on both the HCTZ and the lithium, the drug interaction should not pose a clinical problem.

The treatment of mania is discussed in Section 12, Chapter 35, pages 625–628.

6. WBC with differential: Because lithium produces a leukocytosis without producing a left shift, a baseline WBC should be obtained.

ECG: Because lithium causes ECG changes (flattened T wave), a baseline ECG is needed.

BUN/SCr: Because lithium is excreted by the kidneys.

Thyroid function tests: Because long-term lithium therapy may induce hypothyroidism, one of the symptoms of which is altered mental status, baseline thyroid function tests are needed.

Serum electrolytes: Because a decreased sodium will increase lithium reabsorption in the kidney and thereby increase the lithium level. Also a baseline potassium is needed because lithium causes a flattened T wave similar to that of hypokalemia.

Urinalysis: Because long-term lithium therapy may cause kidney damage.

The laboratory tests required for lithium therapy are discussed in Section 12, Chapter 35, page 626.

7. The side effects in a patient with a lithium level of 1.5–2 mg/dl are: Nausea, vomiting, diarrhea, hand tremor, slurred speech, ataxia, lethargy, and confusion. The side effects in a patient with a lithium level of >2 mg/dl are: Increased deep tendon reflexes, stupor, seizures, hypotension, and irregular pulse.

   Treatment: Discontinue lithium, discontinue the diuretic if the patient is taking a diuretic, initiate hydration and electrolyte replacement if necessary, and increase renal excretion of lithium by (a) osmotic diuresis (mannitol 1–1.5 g/kg, max = 200 g/24 hours or urea 1–1.5 g/kg, max = 120 g/24 hours), (b) urine alkalinization (acetazolamide or sodium bicarbonate).

   The presentation and treatment of lithium intoxication and toxicity are discussed in Section 12, Chapter 35, pages 626–628.

CASE 66

1. A primary feature of Alzheimer's disease is a progressive, and later incapacitating cognitive decline. This includes a loss of recent memory and eventually a loss of long-term memory. Relatives or coworkers may be more aware of this problem than the patient. R.L. has a progressive loss of memory and now frequently forgets food cooking and is unable to engage in social and sports activities he once enjoyed (e.g., cards and golf). He gets lost in once familiar surroundings. In addition to this, his increased restlessness and insomnia are all signs of a progressive decline.

   The characteristics of Alzheimer's disease are discussed in Section 12, Chapter 37, pages 653–654.

2. Inappropriate drug therapy is the most likely cause of R.L.'s sudden change in mental status (delirium or acute confusional state). Elderly patients, especially those with an existing dementia, may be sensitive to central nervous depressants (e.g., diazepam, codeine, triazolam). The initial doses were also too high for patients like R.L. The ibuprofen, as with other NSAIDS at high doses, may produce confusion in patients like R.L.

   The contributing factors to dementia are discussed in Section 12, Chapter 37, page 653, Table 37.2.

3. It is necessary to rule out a possible reversible dementia. Some causes of reversible dementia are: normal pressure hydrocephalus, intracranial tumors, drug toxicity, hypothyroidism, hyperthyroidism, anemia, and subarachnoid hemorrhage.

   Reversible causes of dementia are discussed in Section 12, Chapter 37, page 653.

4. Lecithin and choline, both acetycholine precursors, have been used alone and with cholinesterase inhibitors (e.g., physostigmine) in an attempt to increase acetylcholine levels in the brain and reverse the mental impairment of Alzheimer's disease. While uncontrolled studies have shown some improvement, controlled studies have been disappointing.

5. Currently only Hydergine, a combination of ergoloid mesylates, is FDA approved for the symptoms associated with cognitive impairment. Statistically some symptoms are improved in studies in which patients with a mild to moderate dementia were treated with Hydergine. However, Hydergine does not appear to improve the patient's general functional status at the usual 3-mg-per-day dose. A few studies using larger doses have suggested more promising results. The clinical role and appropriate daily dose of Hydergine remain to be determined.

6. Neuroleptic agents may be used to alleviate and manage inappropriate behavior such as paranoia, agitations, violence, and hallucinations. Antianxiety agents may help in the management of mild to moderate agitation, anxiety, and insomnia. Antidepressants are appropriate if depression further affects the quality of life. For R.L. a high-potency neuroleptic, either haloperidol or fluphenazine, is preferred and should be selected to treat the inappropriate behavior problems. In the elderly, doses of neuroleptics are usually started at one-third to one-half the usual adult dose. While antianxiety agents (lorazepam, oxazepam) are appropriate for mild to moderate agitation or restlessness, they would not be indicated for R.L.'s more severe behavior problems. Antianxiety agents may produce a paradoxical increase in agitation. R.L. should be monitored for diminished agitation and improved behavior. Adverse effects can include Parkinson's disease–like side effects such as tremors, stiffness, and increased restlessness; dizziness when standing; and drowsiness. Patients on long-term neuroleptic therapy should be monitored for signs of tardive dyskinesia. Patients like R.L. should be maintained on the lowest dose possible, and frequent attempts to discontinue neuroleptic therapy should be made.

   The treatment of dementia is discussed in Section 12, Chapter 37, pages 655–660.

SECTION 13
Infectious Disease
CASE 80

1. *Staphylococcus aureus* since the patient reports intravenous drug abuse and the blood culture is positive for Gram-positive cocci in clusters.

   The etiology of endocarditis in a patient who

abuses IV drugs is discussed in Section 13, Chapter 46, pages 770–771.

2. Nafcillin 1.5–2 q4h i.v. Give in sufficient fluid so as to reduce thrombophlebitis.

The treatment of endocarditis is discussed in Section 13, Chapter 46, pages 772–777.

3. Heroin-nephropathy, immune-complex nephritis associated with infective endocarditis, and dissemination of endocarditis to kidneys (pyelonephritis) from microemboli and persistent bacteremia.

The complications of intravenous heroin abuse are discussed in Section 11, Chapter 40, pages 698–699.

The effects of endocarditis on the kidney are discussed in Section 13, Chapter 46.

Pyelonephritis is discussed in Section 13, Chapter 43, page 741.

4. Discontinue aspirin because of the antiplatelet effects of renal failure and because this patient has thrombocytopenia.

Discontinue MOM because of magnesium accumulation in renal failure that would result in CNS changes.

Reduce cimetidine dose in renal failure since it is eliminated by the kidney. Accumulation will result in CNS toxicity.

Drug effects in bleeding disorders are discussed in Section 2, Chapter 5, pages 98–99.

Adjusting doses in renal failure is discussed in Section 4, Chapter 10, pages 222–227.

CASE 81

1. Clean-contaminated.

The classification of surgeries as regards to the risk of infection are discussed in Section 13, Chapter 52, page 854.

2. Enteric Gram-negative, anaerobes, enterococcus.

The organisms most likely to cause infections after surgery are discussed in Section 13, Chapter 52, page 855.

3. Magnesium citrate 10 oz p.o. or Go-lightly 4 liters p.o.

Tap water enemas until clear.

Day prior to surgery: Erythromycin base/neomycin 1 g p.o. at 1300, 1400, 2300.

Bowel preparations prior to surgery are presented in Section 13, Chapter 52, page 856.

4. Most studies have not shown any increased protection against postoperative infection in those patients receiving parenteral antibiotics.

The pros and cons of parenteral antibiotics in this type of surgery are discussed in Section 13, Chapter 52, page 857.

5. The stress of surgery may cause adrenocortical insufficiency; therefore L.D. should be covered

with hydrocortisone 100 mg i.v. q6h and on call on the day of surgery. Thereafter, the hydrocortisone must be gradually tapered. Additionally, steroid use can impair wound healing and the ability to fight off wound infection postoperatively.

The postoperative management of a patient with HPA suppression due to corticosteroid treatment is discussed in Section 3, Chapter 6, pages 132–133.

SECTION 14
Neoplastic Diseases
CASE 94

1. a. HBV infection.
   b. Patient is an immigrant from a geographical area with a high incidence of HBV and an increased consumption of dietary carcinogens.

The predisposing factors for hepatoma are discussed in Section 14, Chapter 56, page 902.

2.

Subjective:	Incidence, %
Right upper quadrant pain	35–70
Early satiety	20–60
Fevers	3–25
Weakness	15–45
Objective:	Incidence, %
HBV positive	
Elevated AFP	75–95
Elevated LFTs	
Icteric sclera	
Pedal edema	15–40
Hepatomegaly	60–95
CT scan (liver lesions)	
Liver biopsy (positive HCC)	
Elevated right hemidiaphragm	

The signs and symptoms of liver tumors are presented in Section 14, Chapter 56, page 903.

3. a. The dose of 120 mg is within the usually accepted range of 60–75 mg/M^2 (106–132 mg), however this patient has hepatobiliary dysfunction and so doxorubicin would require dosage modification in this patient. Give 50% of the usual dose for T. bili of 1.2–3 mg/100 ml, give 25% of the usual dose for T. bili >3.0 mg/100 ml. Therefore D.T. should not receive greater than 25% of the usual dose, making 30 mg an appropriate dose.
   b. Intravenous is the correct route of administration. Doxorubicin should never be given orally, intramuscularly, or subcutaneously because of its ability to cause local skin and/or tissue irritation and necrosis.
   c. Administration every 4 weeks is appropriate.

The treatment of hepatoma is discussed in Section 14, Chapter 56, pages 904–908.

4. Possible adverse effects include nausea/vomiting; stomatitis; bone marrow depression (nadir, 10–14 days; recovery, 18–25 days), decreased WBCs

increase the risk of infection and decreased RBCs and platelets may require transfusion; alopecia; local irritation/necrosis if the drug escapes from the vein (notify the nurse if pain/burning occurs during administration); urine may turn red/orange; and cumulative dose of doxorubicin cannot exceed 25% of 550 mg/M^2 because of increased risk of cardiac damage.

The adverse effects of doxorubicin are discussed in a pharmacology textbook.

SECTION 15
General
CASE 107

1. Acetaminophen (APAP) toxicity can result in serious liver and kidney damage. The clinical course is characterized by four stages. Nausea and vomiting, either prompt or delayed up to 12 hours, mark the first stage. For the next 24–48 hours, symptoms either disappear or diminish, although hepatic necrosis begins at this time. Liver function test (LFT) abnormalities are heralded by an increase in AST, followed by increased ALT, total bilirubin and prothrombin time. The third stage, between 72 and 96 hours after ingestion, is characterized by progressive jaundice and encephalopathy. Acute renal failure, with or without hepatic failure, may also occur. The last stage is the regeneration of the damaged hepatocytes.

   The APAP dose consistent with the development of hepatic necrosis is 140 mg/kg in adults and in children. Since this patient may have ingested about 240 mg/kg of APAP, he is at risk for toxic effects and must be treated.

   Consult an information source on the assessment and treatment of poisonings as suggested in Section 15, Chapter 66, page 1039–40.

2. With the Rumack-Mathew nomogram, a serum APAP level plotted against hours after ingestion can be used to assess the need for antidotal therapy following ingestion of high doses of APAP. Generally, levels greater than 140 μg/ml at 4 hours after ingestion indicate potential toxicity and warrant treatment. M.P.'s serum APAP level of 200 μg/ml at 8 hours after ingestion indicates that he is at risk for developing serious toxic effects. Therefore, he is a candidate for N-acetylcysteine (Mucomyst) antidote therapy.

Consult an information source on the assessment and treatment of poisonings as suggested in Section 15, Chapter 66, page 1039–40.

3. In therapeutic doses, 60% of APAP is metabolized to a glucuronide conjugate and 30% to APAP-sulfate, both of which are nontoxic. About 5% is excreted unchanged in the urine. The cytochrome p-450 system converts about 5% of the remaining APAP to a highly reactive metabolite, which is rapidly inactivated by reacting with reduced glutathione. In an overdose, however, hepatic glutathione is rapidly depleted and the reactive metabolite accumulates, resulting in hepatotoxicity.

   N-acetylcysteine (NAC) serves as a sulfhydryl substitute for glutathione and combines directly with the toxic metabolite. Although therapy with NAC is most effective if initiated within 10 hours of APAP ingestion, it should still be used if fewer than 24 hours have elapsed since ingestion.

   Consult an information source on the assessment and treatment of poisonings as suggested in Section 15, Chapter 66, page 1039–40.

4. The current recommended dosing regimen for NAC is 140 mg/kg loading dose followed by 17 doses of 70 mg/kg every 4 hours. This course should be completed even if repeat serum levels are below the toxic range, as long as the initial level was toxic. Since activated charcoal decreases the bioavailability of NAC by 30% when given concurrently, the loading dose can be increased to 190 mg/kg if activated charcoal has been used.

   NAC is available in the United States as 10% or 20% solutions. In order to minimize its foul taste, smell and irritation to the stomach, dilute NAC to a 5% concentration with a carbonated beverage or fruit juice. If the patient vomits a dose within 1 hour of administration, the dose should be repeated.

   This patient should be treated with NAC without delay. He should receive 50 ml of the 20% solution, diluted 1:3 in a chilled beverage, as the loading dose. This should be followed by 17 maintenance doses (25 ml of the 20% solution). Liver function tests, AST, bilirubin, and prothrombin time, should be drawn serially.

   The dosing of NAC is given in Section 15, Chapter 66, page 1049.

APPENDIX B

Referral Guide

Rather than provide answers, we refer the reader to the corresponding section in the textbook to obtain the answer.

SECTION 3
Endocrine and Metabolic Disease
CASE 14

1. Home blood glucose monitoring and urine testing for glucose and ketones are discussed in Section 3, Chapter 8, pages 184–185.

2. The treatment of diabetes as well as the endpoints of therapy are discussed in Section 3, Chapter 8, pages 186–197.

3. The evaluation of response to medications for hyperthyroidism as well as the treatment for hyperthyroidism is discussed in Section 3, Chapter 7, pages 143–152.

4. The treatment of hyperlipidemia is discussed in Section 3, Chapter 9, pages 202–205.

5. Patient education for drugs for hyperlipidemia is discussed in Section 3, Chapter 9, pages 202–205.

SECTION 5
Gastrointestinal Diseases
CASE 26

1. The treatment of ulcerative colitis is discussed in Section 5, Chapter 13, pages 261–266.

2. The treatment of diabetes is discussed in Section 3, Chapter 8, pages 186–197.

3. The preparation for colonic examination is discussed in Section 5, Chapter 16, page 304.

4. The dose of steroids for patients with suppression of the HPA axis during times of major stress is discussed in Section 3, Chapter 6, page 133.

5. The treatment of nausea and vomiting is presented in Section 5, Chapter 16, pages 291–297.

6. Iatrogenic HPA axis suppression is discussed in Section 3, Chapter 6, page 130.

7. The use of insulin is discussed in Section 3, Chapter 8, pages 193–197.

8. a. Drugs which alter glucose control in a diabetic are discussed in Section 3, Chapter 8, page 195.
   b. The assessment of thyroid function tests is presented in Section 3, Chapter 7, pages 138–143.

SECTION 6
Rheumatic Diseases
CASE 33

1. The treatment of hypoglycemia is discussed in Section 3, Chapter 8, page 196.

2. The treatment of acute gout is discussed in Section 6, Chapter 19, pages 335–338.

3. The treatment of chronic gout and hyperuricemia is discussed in Section 6, Chapter 19, pages 339–341.

4. The use of insulin is discussed in Section 3, Chapter 8, pages 193–197.

SECTION 7
Respiratory Disease
CASE 38

1. Theophylline toxicity is discussed in Section 7, Chapter 21, pages 360–361.

2. Drug-induced hepatitis is discussed in Section 5, Chapter 14, pages 271–273.

SECTION 8
Cardiovascular Disorders
CASE 44

1. Calculation of a loading dose of lidocaine is presented in Section 8, Chapter 25, page 444.

2. Calculation of a maintenance dose of lidocaine is presented in Section 8, Chapter 25, pages 444–445.

3. The use of dopamine and dobutamine in the treatment of severe CHF is discussed in Section 8, Chapter 26, page 473.

4. The dosing of inotropic agents in CHF is discussed in Section 8, Chapter 26, page 473.

5. The treatment of angina is discussed in Section 8, Chapter 27, pages 478–484. The interpretation

of hemodynamic monitoring is discussed in Section 8, Chapter 26, pages 471–472.

6. The treatment of angina is discussed in Section 8, Chapter 27, pages 478–484. The interpretation of hemodynamic monitoring is discussed in Section 8, Chapter 26, pages 471–472.

7. The dosing of drugs in angina is discussed in Section 8, Chapter 27, pages 478–484.

8. The calculation of a loading dose of procainamide is discussed in Section 8, Chapter 25, page 445. The principles of calculating a maintenance dose are discussed in Section 8, Chapter 25, page 445. Consult a pharmacokinetic text for more information.

SECTIONS 9 AND 10
Skin and Eye Diseases
CASE 52

1. The treatment of psoriasis is discussed in Section 9, Chapter 29, pages 520–529.

2. The treatment of rheumatoid arthritis is discussed in Section 6, Chapter 18, pages 323–329.

3. The evaluation and treatment of hypothyroidism is discussed in Section 3, Chapter 7, pages 154–158.

4. The treatment of constipation is discussed in Section 5, Chapter 16, pages 302–305.

SECTION 12
Psychiatric Disorders
CASE 67

1. The treatment of parkinsonism is discussed in Section 11, Chapter 33, pages 595–601.

2. The treatment of COPD is discussed in Section 7, Chapter 22, pages 376–382.

3. The presentation of phenytoin toxicity is discussed in Section 11, Chapter 32, pages 582–583.

4 a. The adverse effects of corticosteroid therapy are discussed in Section 3, Chapter 6, pages 121–123.

4 b. Iatrogenic HPA suppression is discussed in Section 3, Chapter 6, page 130.

4 c. Treatment of rheumatoid arthritis is discussed in Section 6, Chapter 18, pages 323–329.

CASE 68

1. Consult a pharmacokinetic text for phenytoin calculations.

2. The treatment of DT's is discussed in Section 12, Chapter 40, pages 685–688.

3. The medical impact of alcoholism is discussed in Section 12, Chapter 40, pages 680–683.

4. The treatment of alcoholism is discussed in Section 12, Chapter 40, pages 690–692.

5. The drug interactions with phenytoin are discussed in Section 11, Chapter 32, pages 589–591.

6. The treatment of onychomycosis is discussed in a dermatology textbook.

7. The treatment of hyperuricemia is discussed in Section 6, Chapter 19, pages 338–341.

8. Consult a pharmacokinetic text for calculating theophylline doses.

9. The treatment of chronic bronchitis is discussed in Section 7, Chapter 22, pages 376–382.

10. The treatment of chronic bronchitis is discussed in Section 7, Chapter 22, pages 376–382.

CASE 69

1. a. The treatment of gastric ulcers is discussed in Section 5, Chapter 12, pages 251–252.
   b. Drugs exacerbating gastric ulcer disease are discussed in Section 5, Chapter 12, page 245.

2. a. Consult a pharmacokinetic text for calculating theophylline doses.
   b. Consult a pharmacokinetic text for calculating theophylline doses.
   c. The treatment of COPD/chronic bronchitis is discussed in Section 7, Chapter 22, pages 376–382.
   d. The treatment of COPD/chronic bronchitis is discussed in Section 7, Chapter 22, pages 376–382.

3. a. The treatment of alcohol abuse is discussed in Section 12, Chapter 40, pages 684–685.
   b. The prevention of alcohol withdrawal is discussed in Section 12, Chapter 40, pages 685–688.

4. The treatment of depression is discussed in Section 12, Chapter 35, pages 629–635.

5. The treatment of rheumatoid arthritis is discussed in Section 6, Chapter 18, pages 323–329.

6. a. Drug induced constipation is discussed in Section 5, Chapter 16, page 301.
   b. The treatment of constipation is discussed in Section 5, Chapter 16, pages 302–305.

7. The treatment of psoriasis is discussed in Section 9, Chapter 29, pages 520–529.

8. a. The causes of insomnia are discussed in Section 12, Chapter 34, pages 615–616.
   b. The treatment of insomnia is discussed in Section 12, Chapter 34, pages 617–621.

CASE 70

1. Predisposing factors for ulcer disease are discussed in Section 5, Chapter 12, pages 244–245.

2. The treatment of PUD is discussed in Section 5, Chapter 12, pages 247–252.

3. The treatment of COPD is discussed in Section 7, Chapter 22, pages 376–382.

4. The use of phenytoin in alcohol withdrawal seizures is discussed in Section 12, Chapter 40, page 689.

5. The treatment of a Type I diabetic is discussed in Section 3, Chapter 8, pages 193–197.

6. The treatment of tinea corporis is discussed in a dermatology textbook.

SECTION 13
Infectious Disease
CASE 82

1. a. The causes of pneumonia are discussed in Section 13, Chapter 41, pages 719–724.
   b. The treatment of pneumonia is discussed in Section 13, Chapter 41, pages 719–724.

2. The treatment of meningitis is discussed in Section 13, Chapter 47, pages 785–788.

3. The treatment of gonorrhea is discussed in Section 13, Chapter 49, pages 810–811.

4. a. The risks of INH prophylaxis are discussed in Section 13, Chapter 42, page 735.
   b. The treatment of TB is presented in Section 13, Chapter 42, pages 733–734.

CASE 83

1. The organisms likely to be encountered in this surgery and treatment are discussed in Section 13, Chapter 52, pages 855–857.

2. Consult a pharmacology text for adverse reactions to the antibiotic. The monitoring parameters for efficacy are discussed in Section 13, Chapter 52.

3. Consult a pharmacokinetic text for calculations.

CASE 84

1. Consult a pharmacokinetic text for calculations for tobramycin.

2. The most likely organisms in urinary and abdominal infections are discussed in Section 13, Chapters 43, page 741 and 44, pages 754–755 respectively.

3. The treatments of urinary tract infections and abdominal infections are discussed in Section 13, Chapters 43, pages 743–745 and 44, pages 757–759 respectively.

4. The treatment of endocarditis is discussed in Section 13, Chapter 46, pages 772–777.

5. The treatment of infectious diarrhea is discussed in Section 13, Chapter 45, pages 764–768.

6. The treatment of urinary tract infections is discussed in Section 13, Chapter 43, pages 743–745.

SECTION 14
Neoplastic Diseases
CASE 95

1. Prophylaxis for surgical infections is discussed in Section 13, Chapter 52, page 857.

2. The side effects of cancer chemotherapy agents are discussed in pharmacology texts.

3. a. The side effects of cancer chemotherapy agents are discussed in pharmacology texts.
   b. The side effects of cancer chemotherapy agents are discussed in pharmacology texts.
   c. The treatment of fungal infections is presented in Section 13, Chapter 50, page 829.

CASE 96

1. Consult a pharmacokinetic textbook for calculations.

2. Consult a pharmacokinetic textbook for calculations.

3. The treatment of an infection in an immunocompromised patient is discussed in Section 13, Chapter 51, pages 843–846.

4. The treatment of fungal infections is discussed in Section 13, Chapter 50, page 828.

5. The treatment of nausea and vomiting is discussed in Section 5, Chapter 16, pages 291–297.

6. The side effects of the cancer chemotherapeutic agents are discussed in a pharmacology textbook.

CASE 97

1. Pain management is discussed in Section 15, Chapter 60, pages 950–961.

2. The treatment of meningitis is discussed in Section 13, Chapter 47, pages 783–788.

3. The treatment of urinary tract infections is discussed in Section 13, Chapter 43, pages 743–745.

4. Consult a pharmacokinetic textbook for calculating vancomycin doses.

5. The treatment of constipation is discussed in Section 3, Chapter 16, pages 302–305.

6. a. The treatment of lung cancer is discussed in Section 14, Chapter 59, pages 738–743.
   b. Consult a pharmacology text for the adverse reactions of chemotherapeutic agents.

c. The treatment of nausea is discussed in Section 3, Chapter 16, pages 291–297.

SECTION 15
General
CASE 108

1. Birth control pills are discussed in Section 15, Chapter 62, pages 977–985.

2. Birth control pills are discussed in Section 15, Chapter 62, pages 977–986.

3. Treatment of PID is discussed in Section 13, Chapter 49, pages 811–813.

4. Teratogenicity is discussed in Section 15, Chapter 61, pages 972–974.

5. The treatment of urinary tract infections is discussed in Section 13, Chapter 43, pages 743–745.

6. The treatment of hypertension is discussed in Section 8, Chapter 24, pages 403–421.

7. a. Prophylaxis for surgical infections is discussed in Section 13, Chapter 52, pages 857–858.
b. Postmenopausal estrogen therapy is discussed in Section 15, Chapter 61, pages 968–971.

8. The treatment of breast cancer is discussed in Section 14, Chapter 55, pages 892–898.

CASE 109

1. The treatment of schizophrenia is discussed in Section 12, Chapter 36, pages 640–645.

2. The treatment of depression is discussed in Section 12, Chapter 35, pages 629–635.

3. a. The contributing factors for dementia and drug use in the elderly are discussed in Section 12, Chapter 37, page 653 and Section 15, Chapter 63, page 1003 respectively.
b. Drug treatment in the elderly is discussed in Section 15, Chapter 63.

4. The evaluation of thyroid function tests and treatment of hypothyroidism are discussed in Section 3, Chapter 7, pages 154–160.

5. The treatment of diabetes is discussed in Section 3, Chapter 8, pages 186–197.

CASE 110

1. The treatment of otitis media is discussed in Section 13, Chapter 41, pages 712–713.

2. The prophylaxis of meningitis is discussed in Section 13, Chapter 47, pages 789–790.

3. The treatment for TB is discussed in Section 13, Chapter 42, pages 730–734.

4. The treatment of fever is discussed in Section 15, Chapter 64, pages 1027–1028.

5. The treatment of campylobacter is discussed in Section 13, Chapter 45, pages 764–768.

6. Vaccination schedules are given in Section 15, Chapter 64, pages 1022–1026.

7. The treatment of poisonings including iron is discussed in Section 15, Chapter 66, pages 1041–1050.